REVISE EDEXCEL GCSE
Combined Science
Foundation

GUIDED REVISION WORKBOOK

Series Consultant: Harry Smith

Authors: Hanna Beyer, Ann Fullick and Gemma Young

Also available to support your revision:

Revise GCSE Study Skills Guide   9781447967071

The **Revise GCSE Study Skills Guide** is full of tried-and-trusted hints and tips for how to learn more effectively. It gives you techniques to help you achieve your best – throughout your GCSE studies and beyond!

Revise GCSE Revision Planner   9781447967828

The **Revise GCSE Revision Planner** helps you to plan and organise your time, step-by-step, throughout your GCSE revision. Use this book and wall chart to mastermind your revision.

For the full range of Pearson revision titles across KS2, KS3, GCSE, Functional Skills, AS/A Level and BTEC visit:
www.pearsonschools.co.uk/revise

Question difficulty
Look at this scale next to each exam-style question. It tells you how difficult the question is.

Contents

BIOLOGY PAPERS 1 & 2

1   Plant and animal cells
2   Different kinds of cell
3   Microscopes and magnification
4   Dealing with numbers
5   Using a light microscope
6   Drawing labelled diagrams
7   Enzymes
8   pH and enzyme activity
9   The importance of enzymes
10 Getting in and out of cells
11 Osmosis in potatoes
12 Extended response – Key concepts

BIOLOGY PAPER 1

13 Mitosis
14 Cell growth and differentiation
15 Growth and percentile charts
16 Stem cells
17 Neurones
18 Responding to stimuli
19 Extended response – Cells and control
20 Meiosis
21 DNA
22 Genetic terms
23 Monohybrid inheritance
24 Family pedigrees
25 Sex determination
26 Variation and mutation
27 The Human Genome Project
28 Extended response – Genetics
29 Evolution
30 Human evolution
31 Classification
32 Selective breeding
33 Genetic engineering
34 Extended response – Genetic modification
35 Health and disease
36 Common infections
37 How pathogens spread
38 STIs
39 Human defences
40 The immune system
41 Immunisation
42 Treating infections
43 New medicines
44 Non-communicable diseases
45 Alcohol and smoking
46 Malnutrition and obesity
47 Cardiovascular disease
48 Extended response – Health and disease

BIOLOGY PAPER 2

49 Photosynthesis
50 Limiting factors
51 Light intensity
52 Specialised plant cells
53 Transpiration
54 Translocation
55 Water uptake in plants
56 Extended response – Plant structures and functions
57 Hormones
58 The menstrual cycle
59 Blood glucose regulation
60 Diabetes
61 Extended response – Control and coordination
62 Exchanging materials
63 Alveoli
64 Blood
65 Blood vessels
66 The heart
67 Aerobic respiration
68 Anaerobic respiration
69 Rate of respiration
70 Changes in heart rate
71 Extended response – Exchange
72 Ecosystems and abiotic factors
73 Biotic factors
74 Parasitism and mutualism
75 Fieldwork techniques
76 Organisms and their environment
77 Human effects on ecosystems
78 Biodiversity
79 The carbon cycle
80 The water cycle
81 The nitrogen cycle
82 Extended response – Ecosystems and material cycles

CHEMISTRY CORE

83 Formulae
84 Equations
85 Hazards, risk and precautions

CHEMISTRY PAPERS 3 & 4

86 Atomic structure
87 Isotopes
88 Mendeleev's table
89 The periodic table
90 Electronic configurations
91 Ions
92 Formulae of ionic compounds
93 Properties of ionic compounds
94 Covalent bonds
95 Simple molecular substances
96 Giant molecular substances
97 Other large molecules
98 Metals
99 Limitations of models
100 Relative formula mass
101 Empirical formulae
102 Conservation of mass
103 Concentration of solution
104 Extended response – Types of substance

CHEMISTRY PAPER 3

105 States of matter
106 Pure substances and mixtures
107 Distillation
108 Filtration and crystallisation
109 Paper chromatography
110 Investigating inks
111 Drinking water
112 Extended response – Separating mixtures
113 Acids and alkalis
114 Bases and alkalis
115 Neutralisation
116 Salts from insoluble bases
117 Salts from soluble bases
118 Making insoluble salts
119 Extended response – Making salts
120 Electrolysis

121 Electrolysing solutions
122 Investigating electrolysis
123 Extended response – Electrolysis
124 The reactivity series
125 Metal displacement reactions
126 Explaining metal reactivity
127 Metal ores
128 Iron and aluminium
129 Recycling metals
130 Life-cycle assessments
131 The Haber process
132 Extended response – Reactivity of metals

CHEMISTRY PAPER 4

133 The alkali metals
134 The halogens
135 Reactions of halogens
136 Halogen displacement reactions
137 The noble gases
138 Extended response – Groups
139 Rates of reaction
140 Investigating rates
141 Exam skills – Rates of reaction
142 Heat energy changes
143 Reaction profiles
144 Crude oil
145 Fractional distillation
146 Alkanes
147 Incomplete combustion
148 Acid rain
149 Choosing fuels
150 Cracking
151 Extended response – Fuels
152 The early atmosphere
153 Greenhouse effect
154 Extended response – Atmospheric science

PHYSICS PAPERS 5 & 6

155 Key concepts

PHYSICS PAPER 5

156 Scalars and vectors
157 Speed, distance and time
158 Equations of motion
159 Velocity/time graphs
160 Determining speed
161 Newton's first law
162 Newton's second law

163 Weight and mass
164 Force and acceleration
165 Newton's third law
166 Human reaction time
167 Stopping distance
168 Extended response – Motion and forces
169 Energy stores and transfers
170 Efficient heat transfer
171 Energy resources
172 Patterns of energy use
173 Potential and kinetic energy
174 Extended response – Conservation of energy
175 Waves
176 Wave equations
177 Measuring wave velocity
178 Waves and boundaries
179 Waves in fluids
180 Extended response – Waves
181 Electromagnetic spectrum
182 Investigating refraction
183 Dangers and uses
184 Changes and radiation
185 Extended response – Light and the electromagnetic spectrum
186 Structure of the atom
187 Atoms and isotopes
188 Atoms, electrons and ions
189 Ionising radiation
190 Background radiation
191 Measuring radioactivity
192 Models of the atom
193 Beta decay
194 Radioactive decay
195 Half-life
196 Dangers of radiation
197 Contamination and irradiation
198 Extended response – Radioactivity

PHYSICS PAPER 6

199 Work, energy and power
200 Extended response – Energy and forces
201 Interacting forces
202 Circuit symbols
203 Series and parallel circuits
204 Current and charge
205 Energy and charge
206 Ohm's law
207 Resistors

208 I–V graphs
209 Electrical circuits
210 The LDR and the thermistor
211 Current heating effect
212 Energy and power
213 a.c. and d.c. circuits
214 Mains electricity and the plug
215 Extended response – Electricity and circuits
216 Magnets and magnetic fields
217 Current and magnetism
218 Extended response – Magnetism and the motor effect
219 Transformers
220 Extended response – Electromagnetic induction
221 Changes of state
222 Density
223 Investigating density
224 Energy and changes of state
225 Thermal properties of water
226 Pressure and temperature
227 Extended response – Particle model
228 Elastic and inelastic distortion
229 Springs
230 Forces and springs
231 Extended response – Forces and matter

232 Biology answers
249 Chemistry answers
258 Physics answers
270 The Periodic Table of the Elements
271 Physics Equations List

- - - - - - - - - - - - - - - -

A small bit of small print
Edexcel publishes Sample Assessment Material and the Specification on its website. This is the official content and this book should be used in conjunction with it. The questions have been written to help you practise every topic in the book. Remember: the real exam questions may not look like this.

Plant and animal cells

1 In cell X, which structure is labelled A? Tick **one** box.

    ☐ **A**   nucleus

    ☐ **B**   mitochondria

    ☒ **C**   cell wall

    ☐ **D**   cell membrane

> Cell X is a plant cell. Three of these structures are found in both animal and plant cells, so read through the whole list before putting your tick in one box.

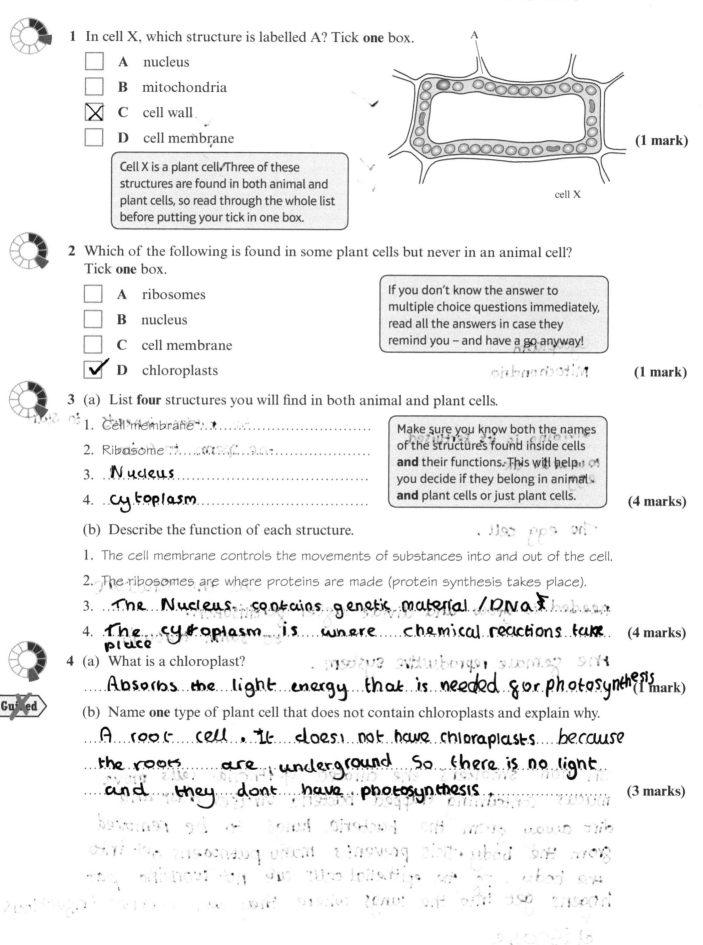

A

cell X

(1 mark)

2 Which of the following is found in some plant cells but never in an animal cell? Tick **one** box.

    ☐ **A**   ribosomes

    ☐ **B**   nucleus

    ☐ **C**   cell membrane

    ☑ **D**   chloroplasts

> If you don't know the answer to multiple choice questions immediately, read all the answers in case they remind you – and have a go anyway!

(1 mark)

3 (a) List **four** structures you will find in both animal and plant cells.

    1. Cell membrane

    2. Ribosome

    3. Nucleus

    4. cytoplasm

> Make sure you know both the names of the structures found inside cells **and** their functions. This will help you decide if they belong in animal **and** plant cells or just plant cells.

(4 marks)

(b) Describe the function of each structure.

    1. The cell membrane controls the movements of substances into and out of the cell.

    2. The ribosomes are where proteins are made (protein synthesis takes place).

    3. The Nucleus contains genetic material / DNA

    4. The cytoplasm is where chemical reactions take place

(4 marks)

4 (a) What is a chloroplast?

Absorbs the light energy that is needed for photosynthesis

(1 mark)

(b) Name **one** type of plant cell that does not contain chloroplasts and explain why.

A root cell. It doesn't have chloroplasts because the roots are underground so there is no light and they dont have photosynthesis

(3 marks)

Different kinds of cell

1 Would you find each of these structures in a bacterial cell, in a plant cell or in both?

Structure	Bacterial cell	Plant cell
cell membrane	✓	✓
plasmid DNA	✓	
nucleus		✓
mitochondria		✓
ribosomes	✓	✓
cell wall	✓	✓

(2 marks)

> Think carefully about the similarities and differences between the different types of cells before you answer a question like this.

2 The diagram shows an egg cell and a sperm cell. They are not drawn to scale.

(a) Name the structures labelled A and B in the diagrams.

A   Cytoplasm

B   Mitochondria   (2 marks)

(b) Describe the function of the structures labelled A and B.

A   The nutrients in the cytoplasm provide the egg with the nutrients it needs to start dividing if it's fertilised

B   The mitochondria provide the energy needed for the sperm to swim towards the egg   (2 marks)

> Structures A and B are very important to the purpose of these cells.

(c) If the cells were drawn to scale, which cell would be bigger?

The egg cell.   (1 mark)

(d) Give **two** reasons for the difference in size.

The egg needs to be big to contain the nutrients and all the structure needed to grow and divide after fertilisation.

The sperm are small because they need to be able to swim through the female reproductive system.   (2 marks)

3 In smokers, the ciliated epithelial cells which line the tubes leading to the lungs often do not work. Explain why this is a health risk.

> Think! How do these specialised cells help prevent disease when they are working?

In non smokers the ciliated epithelial cells move mucus containing trapped bacteria viruses dust and dirt away from the bacteria lungs to be removed from the body. This prevents many pathogens get into the body. If the epithelial cells are not working pat (3 marks) hogens get into the lungs where they can cause infectious disease

Microscopes and magnification

1 A student is given an image of a cell taken using a light microscope and asked to estimate the magnification used. Which of these answers cannot be correct? Tick **one** box.

☑ **A** ×40

☐ **B** ×100

☐ **C** ×1000

☑ **D** ×100 000

> Remember the maximum magnification for a light microscope is around ×2000.

(1 mark)

2 Here are two electron micrographs labelled X and Y.

> Remember only eukaryotic cells have a nucleus. Use this to help you answer.

(a) Which of these cells is a prokaryote?

X

(1 mark)

(b) Give **two** reasons for your choice.

This cell does not have a nucleus, it has a single chromosome, but cell y has a nucleus Eukryotic cells have a nucleus procryotic cells do not

(2 marks)

This cell is an order of magnitude smaller than cell Y. Prokaryotic cells are much smaller than Eukryotic cells .

(2 marks)

(c) Calculate the magnification used to view cell Y.

2.5 cm = 25 mm = 25 000 μm

$$\text{Magnification} = \frac{\text{image size}}{\text{real size}} = \frac{25\,000}{10} = \times 2500$$

(3 marks)

3 The electron microscope has a much greater resolution than a light microscope.

(a) What is the resolution of a microscope? Resolution is the smallest distance between two points that can still be seen as two Seperate points **(1 mark)**

(b) Why do electron microscopes enable us to see inside a cell in a lot more detail than a light microscope?

They have a much higher magnification and much higher resolution **(2 marks)**

4 (a) A student looks at a plant cell through a light microscope using the ×5 eyepiece lens and the ×40 objective lens. What magnification are they using?

5 x 4 = X200 piece lense magnification. **(1 mark)**

(b) Give **three** differences between a light microscope and an electron microscope.

one uses light to form an image the other one uses a beam of electrons. electron microscope has greater magnification than light microscope. electron microscope has greater resolution than a light microscope. **(3 marks)**

Maths skills

Maths skills

Guided

3

Had a go ☐   Nearly there ☐   Nailed it! ☐

Dealing with numbers

1 Which of the following lists of units are in the correct order of decreasing size?
Tick **one** box.

☑ **A** kilogram   milligram   gram   picogram

☐ **B** microgram   milligram   gram   kilogram

☐ **C** milligram   gram   kilogram   tonne

☑ **D** kilogram   gram   milligram   microgram

> You are asked for **decreasing** size so you can eliminate (b) and (c) as they give units in **increasing** size.

(1 mark)

2 For each of the following, state the correct measurement for the second value:

(a) 1000 nanometres = 1 micrometre

(b) 1000 micrograms = 1 ~~millimetre~~ gram

(c) 0.000 000 000 001 metres = 1 ~~nanometre~~ picometre

> pico × 1000 = nano;
> nano × 1000 = micro;
> micro × 1000 = milli

(3 marks)

3 The length of a plant cell measures 100 μm. A small animal cell measures 10 μm.

(a) How much longer is the plant cell than the animal cell?

....

.... **(1 mark)**

(b) Give the length of the plant cell in millimetres.

....

.... **(2 marks)**

(c) An ostrich egg weighs 1.5 kg. A hummingbird egg weighs 0.5 g.

   (i) What is the mass of the ostrich egg in grams?

....

.... **(2 marks)**

   (ii) How much heavier is the ostrich egg than the hummingbird egg?

....

.... **(2 marks)**

4 We always put a scale or a magnification on micrographs and drawings of biological specimens.

(a) Why is this important?

.... **(1 mark)**

(b) Look at the plant cell below. Estimate the diameter of a chloroplast in this cell.

nucleus

....

chloroplasts   40 μm   **(2 marks)**

🧪 **Practical skills** # Using a light microscope

1 (a) Name the following parts.

A the eyepiece lens

B the .... lens

C ....

> Make sure you know all of the main parts
> of the light microscope and what they do.

A
coarse focus
fine focus
B
C
mirror

(3 marks)

(b) How do you calculate the magnification you are using when you look at a
specimen through a light microscope?

....

.... **(1 mark)**

> You use two lenses at a time when using a microscope – multiply the top one by the bottom one.

(c) Give **one** precaution you should always take to protect yourself when you are
using a light microscope and explain why it is important.

Never point the mirror directly at the Sun because ....

....

.... **(2 marks)**

(d) Give **one** precaution you should take to protect the microscope and/or slide
from damage.

....

.... **(2 marks)**

2 (a) A class of students collect their own cheek cells to make slides to look at under light
microscopes. They collect the cells on a swab, smear them onto a microscope slide and
put a coverslip in place. Explain **two** steps that would make it easier to see the cells.

.... so the cells show up more clearly.

.... to avoid trapping air bubbles

which form black circles on the slide, making it harder to see the cells. **(2 marks)**

(b) Explain how to use a light microscope safely to
look at a prepared slide of human cells under
low magnification.

> Make your explanation clear –
> imagine using the instructions
> you write to use a microscope.

....

....

....

....

....

.... **(4 marks)**

Practical skills — Drawing labelled diagrams

1 When you make an accurate labelled diagram of a cell based on what you can see down a microscope, you should always use a sharp HB pencil to make your drawings, not a pen. Why?

So that if you make a mistake .... **(1 mark)**

2

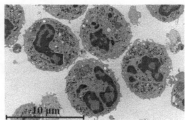

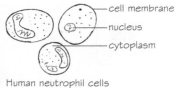

cell membrane
nucleus
cytoplasm

Human neutrophil cells

> You only need to show the detailed internal structure of one of the cells in a micrograph if there is more than one of the same type.

(a) Give **two** good points about this diagram drawn from the electron micrograph of a human neutrophil.

It is drawn in pencil /.................................... **(2 marks)**

(b) Give **two** faults with this diagram.

It does not focus ..../ it does not have

.... **(2 marks)**

(c) Draw your own labelled diagram of the slide shown above.

(4 marks)

3 This is a light micrograph of a plant cell. Draw and label a diagram to show what you can see.

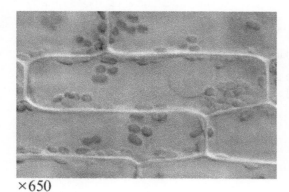

×650

> Remember you might make a mistake and need to rub it out!

(4 marks)

Enzymes

1 (a) What is an enzyme?

An enzyme is a biological catalyst which .... **(1 mark)**

> The reactions in the body would take place without enzymes – just **very** slowly!

(b) What are enzymes made of?

.... **(1 mark)**

(c) This diagram represents the lock-
and-key model of how enzymes work.
What is represented by:

A ....

B ....

C ....   **(3 marks)**

(d) Enzymes are **specific**. Use the diagram to help you explain what this means.

The .... matches the shape of the substrate

molecules and holds them close together so ....

Once the product is formed ....

The shape of the active site of an enzyme only ....

.... **(3 marks)**

2 In a practical, students measured the rate of reaction of a mixture containing an enzyme
and a substrate as they heated up the reacting mixture. Describe each stage of their graph.

> Think about the free movement
> of the molecules *and* the effect of
> temperature on protein structure.

> When the shape of the active site of
> an enzyme is changed by temperature
> so that it no longer works it has been
> **denatured**, not 'killed'.

A ....

....

B ....

....

C ....

....

D ....

.... **(4 marks)**

 **Practical skills** # pH and enzyme activity

You can investigate the effect of pH on the rate of enzyme activity by measuring the rate of an enzyme-controlled reaction at a known pH and then repeating the process at different pHs. By comparing the reaction rates, you can determine how pH affects the enzyme.

A group of students carried out an investigation into the effect of pH on the activity of the enzyme catalase, using the apparatus shown. Catalase catalyses (speeds up) the breakdown of hydrogen peroxide (H_2O_2) into water and oxygen – the oxygen is given off as a gas. By measuring the volume of gas given off in a given time, you can calculate the rate of the reaction at a given pH. Repeating the process with solutions of different pH allows you to observe the effect of pH on the activity of the enzyme.

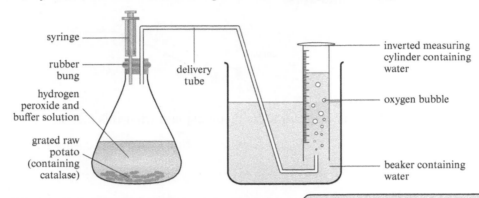

The results they achieved are shown below.

 Maths skills

(a) Complete the table below.

$$\text{rate (cm}^3\text{/min)} = \frac{\text{volume of gas produced}}{\text{time}}$$

pH	Volume of gas produced in 5 min (cm³)	Rate of catalase reaction (cm³ oxygen/min)
4	0	0
5	5	1
6	20	
7		3
8	2	

(3 marks)

 Maths skills

(b) Draw a suitable graph to show the effect of pH on the rate of reaction of catalase.

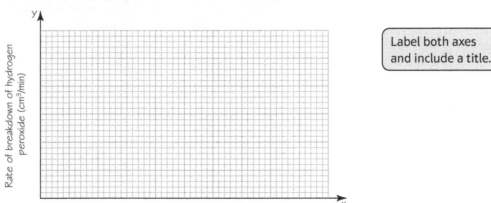

Label both axes and include a title.

(4 marks)

(c) Suggest **one** way in which the students could modify their experiment to make their results more reliable.

....

.... **(1 mark)**

The importance of enzymes

1 (a) What do enzymes do in the human digestive system?

Break down large, complex molecules into ....

....   **(2 marks)**

(b) Complete the following table showing **four** important enzymes.

Enzyme	Where it is found in humans	Reaction catalysed
		Breaking down starch into small sugars
catalase		Breaking down hydrogen peroxide into water and oxygen
protease		
lipase		

(4 marks)

> Learn the names of digestive enzymes and what they help to break down.

2 The enzyme DNA polymerase is an enzyme that helps DNA synthesis.
   What does this mean?

The enzyme catalyses the synthesis of large DNA molecules ....

....   **(2 marks)**

> Make sure you know the difference between synthesis and digestion.

3 Dishwasher powders often contain enzymes as well as detergent. Explain how these
   enzymes help to get dishes and pans clean.

Food contains proteins (in egg, meat, etc.), lipids in fatty foods and

carbohydrates (starches). If ....

....

....

....   **(2 marks)**

4 (a) Give **two** different roles for enzymes in the human body.

....

....   **(2 marks)**

Guided

(b) Normal human body temperature is 37 °C. If your internal body temperature
     falls below 35 °C or goes above 40 °C your body does not work properly and you
     may even die. Using your knowledge of enzymes, explain why your body will not
     function correctly if your body temperature is too hot or cold.

....

....

....

....

....   **(4 marks)**

Getting in and out of cells

1 Which of these transport processes requires energy? Tick **one** box.

☐ **A** osmosis   ☐ **C** active transport

☐ **B** diffusion   ☐ **D** facilitated diffusion   **(1 mark)**

2 (a) Define diffusion.

The net movement of molecules from .... to ......

.... down a .... **(2 marks)**

(b) How does osmosis differ from diffusion?

Osmosis is .... It involves the net movement of water molecules across

.... **(2 marks)**

> In both diffusion and osmosis there is **net** movement **down** a concentration gradient.

3 This diagram shows an experiment in progress. At the beginning of the experiment, the level of liquid in the beaker and in the capillary tubing were the same, and the bag contained a small volume of concentrated sucrose solution.

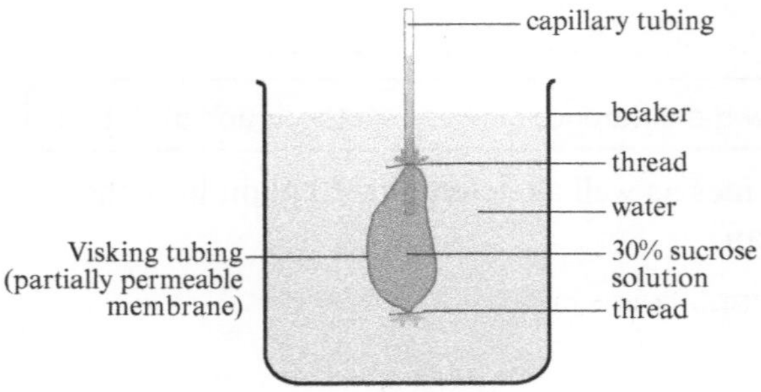

capillary tubing
beaker
thread
water
Visking tubing (partially permeable membrane)
30% sucrose solution
thread

> Always check the concentrations of the different liquids carefully in osmosis investigations.

Name the process and explain what has happened to fill the bag and make the liquid level in the capillary tubing rise.

The process is called .... water molecules crossed the

.... Visking tubing into the tubing than ....

.... This gave a net movement of water .... the

bag, so .... and the bag became................. **(4 marks)**

4 (a) Give **one** similarity between diffusion, osmosis and active transport in cells.

They are all .... **(1 mark)**

(b) Give **one** difference between active transport and the two processes of diffusion and osmosis.

Active transport requires .... from respiration to move molecules

.... The other two processes are passive and ....

.... **(3 marks)**

 **Practical skills** # Osmosis in potatoes

1 This apparatus is used to demonstrate osmosis.

(a) Here are some of the instructions that would allow a student to carry out an investigation into osmosis using potatoes. Complete the remaining instructions.

A Collect five different concentrations of solute solutions, for example, 0, 0.2, 0.4, 0.6, 0.8, and five pieces of potato, all the same length and diameter.

potato —

B Fill a boiling tube two-thirds full with one solution. Mark the value of the solute concentration on the tube. Repeat this for all of the solutions.

C Blot a piece of potato dry, ...

....

D After 20 minutes, remove the pieces of potato, ...

....

.... **(4 marks)**

(b) Why is it important to blot the pieces of potato before measuring the mass?

....

.... **(2 marks)**

2 The table below shows the results of an experiment to investigate osmosis in potatoes.

Solute concentration (mol dm^{-3})	Initial mass (g)	Final mass (g)	Change in mass (g)	Percentage change in mass (%)
0.0	16.52	20.15	3.63	21.97
0.2	15.90	16.70	0.8	5.03
0.4	17.06	15.69	−1.37	
0.6	16.88	14.36	−2.52	
0.8	16.23	12.32	−3.91	

 Maths skills

(a) Complete the table by calculating the percentage change in mass.

Doing lots of calculations is good practice for your exams!

(2 marks)

 Maths skills

(b) (i) Draw a suitable graph to show the effect of solutions of different solute concentrations on osmosis in potato cells.

Label the axes and give the graph a title.

(3 marks)

(ii) Use your graph to estimate the solute concentration of the potato cells in mol dm^{-3}.

.... **(1 mark)**

11

Extended response – Key concepts

You are given a sweet potato and four different concentrations of sugar solution (0.2, 0.4, 0.6 and 0.8 mol dm⁻³). You also have access to all the normal laboratory equipment and distilled water.

Describe how you would use these materials to demonstrate osmosis in plants.

> Plan your answer carefully before you start writing.

> Repeat your measurements and find the mean to make your results as reliable as possible.

> • Describe each step of the experiment you would carry out and what results you would collect.
> • How would you make sure your results were accurate?
> • How do you calculate mass increases/decreases?
> • Describe how you would present the results (graph) and explain the pattern of results you would expect to see.
> • Use your knowledge of osmosis to explain what the results should show.

....

....

....

....

....

....

....

....

....

....

....

....

....

....

....

....

....

....

....

....

....

....

(6 marks)

Mitosis

1 Which of the following processes is involved in the cell cycle? Tick **one** box.

☐ **A** meiosis   ☐ **C** mitosis

☐ **B** gametogenesis   ☐ **D** osmosis

> Be clear about the difference between mitosis and meiosis:
> **Mitosis** – the process of cell division involved in growth and repair.
> **Meiosis** – the process of cell division involved in the formation of the gametes (sex cells).

(1 mark)

2 (a) Body cells are diploid. What does this mean?

They have .... sets of chromosomes.

(1 mark)

> Remember: sex cells (gametes) are haploid – they have one set of chromosomes.
>
> Body cells are diploid – they have twice as many sets of chromosomes, because the original body cell of the organism is formed when an egg from the mother, containing one set of chromosomes, is fertilised by a sperm from the father, containing another set of chromosomes.

(b) Why are body cells diploid?

They get one set of chromosomes from ....

(1 mark)

(c) A body cell divides by mitosis. How do the daughter cells compare to the original cell?

They are both ....

(1 mark)

3 (a) The diagram shows the main stages that occur when an animal cell divides by mitosis. Name the **five** stages of mitosis labelled A–E.

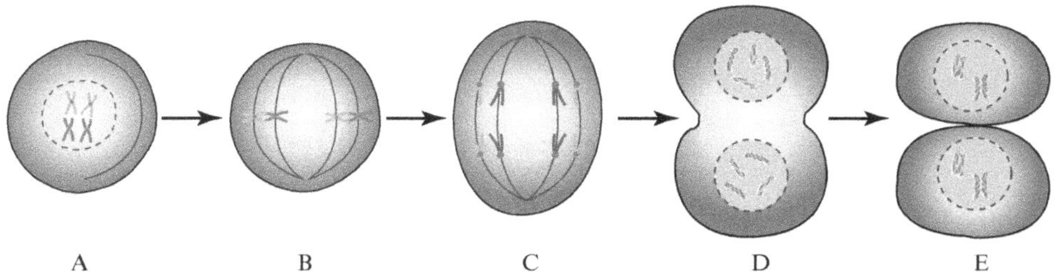

A   B   C   D   E

A Prophase

B ....

C ....

D ....

E ....

> It is important to know the main stages of mitosis and what happens at each stage.

(5 marks)

(b) Describe what is happening in stages A, C and E.

....

....

....

....

....

(4 marks)

Cell growth and differentiation

1 Which of these processes is mitosis **not** involved in? Tick **one** box.

☐ **A** asexual reproduction

☐ **B** growth

☐ **C** repair

☐ **D** formation of the sex cells **(1 mark)**

> Make sure you read through all the options carefully in multiple choice questions.

2 (a) When an egg and a sperm fuse at fertilisation, the new cell that forms is called

the .... **(1 mark)**

(b) What type of cell division takes place as the embryo grows? Explain why this is important.

Mitosis – so all the cells of the new organism .... **(2 marks)**

(c) What happens to the cells as the embryo develops? Explain why this is important.

The cells .... to form .... This is important

because .... **(2 marks)**

> **Growth** involves producing more cells and the cells getting bigger. **Differentiation** is the process that produces specialised cells to do particular functions in the body.

3 Local people in Costa Rica claim the noni fruit (see photo) cures many diseases, including cancer. Scientists are testing the juice and flesh of the noni fruit to see if it has any effect on the stages of mitosis. Explain why they are doing this.

> You are not expected to know anything about the fruit in this photograph. You must use what you know about mitosis and cancer to work out the answer.

Cancer is the result of changes in cells, which leads to ....

.... and the formation of ....

....

.... **(4 marks)**

4 (a) What is the meristem of a plant?

....

.... **(1 mark)**

> Guided

(b) What processes take place in meristems to produce specialised plant cells?

.... **(2 marks)**

(c) Give **one** example of a specialised animal cell and **one** example of a specialised plant cell. For each example you choose, explain how its structure is related to its function.

....

....

....

....

.... **(4 marks)**

Growth and percentile charts

1 (a) What is growth?

A permanent .... **(1 mark)**

(b) Give two common ways in which we measure growth.

Increase in length/height; .... **(2 marks)**

2 Scientists measured the growth of two sets of 10 seedlings. Both sets of plants had lots of light, but one set were grown at 10 °C and the other set grown at 20 °C. The mean wet mass of each set of plants is shown in the table below.

	Mass in grams week 1	Mass in grams week 12
A Plants grown at 10 °C	245	1500
B Plants grown at 20 °C	250	1950

Maths skills

(a) Calculate the increase in mass in (i) plant set A; (ii) plant set B, over the experiment.

(i) .... week 12 mass − week 1 mass = mass increase

(ii) .... **(2 marks)**

Maths skills

(b) Calculate the percentage increase in mass in (i) plant set A; (ii) plant set B. Show your working.

(i) ....

percentage change = $\frac{\text{final value}}{\text{starting value}} \times 100$

(2 marks)

(ii) .... **(2 marks)**

Maths skills

(c) How big was the percentage difference between the plants in set A and set B?

.... **(1 mark)**

(d) Explain the difference you observe.

....
....
....

How does temperature affect the rate of chemical reactions?

(2 marks)

3 (a) What is a percentile chart like this one used to record? .... **(1 mark)**

Guided

(b) A baby boy is weighed at one year old and his weight is plotted on the chart (shown by an x). Which percentile does he belong to?

.... **(1 mark)**

(c) If the weight of a baby falls below the lowest line or rises above the upper line on this chart, what does it indicate?

....
....
....

(1 mark)

Growth chart

Weight-for-age percentiles: Boys, birth to 36 months

Stem cells

1 Which of the following is **not** a type of stem cell? Tick **one** box.

☐ **A** meristem cell

☐ **B** epidermal cell

☐ **C** adult stem cell

☐ **D** embryonic stem cell

> Either knowing the three types of stem cells **or** recognising a differentiated adult cell type will help you answer this question.

(1 mark)

2 (a) What is a stem cell?

> Always check the number of marks – you don't need to give a very long answer if you are only going to get one mark.

Unspecialised cells which .... **(1 mark)**

(b) Give **one** similarity and **one** difference between embryonic stem cells and meristem cells.

Embryonic stem cells and meristem cells can both ....

Embryonic stem cells are ...., meristem cells are .... **(2 marks)**

> When asked for similarities, you only have to think of one property seen in both cell types. For differences, you need to comment on both of the cell types you are comparing.

(c) How do adult stem cells differ from both embryonic stem cells and meristem cells?

Embryonic stem cells and meristem cells can ....,

but adult stem cells can .... **(2 marks)**

3 (a) Give **two** medical uses of embryonic stem cells.

Replacing or ....

....

Growing .... **(2 marks)**

(b) Give **two** reasons why some people have concerns about using embryonic stem cells to treat human diseases.

> Give two very clearly different reasons, e.g. one scientific and one ethical.

Stem cells are good at dividing. Sometimes ....

....

An early human embryo is destroyed ....

.... **(2 marks)**

4 In general, there are fewer objections to the use of adult stem cells in human treatment than there are about using embryonic stem cells. Discuss the reasons for this.

Guided

....

....

....

....

.... **(4 marks)**

Neurones

1 (a) What is a neurone?

A specialised cell that .... **(1 mark)**

> Don't just refer to 'messages' – what physically passes through a neurone?

(b) There are three types of neurones. Explain the function of each type.

Motor neurones carry impulses ....

Sensory neurones carry impulses ....

Relay neurones are found .... linking

.... **(3 marks)**

2 (a) Label the parts labelled A–D. Write your answers on the diagram.   **(2 marks)**

(b) What are the functions of parts B and C?

(i) Part B carries ....   **(1 mark)**

(ii) Part C insulates the neurone, ...

....

....

....   **(2 marks)**

D ....

B ....

C ....

A ....

3 Complete the table to compare three features of a motor neurone, a sensory neurone and a relay neurone.

> The question asks for features so you can use both structures and functions of the cells in your comparison.

Motor neurone	Sensory neurone	Relay neurone
	impulse travels towards the CNS	
cell body at one end	cell body between the axon and the dendron	
		links only to other neurones

(3 marks)

4 (a) Describe the sequence of events in your nervous system that enables you to see a piece of fruit and pick it up.

Guided

....

....

....

....   **(3 marks)**

(b) In some inherited diseases, the myelin sheath surrounding the motor neurones is gradually destroyed. Affected people gradually lose control of their muscles and cannot move. Explain how this happens.

....

....

....

....   **(3 marks)**

Responding to stimuli

1 (a) What is a synapse?

A gap between ....

(1 mark)

(b) Explain what is happening in this synapse at points A, B and C.

A   An electrical impulse ....,

causing ....

.... **(2 marks)**

B   The neurotransmitter ....

and fits ....

.... **(2 marks)**

C   A new .... **(1 mark)**

> Make sure your answer gives three clear events that occur at the junction between two neurones.

2 Synapses slow down the speed of transmission of nerve impulses, **but** they are very important for the smooth working of the nervous system. Explain **two** advantages of having synapses in the system.

Guided

....

.... **(2 marks)**

3 (a) What is a reflex?

Automatic, ... **(1 mark)**

(b) Why is a reflex arc so fast?

Reflex arcs only involve .... If the impulses went to the ....

.... **(2 marks)**

(c) Give **two** reasons why reflexes are so important.

....

.... **(2 marks)**

> Remember: reflexes are fast and don't involve your conscious brain.

4 Draw a flow chart to show the sequence of events in a reflex arc from the stimulus to the response.

> Do what the question asks for and produce a flow chart – don't write sentences or produce bullet points.

(4 marks)

Extended response – Cells and control

Curare is a poison. It has been used by hunters in some South American countries for centuries. A little drop of curare on the tip of an arrow means that if the arrow hits an animal, it will quickly become paralysed and stop breathing.

Scientists have discovered that curare fits into the receptors in the synapses between the motor neurones and the muscles. Use this information to explain how curare can cause paralysis, stop breathing and cause death.

> In this question, you have to explain a situation you will not have seen before. **Don't panic!** What you have learned about the way neurones work means you know everything you need to know to give a perfect answer.
>
> Always plan out your extended response before you start writing. It's a good idea to make a list of bullet points of the main things you want to cover and to get them in the right order before you start writing. Then, cross off each bullet point as you cover it in your answer.
>
> Make sure you keep referring your answer to the content of the question.
>
> Your answer should include:
> * The role of motor neurones, synapses and muscles.
> * How synapses work.
> * How curare would block the transmission of impulses between motor neurones and muscles if it fits into the receptors of the synapses between motor neurones and muscles, and how this would cause paralysis and death.

Motor neurones	What happens at junction	What curare blocks
CNS ↓ electrical impulses ↓ muscles	impulse causes ↓ neurotransmitter chemicals ↓ stimulate muscles to contract	receptors inc. effect of specific muscles not working

....

....

....

....

....

....

....

....

.... **(6 marks)**

Had a go ☐ Nearly there ☐ Nailed it! ☐

Meiosis

1 Which of the following processes are involved in the formation of the gametes?
Tick **two** boxes.

☐ **A** meiosis

☐ **B** gametogenesis

☐ **C** mitosis

☐ **D** osmosis

> Be clear about the difference between mitosis and meiosis:
> **Mitosis** – the process of cell division involved in growth and repair.
> **Meiosis** – the process of cell division involved in the formation of the sex cells.

(1 mark)

2 (a) Body cells are diploid, but gametes are haploid. What do the terms diploid and haploid mean?

Diploid means a cell has .... of chromosomes and haploid

means a cell has .... **(1 mark)**

> When gametes fuse to form a zygote, this has twice as many sets of chromosomes.

(b) Why are body cells diploid?

Because two gametes join together to form a new diploid cell. **(1 mark)**

(c) Gametes are formed when a cell divides by meiosis. How do the daughter cells (formed by meiosis) compare to the original cell?

The original cell is ...., but the daughter cells are ....

.... **(1 mark)**

3 The cells that make the gametes of an animal or plant divide by meiosis. Use diagrams A–D to help you explain what happens in this process.

Guided

> You will not be asked to name the stages of meiosis.

A   B   C   D

....

....

....

....

....

.... **(4 marks)**

DNA

1 A single, long DNA molecule, tightly coiled and held together by proteins. What is this a definition of? Tick **one** box.

☐ **A** gene

☐ **B** base

☐ **C** chromosome

☐ **D** nucleus

> Make sure you are clear about the differences between DNA, genes and chromosomes.

(1 mark)

2 Describe the difference between chromosomes, genes and DNA.

A chromosome consists of a long molecule ....

A gene is a section ....

DNA is the .... material ....   **(3 marks)**

> You need to know how the base pairs are arranged: **A** pairs with .... and **G** pairs with .... Write a mnemonic to help you remember.

3 The diagram shows two models of the structure of DNA.

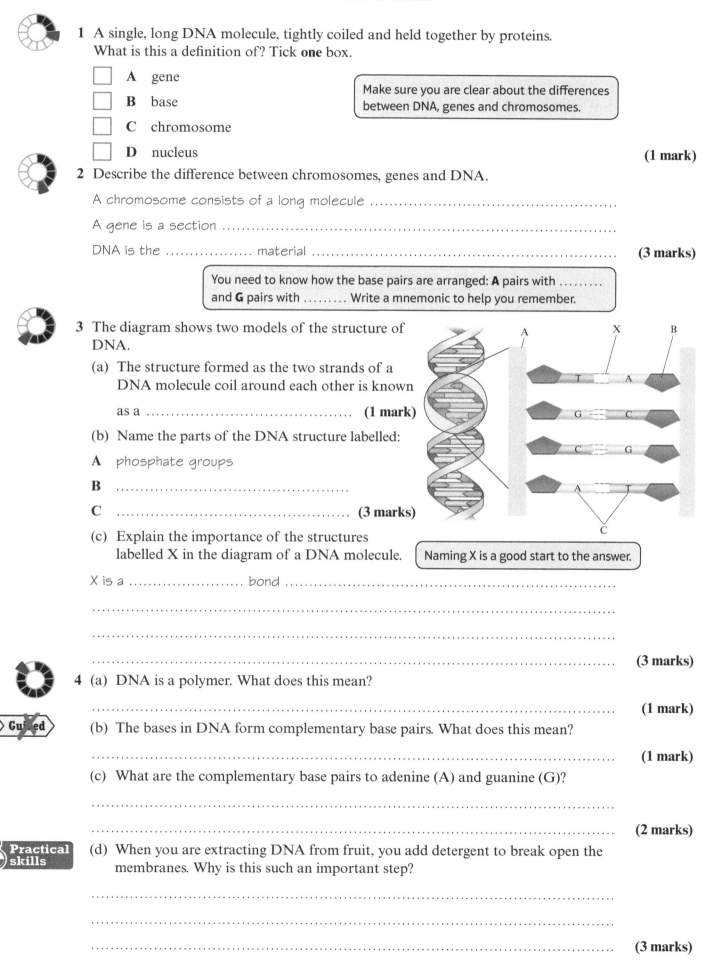

(a) The structure formed as the two strands of a DNA molecule coil around each other is known

   as a .... **(1 mark)**

(b) Name the parts of the DNA structure labelled:

A phosphate groups

B ....

C .... **(3 marks)**

(c) Explain the importance of the structures labelled X in the diagram of a DNA molecule.

> Naming X is a good start to the answer.

X is a .... bond ....

....

....

.... **(3 marks)**

4 (a) DNA is a polymer. What does this mean?

.... **(1 mark)**

⟩ **Guided** ⟩ (b) The bases in DNA form complementary base pairs. What does this mean?

.... **(1 mark)**

(c) What are the complementary base pairs to adenine (A) and guanine (G)?

....

.... **(2 marks)**

🧪 **Practical skills** (d) When you are extracting DNA from fruit, you add detergent to break open the membranes. Why is this such an important step?

....

....

.... **(3 marks)**

Genetic terms

1 List the following genetic terms in order of size, from the smallest to the largest: genome, allele, chromosome, gene, base.

Base, ... **(2 marks)**

2 (a) What is a gene?

A short piece ....

which .... **(1 mark)**

(b) Explain the difference between a gene and an allele.

Alleles are ....

which .... **(2 marks)**

> Make sure you know the difference between a gene and an allele and use the terms correctly. Students often lose marks by getting them muddled.

3 This is a brown mouse. Its mother was a brown mouse and its father was a white mouse. Some of the other mice in the litter were white. The allele for a brown coat is represented by **B** and the allele for a white coat by **b**.

> Guided

(a) Complete a Punnett diagram to show the genotypes of the parents of the mouse described, the mouse and his siblings.

(1 mark)

(b) Define 'genotype':

.... **(1 mark)**

(c) What is the mouse's genotype?

.... **(1 mark)**

(d) What allele did the mouse inherit from its:

(i) mother ....

(ii) father? .... **(2 marks)**

(e) Which of the alleles B and b are dominant? .... **(1 mark)**

(f) Define the following terms:

(i) phenotype ....

(ii) recessive allele .... **(2 marks)**

4 Peas can be round or wrinkled. Their shape is inherited. There is a dominant allele for round peas (represented as **R**) and a recessive allele for wrinkled peas (represented as **r**). There are three possible genotypes for the shape of peas. For each of the following, state whether the plant is homozygous or heterozygous and give the phenotype of the plant:

> Guided

(a) RR .... **(1 mark)**   (c) Rr .... **(1 mark)**

(b) rr .... **(1 mark)**

Monohybrid inheritance

1 Manx cats are born with no tails. The allele for no tail is dominant (T) over the allele (t) for having a tail. The homozygous form of the dominant allele is fatal – kittens which inherit TT die before birth.

> Read the information given to you in the question carefully. You must apply the information you are given to calculating genetic probabilities.

(a) Complete this Punnett square to show the expected genotypes and phenotypes of the kittens born to a cross between a normal cat and a Manx cat, and calculate the percentage of the offspring which you would expect to have no tails.

	T	
t		

> Remember: percentage probabilities in Punnett squares are always 0%, 25%, 50%, 75% or 100%.

$\frac{1}{2}$ of the kittens will have the genotype .... and so their phenotype will be .... This is $\frac{2}{4} \times 100 =$ .... **(3 marks)**

(b) Complete the Punnett square to show the expected genotypes of a cross between two Manx cats.

	T	
T		

Manx cat genotype Tt

(2 marks)

(c) What ratio of Manx kittens to normal kittens would you expect from this cross (regardless of survival)?

.... **(1 mark)**

(d) What ratio of Manx kittens to normal kittens is actually likely to survive? Explain your answer.

....

.... **(2 marks)**

2 A gardener crosses two purple flowered plants and records that the flowers of all the offspring plants are also purple. He claims that his plants will always have purple flowers. Another gardener challenges him to breed his purple plants with white flowering plants and see what happens. The allele for purple colour is dominant, represented by the letter **R**. White is recessive, indicated by the letter **r**. Use Punnett squares or genetic diagrams to show the possible genotypes and phenotypes of the crosses.

....

....

....

....

....

....

(4 marks)

Family pedigrees

1 (a) This family pedigree shows the inheritance of albinism in a family. Albinos do not make the pigment melanin in their bodies, so they have very pale skin, white hair and pale eyes. The allele for normal pigmentation is dominant (**A**) and the allele for albinism is recessive (**a**).

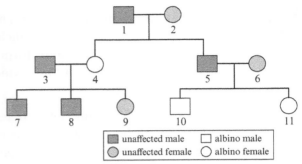

unaffected male ☐ albino male
unaffected female ○ albino female

Which of the following statements is true for anyone affected by albinism? Tick **one** box.

☐ **A** they are homozygous for allele A

☐ **B** they are heterozygous, Aa

☐ **C** they are homozygous for allele a

☐ **D** their bodies make an excess of melanin

> Read the question carefully so you know which allele represents the dominant phenotype and which represents the recessive phenotype.

(b) State the genotypes of individuals 1 and 2 and explain how you know this.

....

....

.... **(3 marks)**

(c) Individual 4 is an albino, but she and her partner have three children who are not affected. Explain two different ways this may have happened (you can explain using words or draw Punnet squares or genetic diagrams).

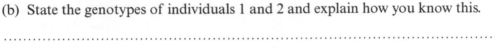

AA × aa

....

....

....

Aa × aa

....

....

.... **(5 marks)**

2 This family pedigree shows the grandparents, parents and children in a family affected by Huntington's disease. This is a genetic disease that develops when people are middle-aged and it is usually fatal. The Huntington's phenotype is dominant and the allele can be represented by a capital **H**. The healthy, recessive allele is shown as **h**.

☐ healthy man ■ man with Huntington's
○ healthy woman ● woman with Huntington's

Couple 3 and 4, and couple 8 and 9 will both be affected by Huntington's. Explain how couple 3 and 4 have no affected children, but couple 8 and 9 have an affected daughter. Draw a Punnett square or genetic diagrams to help you.

> The probabilities apply each time a child is conceived.

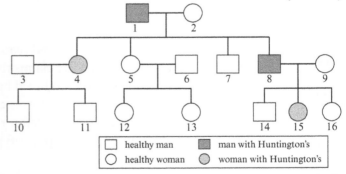

Hh × hh

....

....

.... **(4 marks)**

Sex determination

1 Which of the following is the combination of sex chromosomes you would expect to see in the cells of a human male? Tick **one** box.

☐ **A** XX

☐ **B** X

☐ **C** Y

☐ **D** XY

> Remember – chromosomes come in pairs so there will be two sex chromosomes.

(1 mark)

2 When is the sex of a baby determined? Tick **one** box.

☐ **A** when the gametes are formed

☐ **B** when the baby is born

☐ **C** when the egg is fertilised by the sperm

☐ **D** as the foetus develops in the womb

> Think – the gametes are haploid so it is the moment when the two gametes fuse to form a new individual that the sex will be determined.

(1 mark)

3 A couple have three little boys. They want another child. Some of their friends say that because they have three boys they are sure to have a girl if they have another child. Others say they are bound to have another boy.

(a) Complete the Punnett square below to show how the sex of the new baby is inherited.

	X	Y
X		
X		

(2 marks)

(b) Are either of their sets of friends right about the sex of the baby? Explain your answer.

Each baby gets one set of chromosomes from ....

Each time a baby is conceived there is a ....

.... The outcome is not affected ....

.... so the new baby

has a .... **(4 marks)**

4 Every egg produced by a woman has a chance of becoming a baby girl. Only half of the gametes produced by a man have the chance of becoming a baby girl. Explain this statement.

....

....

....

....

....

....

....

.... **(3 marks)**

Variation and mutation

1 Give **one** example of genetic variation and **one** example of environmental variation between different organisms of the same species.

.... variation, for example, eye colour, natural hair colour.

.... variation, for example, scars, being able to drive. **(1 mark)**

2 Which of the following is an acquired characteristic? Tick **one** box. **(1 mark)**

☐ **A** brown eyes ☐ **C** cystic fibrosis

☐ **B** a tattoo ☐ **D** dimples

Guided ✗

3 (a) What is a mutation?

A change .... **(1 mark)**

(b) Give **two** causes of mutations.

Mistakes made when .... **(2 marks)**

(c) Most genetic mutations have no effect on the phenotype, but some do. Explain how a mutation can affect the phenotype of an organism.

The sequence of bases in the DNA codes for ....

.... If a mutation affects the

base sequences so that different ....

.... **(3 marks)**

4 This bar chart shows the heights of a group of students.

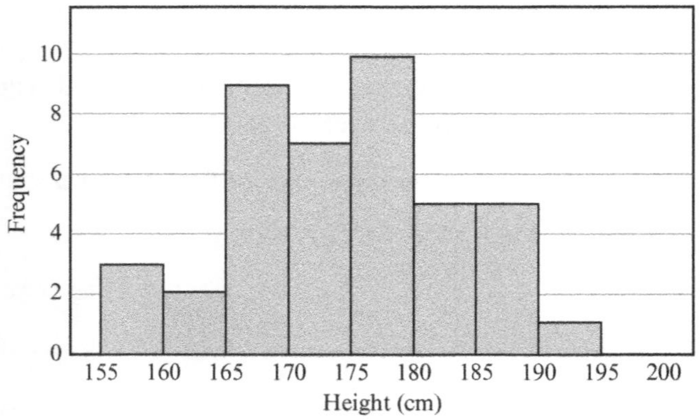

Maths skills

(a) The *y*-axis of this bar chart shows the frequency of the characteristic. What does this mean?

....

.... **(1 mark)**

Maths skills

(b) The bar chart is drawn with no gaps between the bars. What does this tell you?

That the characteristic measured shows .... variation. **(1 mark)**

> Remember: Genetic variation is inherited and gives the basic appearance of an organism. Environmental factors such as the amount of food or light can have a big effect on how the organism eventually looks, whatever genes it has inherited.

The Human Genome Project

1 (a) What is the human genome?

The human genome is .... **(1 mark)**

(b) What is the Human Genome Project?

A collaboration between scientists set up .... **(1 mark)**

(c) How has the Human Genome Project affected the way doctors prescribe medicines?

It may enable them to look at how the genome of the person ....

....

by a particular drug. **(2 marks)**

2 The results of the Human Genome Project are being used to develop new medicines and treatments for diseases.

(a) Give **two** advantages of using the results of the Human Genome Project in medicine.

Advantage 1:

A person who is at risk from a genetic condition or ....

....

.... **(2 marks)**

Advantage 2:

Doctors may be able to ....

....

.... **(2 marks)**

> There are more than two advantages so make sure you use two that are as different as possible.

(b) Some people think there will be disadvantages to having all this information about the human genome. Give **one** possible disadvantage:

If you know you have an increased risk of developing ....

.... **(1 mark)**

3 Many different genes are involved in the risk of developing heart disease. Discuss the advantages and disadvantages of a genetic test that would tell you the balance of low risk and high risk alleles in your cells.

....

....

....

....

....

....

....

.... **(5 marks)**

Extended response – Genetics

There is a dominant mutation that results in Huntington's disease. This disease does not usually develop until the affected person is between 30 and 50 years old, although it can start much earlier or much later. The disease affects many aspects of life and there is currently no cure.

However, using the knowledge we have from the Human Genome Project, people who are at risk can be tested to see if they have the affected dominant allele. Explain how Huntington's disease is passed from one generation to the next, and discuss the advantages and disadvantages of having this test if a grandparent has been affected by the disease.

> You will always be more successful in extended response questions if you plan your answer before you start writing.
>
> You should understand how a dominant disease such as Huntington's is inherited and you should make this clear in your answer. You could sketch a genetic diagram, a Punnett square or a family tree.
>
> When you are asked to discuss, do not waffle. Identify the issues highlighted in the question and make very clear points so the examiner can see you have considered different sides of the question.
>
> In Huntington's disease you need to consider the question of having a family, as the disease usually doesn't show until middle age when children and even grandchildren can already be affected.

Include description	Test advantages	Test disadvantages
mutation	plan your life	can't change outcome
dominant mutation	make decisions about having kids	stress of knowing you have/will have a disease
HGP means it's poss. to test for faulty genes	relief if don't have faulty gene	difficult life choices
chances of inheriting H (Punnett)		impact on other family members

....

....

....

....

....

....

....

....

....

....

....

.... **(6 marks)**

Evolution

1 Produce a flow diagram to explain the process of natural selection.

> Adult organisms usually produce more offspring than an environment can
> support. As a result, there is ....
> between the young to survive and reproduce.

↓

> Some of the offspring inherit advantageous variations ....
> ....
> Others inherit variations ....

↓

> Individuals with the advantageous ....
> ....

↓

> ....

(4 marks)

> Remember: **natural** selection is the process by which evolution takes place.
> **Evolution** is the emergence of a new species as a result of natural selection
> after a change in the environment or some form of isolation.

2 Aloes and agaves look very similar. They have pointed, fleshy leaves and spines, they can both store water and they both grow in desert environments. You might think they are closely related plants, but in fact they are very different. Aloes originally come from north Africa, while agaves come from South America. DNA evidence shows that their last common ancestor lived about 93 million years ago, when there were dinosaurs on the Earth. Explain how the similarities between these two very different groups of plants have evolved.

> Make sure you include the following in your answer:
> • natural selection (what is it?)
> • habitat (where do they live? how are they adapted?)
> • plant features (how do they look? why?)
> • evolution (how does it work?)

....
....
....
....
....
....
....

(5 marks)

Human evolution

1

Species	Age (millions of years)	Skull volume (cm³)
Ardi (*Ardipithecus ramidus*)	4.4	350
Lucy (*Australopithecus afarensis*)	3.2	400
Modern human (*Homo sapiens*)	current	1450

The table gives you some information about two famous ancestral human-like species and modern human beings.

(a) What is our main source of information about early human ancestors?

.... **(1 mark)**

(b) What is the main limitation to our understanding of human evolution?

The lack of .... **(1 mark)**

(c) Why is measuring the skull volume of early human fossils so important in helping us to understand the progress of human evolution?

The volume of the skull ...., and the big increase

....

.... **(2 marks)**

2 Explain how scientists use stone tools as evidence for human evolution.

The layers of rock where stone tools were found have been dated. The earliest stone tools found are relatively simple, because those human ancestors had

relatively small brains. ....

.... **(2 marks)**

3

> Remember: Our main sources of evidence about human evolution come from a limited number of fossils and objects such as stone tools.

Ardipithecus ramidus ('Ardi') Skull volume: 350 cm³ — *Australopithecus afarensis* ('Lucy') Skull volume: 400 cm³ — *Homo habilis* Skull volume: 500–600 cm³ — *Homo erectus* Skull volume: 850 cm³ — *Homo sapiens* Skull volume: 1450 cm³

This diagram shows some of our early ancestors, although this is **not** a direct line of evolution from Ardi to modern humans. Using this diagram and your own knowledge, give four ways in which human-like species and humans have evolved over time, with evidence where possible.

....

....

....

....

.... **(5 marks)**

Classification

1 Which of these groups of organisms is a classification domain? Tick **one** box.

☐ **A** mammals

☐ **C** animals

☐ **B** flowering plants

☐ **D** bacteria

(1 mark)

2 Complete the table giving **three** characteristics of each kingdom of organisms listed.

Kingdom	Characteristics
Animals	1 multicellular 2 3
Plants	1 multicellular/cells have nuclei 2 3
Fungi	1 multicellular (apart from yeasts)/cells have nuclei 2 3
Protists	1 mostly unicellular 2 3
Prokaryotes	1 unicellular 2 3

(5 marks)

> Learn the key features of the five kingdoms and the three domains.

3 The three domain system of classification was suggested relatively recently.

(a) What is the three domain system?

.... **(1 mark)**

(b) Name and describe the three domains.

....

....

.... **(3 marks)**

(c) Explain why the three domain classification system has only been developed relatively recently.

....

....

....

....

....

.... **(3 marks)**

Selective breeding

1 Which of the following organisms is **not** the result of selective breeding? Tick **one** box.

☐ A   Jersey cows

☐ B   golden labrador dogs

☐ C   garden roses

☐ D   red squirrels

> Almost all organisms kept by people –
> farm animals and pets and the plants we
> grow for food and to look nice – are the
> result of **many years** of selective breeding.

(1 mark)

2 (a) What is meant by selective breeding?

It is when plants or animals with ....

so the offspring produced ....   **(1 mark)**

(b) Farmers have carried out selective breeding on plants for centuries. Give **three**
possible characteristics they might try to improve.

Disease resistance/..

....   **(3 marks)**

3 Some people love cats, but are allergic to cat hair. Explain how a breeder might
produce a breed of cats with very little fur, so that people allergic to cats can
enjoy having them as pets.

First, the breeder would choose two cats – male and female – with very little hair.

Then, ...

....   **(3 marks)**

4 (a) Describe the change in the yields of
wheat in the UK since 1887.

Maths skills

....

....

....

....

....   **(3 marks)**

> This answer is worth three marks – so just saying
> the yields increased isn't enough! '**Describe**'.

UK wheat yields 1885–2020

(b) Suggest **two** factors that might have brought about this increase in yield.

....

....   **(2 marks)**

(c) Suggest **one** problem that might arise from changing yields like this, and explain
how such problems might be overcome.

....

....

....

....   **(3 marks)**

Genetic engineering

1 (a) What is genetic engineering?

Genetic engineering is changing ....

.... **(1 mark)**

(b) In many areas of the world, people become ill and die through a lack of vitamins in their diet. How could genetic engineering help to solve this problem?

.... **(1 mark)**

2 In America, parents can buy glowing fish for their children. These fish are bred from genetically modified organisms – fish that have had genes added from jelly fish or sea anemones, which make them fluoresce bright colours. Glowing fish were originally developed to help scientists monitor pollution in waterways.

(a) What is a genetically modified organism?

An organism which has .... **(1 mark)**

(b) Give **one** advantage of producing genetically modified organisms such as glowing fish and **one** disadvantage.

> Glowing fish are only being used as an example – think of all the different advantages and disadvantages of genetically modifying organisms you have considered.

Advantage: they can be ....

....

Disadvantage: some people feel ....

.... **(2 marks)**

3 People with type 1 diabetes cannot live without insulin injections. In the past, they had to use insulin extracted from cows and pigs. The supply was limited and some people reacted to the insulin from other animals, because it was not quite the same as human insulin. Scientists then discovered how to genetically modify bacteria to produce human insulin. They grow the bacteria in huge containers and now there is plenty of human insulin for everyone who needs it.

(a) Why did the scientists use genetic engineering rather than selective breeding to make insulin-producing bacteria?

....

.... **(2 marks)**

(b) Describe how the GM bacteria which make human insulin are produced, and why scientists do not need to keep repeating the process.

....

....

....

.... **(3 marks)**

Guided

Extended response – Genetic modification

The Light Sussex cockerel on the left is the result of hundreds of years of selective breeding, while the scarlet macaw on the right is the result of millions of years of evolution. Bacteria that have been genetically engineered to produce human proteins have been developed over a matter of months and years.

Compare and contrast evolution, selective breeding and genetic engineering, and evaluate the usefulness of selective breeding and genetic engineering to people.

> To be successful in extended response questions, plan your answer before you start writing.
>
> When you are asked to compare and contrast processes, look for similarities **and** differences.
>
> There are two command terms here: 'compare and contrast' and 'evaluate'. Both mean you need to look for pros and cons, advantages and disadvantages, but when you evaluate you must make some judgement on the advantages and disadvantages of the processes. Your answer could explain the following points:
>
> * similarities between the three processes of evolution, selective breeding and genetic engineering
> * differences between the processes of evolution, selective breeding and genetic engineering
> * consider the usefulness to people of selective breeding compared with genetic engineering.

Evolution	Selective breeding	Genetic engineering
Huge periods of time	Decades/centuries	Relatively fast
Characteristics selected by environmental factors	Desired and undesired characteristics selected	Only chosen characteristics selected
	Same species only	Genes from different species can be used

....

....

....

....

....

....

....

....

....

.... **(6 marks)**

Health and disease

1 (a) What is a communicable disease?

A disease which ....

.... **(1 mark)**

(b) What causes communicable diseases?

.... **(1 mark)**

(c) Which of the following diseases is non-communicable? Tick **one** box.

☐ **A** influenza   ☐ **C** tuberculosis

☐ **B** lung cancer   ☐ **D** common cold   **(1 mark)**

> Remember the difference!
>
> .... diseases can be passed from one person to another and are caused by pathogens.
>
> .... diseases cannot be passed from one person to another **and** are not caused by pathogens.

2 The World Health Organization defines good health as a state of 'complete physical, social and mental well-being'. What is meant by:

(a) physical well-being?

Being free .... **(1 mark)**

(b) Social well-being?

Getting on well .... **(1 mark)**

(c) Mental well-being?

.... **(1 mark)**

3 (a) What is a pathogen?

A microorganism which .... **(1 mark)**

(b) Complete the following table showing the four main types of pathogens.

Pathogen	How do they make you ill?
Bacteria	May release ....
Viruses	Take over ....
....	Eukaryotic organisms that dissolve and damage cells
....	Eukaryotic organisms that can live in the body and damage cells

(4 marks)

> Learn how the different types of pathogens cause the symptoms of disease.

4 Explain why having a non-communicable disease makes you more likely to become ill from other diseases.

Guided

....

....

.... **(2 marks)**

Common infections

1 Which of the following is a communicable disease only affecting plants? Tick **one** box.

     ☐   **A**   tuberculosis

     ☐   **B**   cholera

     ☐   **C**   chalara

     ☐   **D**   malaria   **(1 mark)**

2 Botswana is an African country with a population of just over 2.26 million. The data in the graph shows the relationship between HIV infection and the numbers of people infected with TB each year.

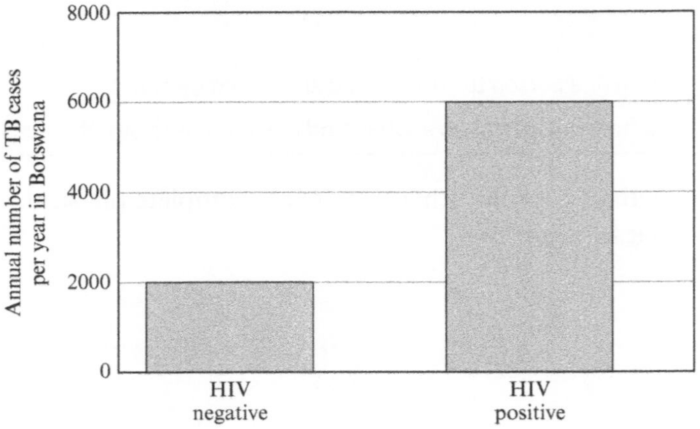

[Bar chart: x-axis shows "HIV negative" (~2000) and "HIV positive" (~6000); y-axis labelled "Annual number of TB cases per year in Botswana" from 0 to 8000]

Maths skills

(a) Give the total number of people infected each year with TB in Botswana.

....   **(1 mark)**

Maths skills

(b) What percentage of the people infected with TB are also infected with HIV?

$\frac{6000}{8000} \times$ ....   **(2 marks)**

(c) Explain why people infected with HIV are so much more likely to also become infected with TB.

....

....

....

....   **(3 marks)**

3 Complete the table to give three common human infections, with the symptoms of each.

Pathogen	Disease	Symptoms
Bacterium	....	....
Virus	....	....
Protist	....	....

     (6 marks)

How pathogens spread

1 How do the viruses that cause colds and flu spread from one person to another?
   Tick **one** box.

   ☐ **A**   through a cut in the skin

   ☐ **B**   through insect bites

   ☐ **C**   through the mouth in food or water

   ☐ **D**   by droplet infection from the air   **(1 mark)**

2 Cholera is an infection that kills thousands of people.

   (a) What type of pathogen causes cholera?

   ....   **(1 mark)**

   (b) Describe the main symptoms of cholera.

   Large amounts ....   **(1 mark)**

   (c) Cholera is a particular problem after natural disasters, such as floods and
        earthquakes. Explain this observation.

   The bacteria that cause cholera .... If there is a good

   sewage system, they ....

   After natural disasters...................................... so diarrhoea gets into water

   used for ....   **(3 marks)**

3 Describe the difference between a pathogen and a vector.

   A pathogen is ....

   A vector is a living ....   **(2 marks)**

   > Mosquitoes are the vectors for the protist that causes
   > malaria, carrying it from host to host in their bodies.

4 Here are three ways of reducing the spread of pathogens and so reducing infectious
   diseases. Explain how each way works:

   (a) Washing hands thoroughly after using the toilet.

   ....

   ....   **(2 marks)**

   (b) Boiling water before using it to drink or wash salads in hot countries with poor
        sanitation.

   ....

   ....   **(2 marks)**

   (c) Using tissues when you cough, sneeze or blow your nose, putting the used tissue in
        a bin and then washing your hands.

   ....

   ....

   ....   **(2 marks)**

STIs

1 Which of the following statements about STIs is **not** correct? Tick **one** box.

☐ **A** An STI is a sexually transmitted infection.

☐ **B** STIs are usually transmitted through sexual activity.

☐ **C** Many people with STIs do not know they are infected.

☐ **D** STIs are always incurable.   **(1 mark)**

> STIs caused by bacteria such as *Chlamydia*, gonorrhoea and syphilis can all be cured using antibiotics if they are picked up early, before they cause permanent damage.
>
> STIs caused by viruses such as herpes and HIV can be treated to greatly reduce the symptoms.

2 Explain the following statements about STIs.

(a) The spread of many STIs can be prevented if men wear condoms when having sex.

STIs are spread ....

If a man wears a condom, ...

....

....   **(3 marks)**

(b) All pregnant women are routinely screened for STIs including *Chlamydia* and HIV.

A woman can have these STIs without knowing. The pathogens can be passed

from ....

If the infection is picked up by screening ....

....

....   **(3 marks)**

3 There are a number of ways in which we can reduce the incidence, and prevent the spread, of STIs. For each of the methods given below, explain how they have their effect.

(a) Using condoms during sexual intercourse.

....

....   **(1 mark)**

(b) Screening blood transfusions for STIs.

....

....   **(2 marks)**

(c) Increasing sex education for young people.

....

....

....

....   **(2 marks)**

(d) Supplying intravenous drug users with sterile needles.

....

....   **(2 marks)**

Human defences

1 Which of the following acts as both a physical and a chemical barrier to the entry of
pathogens into your body? Tick **one** box.

☐ **A** tears

☐ **B** saliva

☐ **C** mucus

☐ **D** skin

> Many **chemical barriers** contain enzymes or acids to kill pathogens
> whereas a **physical barrier** stops pathogens entering your body.
> This question is asking you to identify a barrier that does both.

(1 mark)

2 The human body is surrounded by microorganisms all the time and some of them
are pathogens. Explain how each of the following helps to defend the body against
these pathogens.

(a) The skin.

> The command word here is 'explain' and you get 2 marks – so just saying the
> skin acts as a barrier isn't enough to get full marks – that is just a description!

Unbroken skin forms ....

because it is .... **(2 marks)**

(b) The acid in the stomach.

The acid in the stomach acts as ....

.... **(2 marks)**

(c) The tears.

Tears act as ....

.... **(2 marks)**

3 Children in households where one or both
of their parents smoke are much more likely
to get infections, especially chest infections.

(a) Name the structures labelled A, B and C.

A ....

B ....

C .... **(3 marks)**

(b) Suggest how these structures protect
our lungs.

....

....

> The air you breathe contains lots of dirt and pathogens.
> Think about how your body keeps your lungs clean.

....

....

.... **(2 marks)**

(c) Explain how breathing in second-hand smoke can increase the risk of children
getting chest infections.

....

....

....

.... **(3 marks)**

The immune system

1 The immune system uses chemicals found on the outside of cells and viruses to identify if something is a cell of the body or if it has come from outside the body. What are these special identifying chemicals called? Tick **one** box.

☐ **A** antigens
☐ **B** antibodies
☐ **C** antivirals
☐ **D** antibiotics

> **Antigens** are chemicals on the outside surface of **all** cells. White blood cells produce **antibodies** that match the shape of specific antigens on the pathogen cells or viruses so that the body can recognise its own cells from foreign cells or viruses. Make sure you learn the difference between these two similar sounding words.

(1 mark)

2 When you get a disease, your immune system will attack and destroy the pathogens causing your illness.

(a) Describe how your immune system recognises the pathogens.

White blood cells called .... have ....

on their surfaces. The shape ....

.... If the pathogen is present ....

....   **(3 marks)**

(b) Explain how your immune system destroys the pathogens so that you recover from the disease.

A l.................…... is activated when an .... from a ....

fits into ....

....   **(3 marks)**

(c) Once you have had a disease once, you are unlikely to get it again because you will develop natural immunity. Explain how this works.

Some of the activated ....…... form .... When you meet

the same .... again, they can ....

.... before you develop symptoms.   **(3 marks)**

3 (a) What event has happened at point X?

....
....
....   **(1 mark)**

(b) What events are indicated by the letters A and B?

A ....

B ....   **(2 marks)**

(c) The antibody numbers per cm^3 of blood climb faster and get much higher in response B than in response A. Explain both of these differences.

....
....
....
....   **(3 marks)**

Immunisation

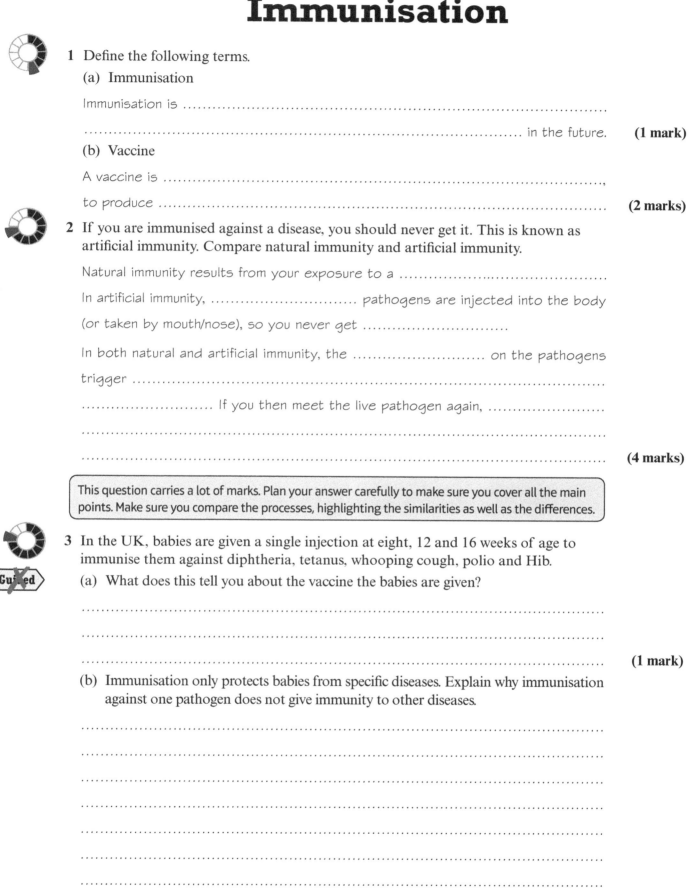

1 Define the following terms.

(a) Immunisation

Immunisation is ....

.... in the future. **(1 mark)**

(b) Vaccine

A vaccine is ....,

to produce .... **(2 marks)**

2 If you are immunised against a disease, you should never get it. This is known as artificial immunity. Compare natural immunity and artificial immunity.

Natural immunity results from your exposure to a ....

In artificial immunity, ... pathogens are injected into the body

(or taken by mouth/nose), so you never get ....

In both natural and artificial immunity, the .... on the pathogens

trigger ....

.... If you then meet the live pathogen again, ...

....

.... **(4 marks)**

> This question carries a lot of marks. Plan your answer carefully to make sure you cover all the main points. Make sure you compare the processes, highlighting the similarities as well as the differences.

3 In the UK, babies are given a single injection at eight, 12 and 16 weeks of age to immunise them against diphtheria, tetanus, whooping cough, polio and Hib.

Guided

(a) What does this tell you about the vaccine the babies are given?

....

....

.... **(1 mark)**

(b) Immunisation only protects babies from specific diseases. Explain why immunisation against one pathogen does not give immunity to other diseases.

....

....

....

....

....

....

....

....

.... **(5 marks)**

Treating infections

1 Which of the following is a type of medicine that can kill bacteria and so cure bacterial diseases? Tick **one** box.

☐ **A** antigens

☐ **B** anti-inflammatories

☐ **C** antibodies

☐ **D** antibiotics

> Don't get muddled between words linked to the immune response and the drugs that cure bacterial diseases.

(1 mark)

2 (a) Why are antibiotics so useful at treating bacterial infections in humans?

Because they ...., but do not affect .... **(1 mark)**

(b) Give **two** ways antibiotics can affect bacteria.

They can .... or they can ....

.... **(2 marks)**

(c) A worried mother goes to the doctor with her toddler, who has a bad cold. She wants some antibiotics to make the child better. The doctor does not give any antibiotics. Suggest why this decision was made.

Colds are caused .... Antibiotics do not ....

so they would .... **(2 marks)**

3 In the early years of the 20th century, many women died from infection shortly after they gave birth.

Guided

Maths skills

(a) What was the highest rate of maternal deaths recorded in the United States between 1900 and 2010?

.... **(2 marks)**

(b) Suggest a reason for the rapid fall in maternal deaths observed in the shaded area of the graph.

....

.... **(1 mark)**

Maternal death rates in the US 1900–2010

(c) The rate of maternal deaths from infection has remained very low for many years. Scientists now fear that, as a result of the over-use of antibiotics, the number of women dying from these infections may increase again in the future. Discuss this statement.

> These infections are usually caused by bacteria. Consider antibiotic resistance in your answer.

....

....

....

....

....

....

.... **(4 marks)**

New medicines

1 Which process is **not** involved in the development of new medicines? Tick **one** box.

☐ **A** discovery   ☐ **C** immunisation

☐ **B** clinical testing   ☐ **D** development   **(1 mark)**

2 Scientists have discovered a new chemical in the fruit of a tree from the rain forests of South America. Local people use the fruit to cure many types of disease, including some cancers. Scientists observe that people who take the fruit do seem to recover from some of their illnesses.

(a) Suggest **two** reasons why the scientists don't bring the fruit back to the UK and start using it to treat ill people immediately.

Because they don't know .... There may be

.... **(2 marks)**

(b) Once the chemicals have been isolated from the fruit, they will have to go through several stages of pre-clinical testing.

(i) What is pre-clinical testing?

Testing new medicines ....

.... **(2 marks)**

(ii) Describe **three** different stages of pre-clinical testing.

Testing on ....

Testing on ....

Testing on ....   **(3 marks)**

(c) Describe what happens if the pre-clinical testing of the new medicine is successful.

It goes into .... First it is tried on ....

................................, and then it is tried on .... **(3 marks)**

3 New drugs are being developed all the time. It takes many years and costs enormous amounts of money to bring new medicines into your doctor's surgery.

(a) Give **one** reason new medicines are tested so carefully before they are used on patients.

.... **(1 mark)**

(b) What is the efficacy of a drug?

.... **(1 mark)**

(c) What is the optimum dose of a drug?

.... **(1 mark)**

(d) What does it mean if a drug is found to be toxic during pre-clinical or clinical trials?

.... **(1 mark)**

(e) Even when a new medicine has passed all of the stages of development, doctors will still always report any problems their patients have when they use the medicine. Suggest a reason why this final stage of constant testing is so important.

....

....

.... **(3 marks)**

43

Non-communicable diseases

1 (a) What is the one thing all non-communicable diseases have in common?

They cannot be .... **(1 mark)**

(b) Many non-communicable diseases are caused by the interaction of a number of factors. List **four** of the factors that can affect your risk of developing a non-communicable disease.

Genes, ..., ..., ... **(4 marks)**

2 A mutation in the BRCA gene affects the risk of developing both breast and ovarian cancer in women. It also affects the risk of developing some other cancers in men. The data in this bar chart looks at the effect of the BRCA allele in women.

> Always look carefully at any data you are given – you will be expected to use it in your answers.

Bar chart to show the impact of the BRCA mutation on cancer risk

(a) What is the increased percentage risk of developing breast cancer for a woman before the age of 50 if she has the BRCA allele?

....

.... **(1 mark)**

(b) How does the risk of developing breast cancer by the age of 70 compare with the risk of developing ovarian cancer by the age of 70 for a woman who has inherited the BRCA mutation?

.... for breast cancer compared with .... **(1 mark)**

(c) Breast cancer and ovarian cancers are examples of non-communicable disease. From the data in the bar chart describe the effect age and the presence of the BRCA gene have on the risk.

Age .... the risk – from around ....

to around .... Over those 20 years ....

.... **(3 marks)**

> Use data from the graph where you can to support your answer and get all of the marks.

3 Here are four factors that increase your risk of developing a non-communicable disease. For each factor, give an example of how it affects your risk.

Age: ....

Lifestyle factors: ....

....

Environmental factors: ....

....

Sex: ....

.... **(4 marks)**

Alcohol and smoking

1 The table below gives the alcohol drunk per person per year and the incidence of liver disease per 100 000 of the population in several countries, listed alphabetically.

Country	Alcohol drunk per person per year (dm³)	Deaths from liver disease (per 100 000 people)
Australia	10.00–12.49	6.8
Brazil	7.5–9.99	28.8
Russia	≥12.50	48.7
UK	≥12.50	16.0
USA	7.5–9.99	14.9

Maths skills

(a) List the countries in order of amounts of alcohol drunk per year, from the least to the most.

Brazil, USA, ..., ..., ... **(1 mark)**

Maths skills

(b) List the countries in order of the number of deaths from liver disease per year.

Australia, USA, ..., ..., ... **(1 mark)**

(c) Here are two statements about non-communicable diseases:

A Non-communicable diseases may be caused by a single lifestyle factor.

B Non-communicable diseases are often the result of several different factors.

Using the data from the table, give examples that illustrate both of these points.

A ....

....

B ....

....

.... **(3 marks)**

(d) Suggest one problem with the data given in the table that makes it harder to draw conclusions about the cause of liver disease.

> Think carefully about the limitations of the data you have been given. What more do you need to know?

....

.... **(1 mark)**

2 (a) What is meant by a lifestyle disease?

Guided

....

.... **(1 mark)**

(b) Cigarette smoke contains many substances that have negative effects on health. List **four** of them and describe how they affect the body.

....

....

....

.... **(4 marks)**

Malnutrition and obesity

1 (a) What is malnutrition?

When someone eats too .... or too .... **(1 mark)**

(b) Give an example of a lifestyle disease caused by eating too little of a named nutrient.

.... **(1 mark)**

> Learn a few examples of diseases caused by lack of specific nutrients or by excess food/fat.

2 (a) A woman visits her doctor and is told her BMI is too high. What does BMI stand for?

Body .... **(1 mark)**

(b) How do you calculate the BMI of a person?

$$BMI = \frac{.........................}{.........................}$$ **(1 mark)**

(c) A man has a health check for his job. He weighs 70 kg and he is 1.6 m tall. Is he obese? Explain your answer.

BMI = 70 .... = ... = ...

A BMI of over .... is obese, so .... **(3 marks)**

3 The charts below show how death from CVC relates to BMI and waist:hip ratio.

(a) What is waist:hip ratio?

....

.... **(2 marks)**

Charts to show the relationships between BMI and waist:hip ratio with death from cardiovascular disease in over 4000 Australian men

(b) What do both of the charts tell us about the relationship between obesity and cardiovascular disease?

....

.... **(2 marks)**

(c) Suggest why your waist:hip ratio is a better predictor of your risk of cardiovascular disease than your BMI.

....

....

.... **(3 marks)**

Cardiovascular disease

1 These diagrams show how blood vessels can be damaged as a result of smoking. This leads to cardiovascular disease. Explain what is happening at:

A Substances from tobacco smoke damage

....**(1 mark)**

> The question refers to smoking, so make sure you relate your answer to the damage caused by smoking.

B Fat builds up on the artery wall at the site

of ...., making the artery

.... **(2 marks)**

C A blood clot may block the artery where ....,

or ....,

causing a heart attack or .... **(3 marks)**

2 (a) Give **four** lifestyle changes a doctor might suggest to treat early signs of cardiovascular disease or to prevent cardiovascular disease from developing.

Lose ....; give up ....; take ....;

eat .... **(4 marks)**

(b) Give **two** advantages and **one** disadvantage of these treatments for cardiovascular disease.

Advantages: no side effects/ ....

Disadvantages: .... **(3 marks)**

3 If a patient has a narrowed coronary artery which does not respond well to lifestyle changes or medication, they might be offered surgery. One option is to insert a stent. Another is bypass surgery.

(a) Why is it so important to treat a narrowed coronary artery successfully?

....

.... **(3 marks)**

(b) What is a stent?

.... **(1 mark)**

(c) Describe what happens during bypass surgery.

.... **(1 mark)**

(d) Surgery offers a long-term solution to the problems of cardiovascular disease, which is good news. Give **three** clear reasons why it is not normally the first choice of treatment.

....

....

.... **(3 marks)**

Extended response – Health and disease

In 2010, UK newspapers reported a woman who had just turned 100 years old – and had been a regular smoker for 70 years, as well as enjoying a regular drink of whisky and beer. She was quoted as saying 'I've been smoking since I was 30 and have had no problems at all!'

Scientists often describe non-communicable diseases such as lung cancer and heart disease as multifactorial.

Discuss how this story confirms that view of disease.

> You will always be more successful in extended response questions if you plan your answer before you start writing.
>
> When you are asked to discuss, do not waffle. Identify the issues highlighted in the question and make very clear points so the examiner can see you have considered different sides of the question.
>
> In this question, you have to cover factors that can affect multifactorial diseases, the expected results of long term smoking and the other factors which mean some people remain healthy in spite of smoking.
>
> Your answer could explain the following points:
>
> • factors affecting health and the development of non-communicable diseases
>
> • the known impacts of smoking on health
>
> • the known impacts of drinking on health
>
> • the factors that would make you expect this lady to have some type of serious non-communicable disease
>
> • the factors that might have protected her from diseases such as lung cancer and heart disease.
>
> Make sure you refer to scientific evidence about links between lifestyle factors and disease – but emphasise that statistics refer to populations, not individuals.

....

....

....

....

....

....

....

....

....

....

....

....

....

(6 marks)

Photosynthesis

1 (a) Which of the following is **not** needed for photosynthesis to take place? Tick **one** box.

☐ **A** carbon dioxide   ☐ **C** oxygen

☐ **B** water   ☐ **D** light   **(1 mark)**

(b) Complete this word summary to show the reactants and products of photosynthesis.

carbon dioxide + ... → .... + oxygen   **(2 marks)**

(c) Where does photosynthesis take place in the plant cells?

....   **(1 mark)**

> **Chloroplasts** are the organelles where photosynthesis takes place.
> **Chlorophyll** is the green pigment in the chloroplasts which traps the light needed for the process.

2 (a) What is biomass?

....   **(1 mark)**

(b) Why are plants and algae known as producers?

....

....

....   **(3 marks)**

3 A student investigated the importance of light to plants. They left a plant in the dark for 48 hours. Then they completely covered one leaf in black card and another leaf in black card with a circle cut out of it. One leaf was left uncovered. The plant was placed in the light for the day. Then three leaves (A, B and C in the diagram) were removed from the plant and tested for starch using iodine solution.

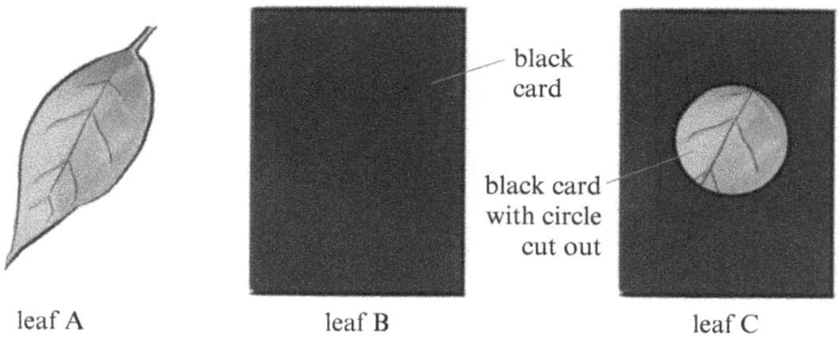

leaf A   leaf B   black card

black card with circle cut out

leaf C

(a) Why is the plant left in the dark for 48 hours before the investigation?

....

....   **(2 marks)**

(b) What would you expect the result to be on leaf A? Explain your answer.

....

....   **(2 marks)**

(c) What would you expect the result to be on leaf B? Explain your answer.

....

....   **(2 marks)**

(d) What would you expect the result to be on leaf C? Explain your answer.

....

....   **(2 marks)**

(e) Suggest one way in which the student could make their results more reliable.

....   **(1 mark)**

Limiting factors

1 Give **three** factors that can limit the rate of photosynthesis if they are in short supply.

....

....

....

> When you think about factors that limit the rate of photosynthesis, think about what is needed for photosynthesis to take place.

> Quantify where you can – light **intensity**, not just light, carbon dioxide **concentration**, not just carbon dioxide.

(3 marks)

2 This graph shows the results of an investigation into the effect of light intensity on the rate of photosynthesis.

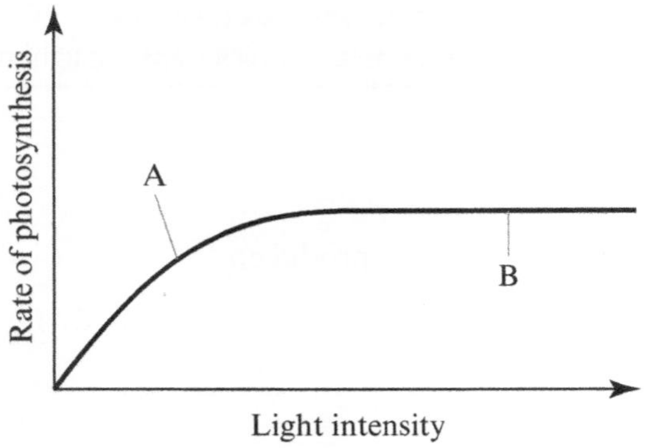

(a) What is happening at point A on the graph?

....

.... **(2 marks)**

(b) What is happening at point B on the graph?

....

....

....

.... **(3 marks)**

> Looking at the marks gives you an idea of how much information you need to give in your answer.

3 (a) Explain why carbon dioxide concentration affects the rate of photosynthesis.

....

.... **(2 marks)**

(b) Explain how temperature affects the rate of photosynthesis.

....

....

....

....

.... **(3 marks)**

> The effect of temperature on the rate of photosynthesis differs from the effect of carbon dioxide or light intensity because very high temperatures denature enzymes and stop photosynthesis permanently.

Light intensity

1 (a) What is this apparatus often used to investigate?

.... **(1 mark)**

(b) How do you measure the rate of photosynthesis?

....

.... **(2 marks)**

(c) Give **one** step you must take to make sure your results are as reliable as possible.

....

....

.... **(1 mark)**

oxygen

oxygen bubbles

water

pondweed

> This question is testing your practical skills so make sure you give practical answers.

2 In an investigation into the effect of light intensity, students placed a lamp at different distances from some Cabomba (pondweed) in water. They measured the volume of the gas produced.

Distance from lamp (cm)	5	10	15	20	25	30
Volume of gas produced (mm³)	83	57	43	28	19	11

(a) Plot a graph of the results of this investigation.

Volume of gas produced (mm³) vs Distance from lamp (cm)

(2 marks)

(b) Use your graph to find the volume of gas likely to be given off if you moved the lamp to 18 cm from the pondweed.

.... **(1 mark)**

(c) Explain the change in the amount of gas given off as the light is moved closer to the plant.

....

.... **(2 marks)**

Specialised plant cells

1 The diagram shows some cells from a plant tissue specialised for transport.

(a) State the name of this plant transport tissue.

....

.... **(1 mark)**

(b) What does it transport?

....

.... **(1 mark)**

(c) Give **two** features of this tissue and explain the importance of each.

Dead cells ....

....

Cell walls strengthened ....

.... **(4 marks)**

the wall that makes the tube is made of lignin

Make sure you can recognise xylem and phloem cells – and know what they do.

2 The diagram shows a root hair cell.

(a) What is the function of a root hair cell?

The uptake of ....

....

.... **(1 mark)**

B

A

(b) Give **two** ways in which the structure labelled A is adapted for the functions of the root hair cell.

Think about the surface area of A as well as the thickness of the cell wall.

....

....

....

.... **(4 marks)**

(c) Explain why structure B is so important in the cytoplasm of the root hair cell.

....

.... **(2 marks)**

Think about what organelle B provides to the cell and what this is used for. Remember that root cells do not photosynthesise because they grow underground.

3 (a) State the name of the tissue that transports sucrose around a plant.

.... **(1 mark)**

Guided

(b) Give **two** ways in which phloem tissue is adapted for its function.

....

.... **(2 marks)**

Transpiration

1 What is the loss of water from a plant by evaporation and diffusion through the leaves known as? Tick **one** box.

☐ **A** translocation

☐ **B** transportation

☐ **C** respiration

☐ **D** transpiration

> Be clear about the difference between **transpiration** and **translocation**.

(1 mark)

2 (a) What is the transpiration stream?

.... **(1 mark)**

(b) Complete this flow chart of the transpiration stream.

> Name the plant **structures** involved in transpiration as well as the **processes**.

| Water enters the .... by .... |

↓

| Water is drawn up .... |

↓

| Water is .... into the leaves and then .... |

↓

| Water ....out through .... |

(4 marks)

3 (a) Describe the role of stomata in plants.

....

....

....

.... **(2 marks)**

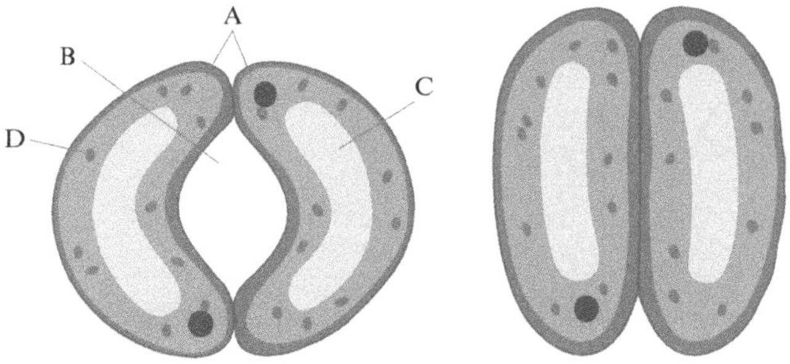

stoma open   stoma closed

(b) Name the structures labelled A, B, C and D in the diagrams showing an open and a closed stoma.

A ....

B ....

C ....

D .... **(2 marks)**

(c) Explain how stomata open when it is light and close when it is dark.

....

....

....

....

.... **(4 marks)**

Translocation

1 Which plant tissue is involved in translocation? Tick **one** box.

☐ **A** xylem

☐ **B** phloem

☐ **C** mesophyll

☐ **D** meristem

> **Phloem** carries **food**. They are spelled differently, but both words sound as if they start with an F. Use this to help you remember the difference between the roles of phloem and xylem.

(1 mark)

2 (a) State what is meant by translocation.

....   **(1 mark)**

(b) A poison that inhibits active transport is applied to the leaves of a plant in an experiment. Explain the effect this would have on translocation.

> Don't forget to include the following in your answer:
> • companion cells
> • active transport.

....

....

....   **(2 marks)**

3 Complete the table below to show the **two** main differences between transpiration and translocation.

	Transpiration	Translocation
Tissue where it takes place		
Substances transported		
Direction of transport		

(3 marks)

4 (a) Give **two** ways in which the sucrose transported in the phloem may be used by the plant.

> Guided

....

....

....   **(2 marks)**

(b) Scientists supply a plant with radioactive water. They also supply the lower leaves with carbon dioxide containing radioactive carbon. They kill a ring of stem tissue with a jet of steam. They find radioactive water in the leaves of the plant from the top to the bottom of the plant, but they only find radioactively labelled sucrose below the ring of dead tissue. Explain these observations in terms of the properties of xylem and phloem.

....

....

....

....

....

....

....   **(3 marks)**

 **Practical skills** # Water uptake in plants

1 (a) What does this apparatus measure?

.... **(1 mark)**

(b) Explain what happens to the air bubble:

  (i) if the stem is placed next to a table fan.

....

....

.... **(3 marks)**

  (ii) if the underside of the leaves is covered with petroleum jelly.

....

.... **(3 marks)**

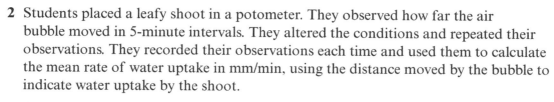

Think your answers through clearly a step at a time to get all the marks.

2 Students placed a leafy shoot in a potometer. They observed how far the air bubble moved in 5-minute intervals. They altered the conditions and repeated their observations. They recorded their observations each time and used them to calculate the mean rate of water uptake in mm/min, using the distance moved by the bubble to indicate water uptake by the shoot.

 Maths skills

(a) Complete the table below.

Movement of air bubble in 5-minute intervals (mm)	Plant A at 15 °C	Plant B at 25 °C	Plant C at 25 °C with a fan blowing at the leaves
Reading 1	50	80	105
Reading 2	45	84	106
Reading 3	55	91	104
Mean result	50		
Mean rate of water uptake (mm/min)	$\frac{50}{5} = 10$		

(4 marks)

(b) Why did the students take three readings under each set of conditions?

.... **(1 mark)**

(c) Explain the differences between the results seen for:

  (i) plant A and plant B.

....

.... **(4 marks)**

  (ii) plant B and plant C.

....

....

....

.... **(4 marks)**

55

Extended response –
Plant structures and functions

(6 marks)

Cactus

Palo verde

These two plants live in the deserts of Arizona in the USA. The cactus has a huge green stem and the leaves are reduced to tough spines. The palo verde is a very special tree. Most of the year it has no leaves, but the bark is green and contains chloroplasts. Only in the rare wet seasons does the tree produce leaves.

Use your knowledge of plants to explain how these adaptations allow the cactus and the palo verde to survive in the deserts.

> You might not know much about deserts – but you know a lot about plant structures, photosynthesis and transpiration, and this will allow you to answer the question.
>
> Always plan out your extended response before you start writing. Make sure you keep referring your answer to the content of the question.
>
> Your answer should include:
> • what plants need for photosynthesis
> • role of the stomata and chloroplasts
> • problems of desert life
> • adaptations of the cactus
> • adaptations of the palo verde.

....
....
....
....
....
....
....
....
....
....
....

Hormones

1 Which of the following endocrine glands releases the hormone ADH? Tick **one** box.

☐ **A** adrenal glands

> The pituitary gland produces several different hormones and it's important to remember what they are and what they do.

☐ **B** pituitary gland

☐ **C** ovaries

☐ **D** thyroid gland

(1 mark)

2 Define a hormone.

> Make three clear points to get the three marks here.

....

....

....

(3 marks)

3

Guided

A ▢

B ▢

C ▢

(a) Name the endocrine gland labelled A and state one of the hormones it produces.

.... **(2 marks)**

(b) Name the endocrine gland labelled B and state one of the hormones it produces.

.... **(2 marks)**

(c) Name the endocrine gland labelled C and state one of the hormones it produces.

.... **(2 marks)**

4 Complete the table below stating where each of the hormones is produced and the main target organ/organs for each hormone.

Hormone	Produced in	Target organ/s and tissues
TSH		Thyroid gland
Insulin		Liver, muscles and fatty tissue
Adrenaline	Adrenal glands	........., ..., skin, other organs
Oestrogen		

(4 marks)

The menstrual cycle

1 What is the mean length of menstrual cycles in women? Tick **one** box.

☐ **A** 14 days

☐ **B** 21 days

☐ **C** 9 months

☐ **D** 28 days

> On average, a menstrual cycle lasts 4 weeks, but in fact they are very variable. Pregnancy lasts nine months.

(1 mark)

2 Define the following terms.

> When describing menstruation, don't forget to say what happens to the egg. When describing fertilisation, include where/when it usually occurs.

(a) Ovulation

.... **(1 mark)**

(b) Menstruation

.... **(1 mark)**

(c) Fertilisation

.... **(1 mark)**

3 This diagram represents the menstrual cycle. Explain what happens:

(a) On days 1–5.

....

.... **(1 mark)**

(b) On approximately day 14.

....

.... **(1 mark)**

(c) Through weeks 2, 3 and 4.

....

.... **(1 mark)**

The menstrual cycle

lining thickens — 28 1 2 3 4 5 6 7 8 9 10 11 12 13 14 15 16 17 18 19 20 21 22 23 24 25 26 27

week 4   week 1   week 2   week 3

period

ovulation

4 (a) What is contraception?

.... **(1 mark)**

> Guided

(b) If a couple do not use contraception, when during the menstrual cycle is pregnancy most likely to occur?

.... **(2 marks)**

(c) Give one example of a barrier method of contraception and explain how it works.

....

.... **(2 marks)**

(d) Explain how hormonal methods of contraception work.

....

.... **(2 marks)**

(e) Discuss the advantages and disadvantages of using barrier and hormonal contraception.

....

....

.... **(4 marks)**

Blood glucose regulation

1 Which of the following is a hormone produced in the pancreas and released when blood glucose levels rise? Tick **one** box.

     ☐ **A**   insulin

     ☐ **B**   glycogen

     ☐ **C**   glucose

     ☐ **D**   glucagon   **(1 mark)**

2 (a) Why is glucose so important for the body?

.... **(1 mark)**

(b) Which organ secretes the hormones that control blood glucose levels?

.... **(1 mark)**

(c) Why do blood glucose levels rise after a meal?

.... | Think about how sugars from digested foods get into your blood. |

....

.... **(2 marks)**

(d) Explain why it is so important that blood glucose levels are maintained within a narrow range of concentrations.

....

....

.... **(2 marks)**

3 This graph shows the changes in blood glucose concentration of a person who has just had a meal.

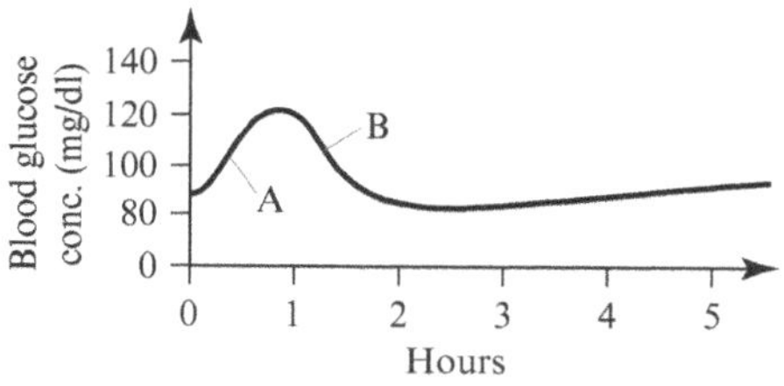

(a) Describe and explain the change in the blood glucose concentration seen at point A on the graph.

....

....

....

.... **(3 marks)**

(b) Describe and explain the change in the blood glucose concentration seen at point B on the graph.

....

....

....

.... **(3 marks)**

Diabetes

1 This graph is a repeat of the graph on the previous page showing the changes in blood glucose concentration of a person who has just had a meal.

Blood glucose conc. (mg/dl)

140
120
100
80
0

B

A

0 1 2 3 4 5
Hours

(a) Describe what you would expect to see if the person had untreated type 1 diabetes.

....

.... **(1 mark)**

> For (a) no explanation is needed for the 1 mark, just a description.

(b) Explain your answer to (a).

....

....

.... **(4 marks)**

(c) How can this be treated?

.... **(2 marks)**

2 Complete this table comparing type 1 diabetes and type 2 diabetes.

	Type 1 diabetes	Type 2 diabetes
Cause		
Control		

(4 marks)

3 This data shows the percentage of UK adults in three BMI categories with type 2 diabetes.

Percentage of adults in each BMI category with type 2 diabetes

(a) Using the data, what can you say about the relationship between BMI category and obesity?

....

....

....

....

....

....

.... **(3 marks)**

Percentage of people in category with type 2 diabetes

16
14
12
10
8
6
4
2
0

☐ men
■ women

normal   overweight   obese
BMI category

(b) A student looks at the data and makes the following claim 'Men are more likely to develop type 2 diabetes than women'. Evaluate this claim.

....

....

....

.... **(4 marks)**

Extended response – Control and coordination

When people want to have sex, but do not want to get pregnant, it is important to use contraception. The following data is taken from the National Health Service website about the effectiveness of different types of contraception. Describe and evaluate the different methods of contraception shown in the bar chart below.

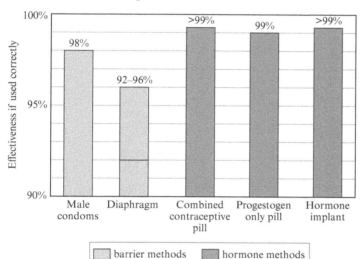

You will always be more successful in extended response questions if you plan your answer before you start writing.

When you are asked to evaluate you need to refer to data. Your answer could explain the following points:

• how the different methods of contraception work

• which types of contraception appear most effective from the data

• what it means if a contraceptive method is described as 98% effective

• what 'if used correctly' means and why it is so important when considering the data

• pros and cons of the different methods beyond statistical effectiveness.

....
....
....
....
....
....
....
....
....
....
....
....
....
....
....
....
....
....
....

(6 marks)

Exchanging materials

1 Which of the following substances needs to be transported **out** of multicellular organisms? Tick **one** box.

☐ **A** oxygen

☐ **B** glucose

☐ **C** carbon dioxide

☐ **D** lipids

> Remember: carbon dioxide is a toxic waste product of cellular respiration.

(1 mark)

2 (a) Calculate the surface area to volume ratio of these two model organisms. (Consider the surface area of just one face.)

small cube
(s.a. = 1 × 1 = 1 cm²)   (vol = 1 × 1 × 1 = 1 cm³)
1:1
big cube

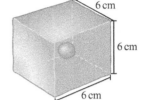

.... **(2 marks)**

(b) Explain why larger, multicellular organisms need transport and exchange systems, but small single-celled organisms do not.

....

....

....

....

(3 marks)

> It is the surface area:volume ratio of an organism that is important when you discuss the need for exchange and transport systems – not just the surface area.

3 (a) Name **two** human organs which are adapted for exchange of materials.

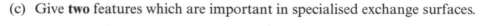

.... **(2 marks)**

Guided

(b) Name **one** human system which is involved in transport of materials around the body.

.... **(1 mark)**

(c) Give **two** features which are important in specialised exchange surfaces.

.... **(2 marks)**

4 A mammal is too large for simple diffusion to supply its needs. Complete this table showing the main substances which need to be exchanged and the site where the exchange takes place.

Guided

Substance	Site of exchange	Reason for exchange
Oxygen		
Carbon dioxide		
Dissolved food molecules		
Mineral ions		
Urea		

(5 marks)

Alveoli

1 (a) Define breathing.

The movement of air .... **(1 mark)**

(b) Describe gas exchange in the lungs.

> Use the term 'diffuses'.

....

.... **(2 marks)**

(c) Explain how breathing affects gas exchange.

> Include the term 'concentration gradient' in your answer.

....

....

.... **(3 marks)**

2 State **three** ways in which the alveoli of the lungs are adapted for gas exchange and explain how each of the features makes gas exchange in the lungs more efficient.

....

....

....

....

....

....

....

.... **(4 marks)**

> Don't forget to say how the concentration gradient is maintained.

3 Here are brief descriptions of three diseases of the lungs. They can all cause breathlessness and low levels of oxygen in the blood. In each case, explain how the problems are caused in terms of the structures and adaptations of the exchange surfaces of the lungs.

(a) COPD is a family of lung diseases where the structure of the alveoli breaks down, forming a few large air sacs instead of many small ones.

....

.... **(2 marks)**

(b) In lung cancer, a solid tumour grows into the lung tissue taking up space where the alveoli should be.

....

.... **(2 marks)**

(c) In a pulmonary embolism, a blood clot blocks the artery leading to the lungs.

....

.... **(2 marks)**

Blood

1 What is the yellow liquid that makes up around 55% of the blood called?
Tick **one** box.

> Learn the main components of the blood and their relative proportions.

☐ **A** phloem

☐ **B** lymph

☐ **C** pus

☐ **D** plasma

(1 mark)

2 (a) Name the **four** main components of the blood shown in this diagram.

> Guided

A .... B .... C .... D .... **(2 marks)**

(b) Give **one** function of each component you named in (a).

A ....

B ....

C ....

D .... **(4 marks)**

3 Explain **three** ways in which erythrocytes are adapted for their role in the body.

> The question says 'Explain…' so your answer needs to refer specifically to how the different features of the red blood cell enable it to carry out its function of transporting oxygen.

....

....

....

> Learn their proper names!
> • red blood cells = **erythrocytes**
> • white blood cells = **phagocytes** and **lymphocytes**

....

.... **(3 marks)**

4 Children born with a genetic condition called SCID do not have functioning white blood cells. The affected children get many infections, one after the other.

> Guided

(a) Describe **two** ways in which white blood cells prevent infection in healthy people.

....

....

....

....

.... **(4 marks)**

(b) Explain why children affected by SCID get many repeated infections which may kill them.

....

....

....

....

.... **(3 marks)**

Blood vessels

Guided

1 (a) Name the types of vessels labelled A, B and C.

....

(b) In which type of blood vessel – A, B or C – is the blood pressure highest? Explain your answer.

....

....

....

....

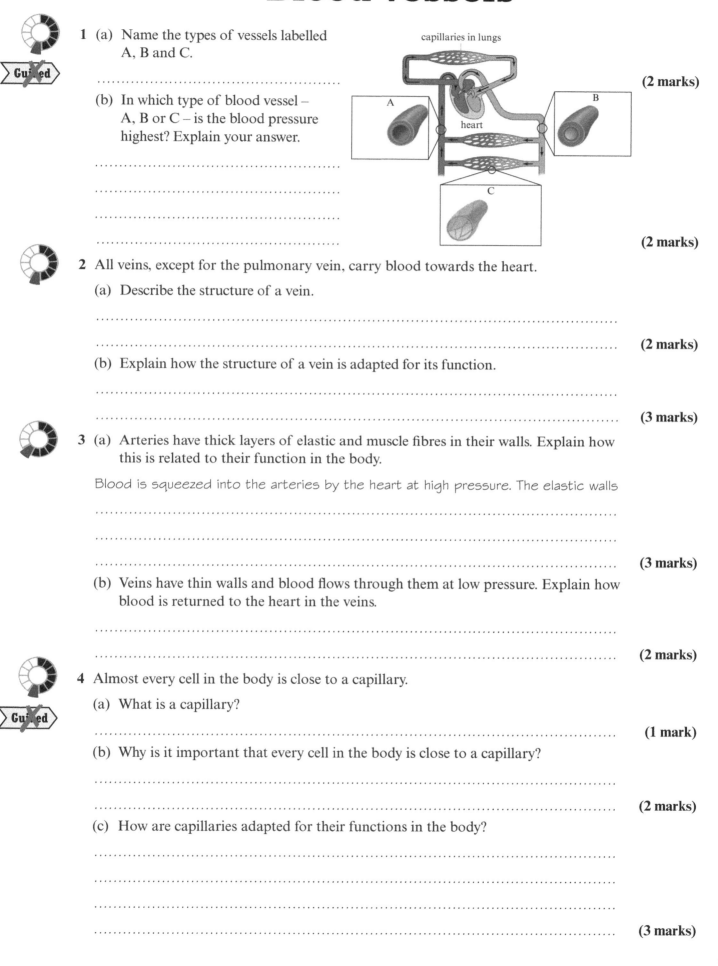

capillaries in lungs

A

B

heart

C

(2 marks)

(2 marks)

2 All veins, except for the pulmonary vein, carry blood towards the heart.

(a) Describe the structure of a vein.

....

....   **(2 marks)**

(b) Explain how the structure of a vein is adapted for its function.

....

....   **(3 marks)**

3 (a) Arteries have thick layers of elastic and muscle fibres in their walls. Explain how this is related to their function in the body.

Blood is squeezed into the arteries by the heart at high pressure. The elastic walls

....

....

....   **(3 marks)**

(b) Veins have thin walls and blood flows through them at low pressure. Explain how blood is returned to the heart in the veins.

....

....   **(2 marks)**

4 Almost every cell in the body is close to a capillary.

Guided

(a) What is a capillary?

....   **(1 mark)**

(b) Why is it important that every cell in the body is close to a capillary?

....

....   **(2 marks)**

(c) How are capillaries adapted for their functions in the body?

....

....

....

....   **(3 marks)**

The heart

1 Which of the following blood vessels carries oxygenated blood from the lungs to the heart? Tick **one** box.

   ☐   **A**   aorta

   ☐   **B**   pulmonary artery

   ☐   **C**   pulmonary vein

   ☐   **D**   vena cava   **(1 mark)**

> Remember: the type of blood carried in the pulmonary artery and pulmonary vein is the opposite to the rest of the arteries and veins. This is because they carry blood to and from the ....

2 This diagram shows a section through a human heart.

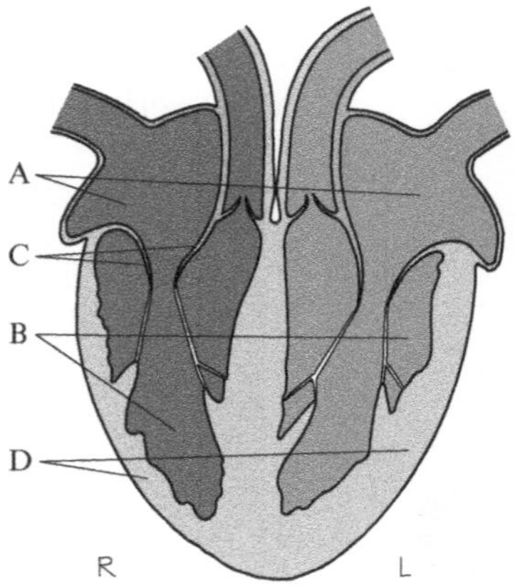

   (a) Name the chambers of the heart labelled A and B.

     .... **(2 marks)**

   (b) Name the structures labelled C and describe their role in the heart.

     ....

     ....

     .... **(2 marks)**

   (c) Explain the difference you can observe in the structures labelled D on the left- and right-hand sides of the heart.

     ....

     ....

     ....

     ....

     .... **(2 marks)**

> Remember! The sides of the heart are labelled as if you are looking at the person, so the left-hand side of the heart is on the right-hand side of the diagram.

3 Complete this simple flow diagram to show the movement of blood through the heart.

> Blood .... the heart from .... in ....
>
> ↓
>
> the .... contract, forcing ....
>
> ↓
>
> the .... close, preventing .... through the heart
>
> ↓
>
> the .... contract, forcing ....
> into .... which carry it to the organs.   **(4 marks)**

Aerobic respiration

1 (a) Define aerobic respiration.

It is a process that .... energy from .... for use in ....

.............................., using ....   **(2 marks)**

(b) Write a simple word summary for this process.

Glucose + ... →............................... + water   **(2 marks)**

(c) Where do the chemical reactions of aerobic respiration take place?

Mainly in the ....   **(1 mark)**

(d) Explain where the glucose and oxygen used in aerobic respiration come from.

Glucose comes from ...., oxygen from ....

....   **(2 marks)**

2 (a) Describe **three** ways in which the energy released in aerobic respiration is used in animals.

For .... processes.

To enable .... contraction.

In birds and mammals, to help ....   **(3 marks)**

(b) Plants also use energy from aerobic respiration. Give **one** example from plant cells.

Building .... molecules from .... molecules. For example, ...

....

....   **(2 marks)**

3 (a) The reactions of respiration are all controlled by enzymes. The body temperature of the human body and the pH of the cells are carefully controlled. Suggest an explanation for these observations.

....

....

....

....

....

....

....   **(4 marks)**

(b) If a culture of cells are given the poison curare, all of the reactions of metabolism fail and the cells die. If the cells are provided with energy in a useable form, they can survive. Suggest an explanation for the way the poison works.

....

....

....

....

....   **(3 marks)**

Anaerobic respiration

1 Which of the following substances is produced in humans during anaerobic respiration, but not in aerobic respiration? Tick **one** box.

☐ **A** carbon dioxide

☐ **B** lactic acid

☐ **C** oxygen

☐ **D** water

> In aerobic respiration in people, glucose is fully broken down into carbon dioxide and water using oxygen. In anaerobic respiration, glucose is not fully broken down.

(1 mark)

2 (a) What is anaerobic respiration?

....

.... **(2 marks)**

(b) Complete the following table to show some of the advantages and disadvantages of anaerobic respiration.

> Think about:
> • why anaerobic respiration is important in muscles
> • organisms that live where there is very little oxygen
> • the amount of energy released by the different types of respiration
> • the chemical produced during anaerobic respiration.

Advantages of anaerobic respiration	Disadvantages of anaerobic respiration

(4 marks)

3 The graph shows the breathing rate and heart rate of a student during and after exercise.

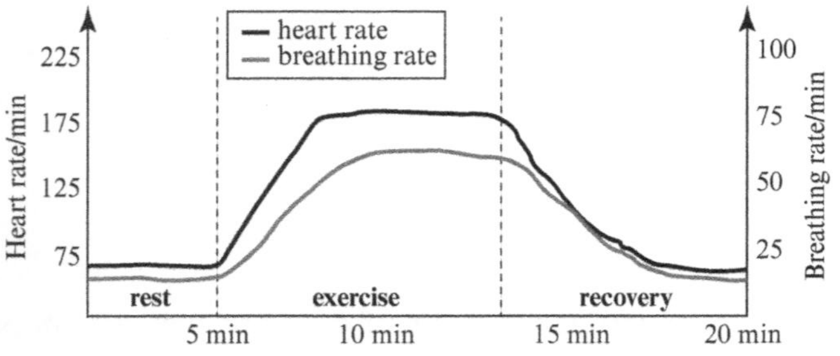

(a) What type of respiration takes place at the start of a period of exercise?

.... **(1 mark)**

(b) Explain what happens in the muscles as the period of exercise continues, and the heart and lungs cannot supply all the glucose and oxygen needed.

....

.... **(3 marks)**

(c) Describe, from the graph, what happens to the breathing rate and heart rate after exercise stops.

....

.... **(2 marks)**

Practical skills **Rate of respiration**

1 The diagram shows a respirometer used to investigate the rate of respiration in germinating peas.

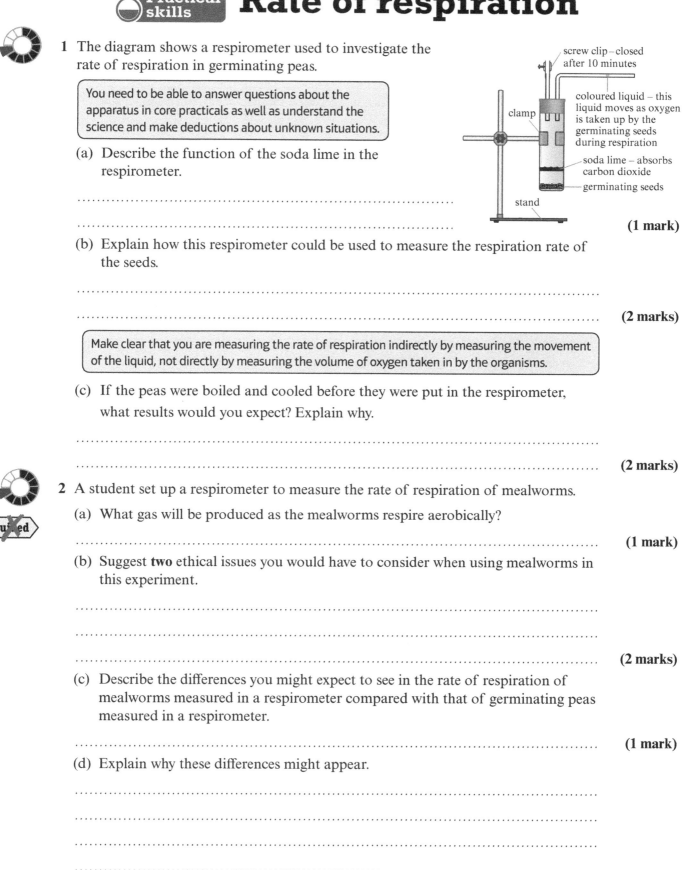

screw clip – closed after 10 minutes

coloured liquid – this liquid moves as oxygen is taken up by the germinating seeds during respiration

clamp

soda lime – absorbs carbon dioxide

germinating seeds

stand

> You need to be able to answer questions about the apparatus in core practicals as well as understand the science and make deductions about unknown situations.

(a) Describe the function of the soda lime in the respirometer.

....

.... **(1 mark)**

(b) Explain how this respirometer could be used to measure the respiration rate of the seeds.

....

.... **(2 marks)**

> Make clear that you are measuring the rate of respiration indirectly by measuring the movement of the liquid, not directly by measuring the volume of oxygen taken in by the organisms.

(c) If the peas were boiled and cooled before they were put in the respirometer, what results would you expect? Explain why.

....

.... **(2 marks)**

2 A student set up a respirometer to measure the rate of respiration of mealworms.

(a) What gas will be produced as the mealworms respire aerobically?

.... **(1 mark)**

(b) Suggest **two** ethical issues you would have to consider when using mealworms in this experiment.

....

.... **(2 marks)**

(c) Describe the differences you might expect to see in the rate of respiration of mealworms measured in a respirometer compared with that of germinating peas measured in a respirometer.

.... **(1 mark)**

(d) Explain why these differences might appear.

....

....

....

....

....

.... **(4 marks)**

Changes in heart rate

1 If a student has a stroke volume of 0.09 litres and at rest their heart beats 70 times a minute. What is their cardiac output? Tick **one** box.

☐ **A** 6.3 centilitres/sec

☐ **B** 6.3 litres/min

☐ **C** 6.3 litres/sec

☐ **D** 6.3 millilitres/min

> Make sure you know the units of different measurements.

(1 mark)

2 One way of measuring the fitness of an individual is to measure how well their heart is pumping blood. Define each of the following and for (a), (b) and (c) state the units in which they are measured.

(a) Stroke volume ....

.... **(2 marks)**

(b) Heart rate ....

.... **(2 marks)**

(c) Cardiac output ....

.... **(2 marks)**

(d) Give the formula for measuring the cardiac output of an individual.

cardiac output = ... × .... **(1 mark)**

3 This bar chart shows the effect of moderate exercise on the cardiac output of three people labelled A, B and C.

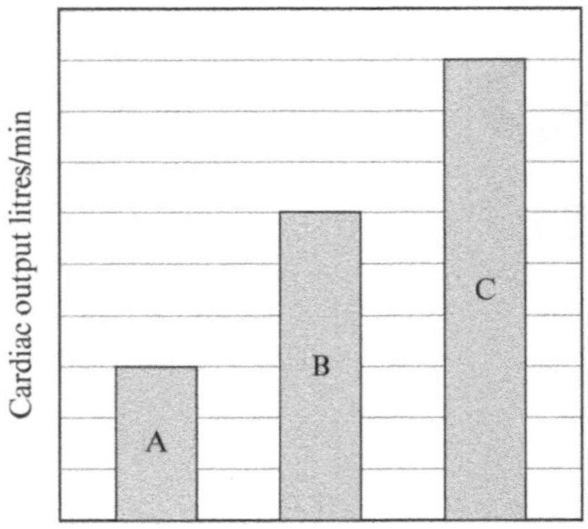

(a) Which of these people is the fittest? Explain your answer.

....

....

....

.... **(2 marks)**

(b) Which person would you expect to have the highest recorded heart rate during the period of exercise? Explain your answer.

....

.... **(2 marks)**

(c) During the period of exercise, person B had a stroke volume of 0.095 litres and a heart rate of 120 beats per minute. Person C had a stroke volume of 0.15 litres and a heart rate of 100 beats per minute. What was the cardiac output of each individual?

B ....

C .... **(2 marks)**

(d) How much more blood, in percentage terms, did person C pump each minute than person B?

.... **(2 marks)**

Extended response – Exchange

These images show Tom taking part in an endurance race. The first image is from the beginning of the race, the second is much later on. Apart from the fact that he is much muddier, Tom's muscles are working hard later in the race and they start to ache. Explain why Tom's muscles are aching, and what happens to his heart and breathing as the race progresses.

To be successful in extended response questions, plan your answer before you start writing.

When you are asked to explain, you need to think carefully about what is happening and why. Here you are asked about three different systems in the body – for a good answer you must cover each of them in turn. Make sure you refer to the context of the question. Your answer could explain the following points:

- what the muscles need to keep working effectively in a race
- why Tom's muscles are aching
- the changes you would expect in his breathing and why they are needed
- the changes you would expect in his heart rate and why they are needed.

....

....

....

....

....

....

....

....

....

....

....

....

....

.... **(6 marks)**

Ecosystems and abiotic factors

1 Which of the following is **not** an abiotic factor affecting the distribution of organisms in an ecosystem? Tick **one** box.

☐ **A** rainfall

☐ **B** light levels

> Remember the difference! Abiotic means non-living; biotic means living.

☐ **C** nitrate levels in the soil

☐ **D** predator numbers

(1 mark)

2 Define the following terms, which are all important in the study of ecology:

Guided

(a) Organism

.... **(1 mark)**

(b) Population

.... **(1 mark)**

(c) Community

.... **(1 mark)**

(d) Ecosystem

.... **(1 mark)**

3 (a) List **three** abiotic factors which can affect the organisms in an ecosystem.

.... **(3 marks)**

Guided

(b) This sundew is a carnivorous plant. It captures insects on the sticky drops on its leaves and digests them. It grows on bogs, where very few other plants can survive. Suggest an explanation for these observations in terms of abiotic factors.

....

....

....

....

....

.... **(3 marks)**

(c) Great tits feed their babies on tiny caterpillars and other insects. When the weather is particularly cold, when there are late frosts or there is a lot of very heavy rain, these birds raise fewer chicks than in warm, dry years. Suggest how these abiotic factors may affect the success of the breeding birds.

....

....

....

....

.... **(3 marks)**

Biotic factors

1 Which of the following is a biotic factor affecting the distribution of organisms in an area? Tick **one** box.

☐ **A** temperature

☐ **B** rainfall

☐ **C** competition

☐ **D** oxygen levels in water

> Biotic factors have **bio**logical causes.

(1 mark)

2 Red deer stags grow large antlers each year and fight each other.

(a) What are they fighting for?

.... **(2 marks)**

(b) What is this process called? .... **(1 mark)**

(c) Male deer of the same species fight against each other. Give an example of competition between two different species.

> Learn three examples of interspecies competition for resources.

....

.... **(2 marks)**

3 In a UK oak woodland, lots of small plants, such as primroses and bluebells, grow and flower early in the year. By the summer, the ground is mainly bare. Explain why plants on the ground grow so early and then disappear until the next spring.

> You won't always be familiar with the example you are given, but you should be able to apply your knowledge and work it out.

....

....

.... **(3 marks)**

4 This graph shows the numbers of snowshoe hares and the lynx, which are their predators, over a period of years in Canada.

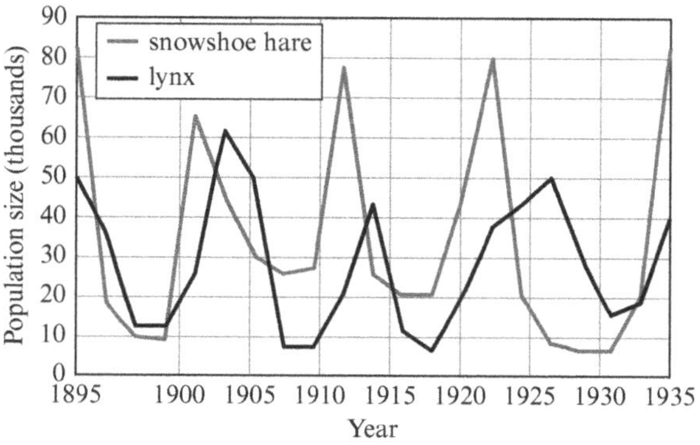

Guided ✗

(a) Define the term predator.

.... **(1 mark)**

(b) The snowshoe hare is a prey animal. What does this mean?

.... **(1 mark)**

(c) Look at the graph. Describe how the hare and the lynx numbers are correlated.

....

.... **(2 marks)**

(d) Suggest an explanation for the pattern you can see.

....

....

....

.... **(4 marks)**

Parasitism and mutualism

1 Which of the following organisms is **not** a parasite? Tick **one** box.

☐ **A** flea

☐ **B** tapeworm

☐ **C** louse

☐ **D** clownfish

> Make sure you know the difference between parasitic organisms and mutualistic organisms.

(1 mark)

2 (a) What is a parasite?

.... **(2 marks)**

(b) Complete this table about three different parasites.

Parasite	How it feeds
Flea	
Tapeworm	
Mistletoe	

(3 marks)

> You will be expected to be able to recall examples of parasitism and mutualism. Make sure you learn three examples of each.

> Different parasites feed in different ways – learn some examples.

3 A tapeworm is a parasite that can live in the gut of mammals.

hook
scolex ('head')
sucker
neck
thin, flat segments
testes
uterus
segments contain no digestive system
ovary

Give **three** adaptations shown by tapeworms and explain how these benefit their parasitic lifestyle.

The hooks and .... attach to the .... of the host.

The .... body gives a big surface area where ....

.... can be .... Segments contain both

.... so .... can take place

inside .... **(3 marks)**

4 (a) What is a mutualistic relationship?

.... **(1 mark)**

> Guided

(b) The nitrogen-fixing bacteria that live in the root nodules of legumes are in a mutualistic relationship. Explain what this means for the bacteria and the plant.

....

.... **(2 marks)**

 **Fieldwork techniques**

1 In a long-running investigation into the numbers of penguin nests on a beach in Argentina, scientists recorded the results shown in the table below.

Quadrat number along transect	1	2	3	4	5	6	7	8	9
Number of nests/100 m²	10	2	15	9	3	22	14	12	20

In the previous two years there was a mean nest density of 5.6 nests/100 m² and 8.4 nests/100 m².

 Maths skills

(a) Calculate the mean number of nests per 100 m² for the data in the table.

.... **(3 marks)**

(b) Do you think this was a good breeding year or a bad one? Explain your answer.

....

.... **(2 marks)**

(c) Suggest **one** biotic factor and **one** abiotic factor which might affect the success of penguins breeding in any given year.

biotic .... abiotic... **(2 marks)**

2 A student measures the abundance of slugs in a garden. They take five random samples of the garden using a 1 m² quadrat. The number of slugs in the quadrats was 10, 6, 5, 9 and 2. The garden has an area of 100 m².

(a) What does abundance measure?

.... **(1 mark)**

Maths skills

(b) Estimate the total population of slugs in the garden.

mean num. slugs in 1 m² = $\frac{(...+...+...+...+...)}{5}$ = ...

The garden is ......m², so approx. slug population in the garden is .... **(3 marks)**

3 A class is going to investigate the effect of abiotic factors on the distribution of plants in a local park. One group suggests looking at random quadrats. Another group suggests taking a belt transect across the park, going across a footpath, under some shady trees and close to a pond. Both groups plan to record the conditions at each quadrat recorded.

(a) What is an abiotic factor?

.... **(1 mark)**

(b) Explain what the term 'the distribution of plants' means.

.... **(1 mark)**

(c) Describe a quadrat.

.... **(1 mark)**

(d) Which method would ensure they sampled different environments?

....

....

.... **(4 marks)**

Organisms and their environment

1 A scientist is looking at the distribution of sundew plants in the New Forest in the UK. Sundews are found in bogs and they capture and digest insects to get the nitrates they need. The scientist is investigating an area of heathland which has some very boggy parts and she begins by doing two belt transects. She uses a 0.25 m² quadrat and places the quadrat at two-metre intervals along the transect. Her data is shown in the table.

| Transects | Number of sundew plants | | | | | | | | Mean |
	Quadrat 1	Quadrat 2	Quadrat 3	Quadrat 4	Quadrat 5	Quadrat 6	Quadrat 7	Quadrat 8	
A	0	0	1	3	1	4	0	0	
B	0	4	6	8	10	10	5	3	

(a) Calculate the mean number of sundew plants in transect A and transect B (to the nearest whole number).

> In this example, the mean is the **sum** of the numbers of organisms **divided** by the number of quadrats taken.

.... **(2 marks)**

(b) Suggest what these results tell you about the ecosystems covered by the two transects.

....

....

....

.... **(3 marks)**

> Think carefully about what you are told in the question and the data you are given. Work out as much detail as you can from the data about how boggy the ground is in the different transects.

(c) Suggest **two** ways in which the scientist could improve her method in future.

1. ....

2. .... **(2 marks)**

2 A student wants to investigate the distribution of shellfish called mussels across a rocky shore. Describe how they might do this.

....

....

....

....

....

....

.... **(5 marks)**

Human effects on ecosystems

1 When too many nutrients are added to a water ecosystem this can eventually result in a lack of oxygen in the water. What is this process known as? Tick **one** box.

☐ **A** fertilising the soil

☐ **B** eutrophication

☐ **C** pollution

☐ **D** conservation

(1 mark)

2 When the prickly pear cactus was introduced to Australia, it rapidly became a pest species. By 1920 it had covered 58 million hectares, ruining lots of good farmland. In the late 1920s, the caterpillars of a moth that feeds only on prickly pear cactus were released onto the cacti in some of the worst hit areas. In a matter of years it had brought the plague of cacti under control.

> In questions like this, you will be given information about a new situation. You are not expected to know about prickly pear cacti or cacti-eating moths, **but** you are expected to be able to show you understand the basic principles which explain all species interactions.

(a) What process is illustrated in the story of the prickly pear cactus and the cactus moth?

....

(1 mark)

(b) Using the prickly pear cactus as an example, explain the dangers of introducing new species to an ecosystem.

....

....

(2 marks)

(c) Using the cactus moth as an example, explain how the introduction of non-indigenous species can have benefits and risks.

....

....

(2 marks)

3 (a) What is fish farming?

....

....

(2 marks)

(b) Explain how farming fish can be a better way of providing fish for people to eat than catching wild fish.

> Which method gives people a reliable supply of protein food that is easy to get?

....

....

....

....

(3 marks)

(c) Suggest **two** harmful effects fish farming can have on the environment.

....

....

(2 marks)

77

Biodiversity

1 (a) What is biodiversity?

.... **(1 mark)**

(b) Give **three** reasons why it is important to maintain biodiversity both at local and global levels.

....

....

....

.... **(3 marks)**

2 (a) Explain the effect of deforestation on biodiversity.

Deforestation removes .... from an area. This also removes the

.... of many different species and may remove the food source

for some animals, so it reduces .... in an area. **(2 marks)**

(b) State what is meant by reforestation and suggest **two** ways it can be carried out.

....

.... **(2 marks)**

(c) Rainforests are thought to contain around 500 species of tree per hectare and UK woodlands about 12 species per hectare. Some people claim deforestation of a rainforest is more damaging to biodiversity than deforestation in the UK. Discuss this claim.

....

....

....

....

.... **(3 marks)**

3 Red squirrels are indigenous to the UK. Their numbers have been declining for centuries. They do best in coniferous woodlands. Climate change means coniferous woodlands now do best in the cooler north. Millions of acres of woodland have been destroyed by people for housing, agriculture, etc. and many people have planted deciduous woodlands rather than conifers. Grey squirrels, introduced in the late 19th century, are more effective at converting food to biomass and so can out-compete red squirrels. Squirrelpox is a disease carried by grey squirrels that can kill red squirrels fast, but many grey squirrels are immune to it.

Suggest how red squirrels might be conserved in the UK.

....

....

....

....

.... **(4 marks)**

The carbon cycle

1 Which of the following processes takes carbon dioxide out of the air during the carbon cycle? Tick **one** box.

  ☐ **A** photosynthesis

  ☐ **B** combustion

  ☐ **C** respiration

  ☐ **D** decomposition

> Make sure you know which of the processes of the carbon cycle put carbon dioxide into the atmosphere and which remove it.

(1 mark)

2 (a) Describe the role of decomposers in the carbon cycle.

....

.... **(1 mark)**

(b) Describe how burning forests affects the levels of carbon dioxide in **two** ways.

....

....

....

> What does burning fuel add to the atmosphere? What do living trees usually remove from the atmosphere?

.... **(4 marks)**

3 This diagram represents the carbon cycle.

(a) Define the carbon cycle.

....

....

....

.... **(1 mark)**

(b) Name the processes listed on the diagram of the carbon cycle. For each one, explain the part it plays in the carbon cycle:

(i) Process A

....

....

.... **(3 marks)**

(ii) Process B

....

.... **(3 marks)**

(iii) Process C

....

....

.... **(3 marks)**

(iv) Process D

....

....

.... **(3 marks)**

The water cycle

1

(a) Define the water cycle.

.... **(1 mark)**

(b) Give **two** reasons why water is so important to living organisms.

....

....

.... **(2 marks)**

(c) Name each of the processes labelled A–D on the diagram of the water cycle.

A .... C ....

B .... D .... **(2 marks)**

2 Clean drinking water (potable water) is in short supply in many places. In some areas, people are using sea water to make drinking water.

(a) Explain why we can't drink sea water.

Sea water contains lots of salt and this would upset the .... **(1 mark)**

(b) Name the process used to turn sea water into potable water.

.... **(1 mark)**

(c) Explain how sea water can be distilled to give potable water.

Seawater is heated until the water evaporates, forming steam. ....

....

.... **(3 marks)**

3 Describe how water cycles through the **abiotic** parts of an ecosystem.

....

....

....

....

....

.... **(5 marks)**

The nitrogen cycle

1 Which of the following processes involves the release of nitrogen back into the air? Tick **one** box.

☐ **A** nitrogen fixation

☐ **B** decomposition

☐ **C** combustion

☐ **D** denitrification   **(1 mark)**

2 Farmers have many ways to make their soil more fertile and to help them grow the biggest, healthiest crops possible. Explain the science behind these three farming methods:

(a) Adding nitrate fertiliser to fields.

Plants need nitrates to make ....

....

....   **(3 marks)**

(b) Rotating crops every year.

Different types of plants ....

....   **(2 marks)**

(c) Planting a crop of peas or clover at regular intervals in their crop rotation.

Peas and clover have root nodules containing bacteria that can ....

....

....

....

....   **(4 marks)**

3 This diagram represents the nitrogen cycle in nature. Nitrogen compounds are very important as they are needed to form proteins and DNA.

(a) What are the key organisms in the nitrogen cycle?

....

(b) Explain what is happening at the stages of the nitrogen cycle labelled A–E.

....

....

....

....

....

....   **(5 marks)**

(1 mark)

Extended response – Ecosystems and material cycles

 Pandas are well-known animals which are at risk of becoming extinct. In the past they have been extensively hunted for their body parts to be used in traditional medicine and much of their habitat of bamboo forests has been destroyed. The following data shows the recorded panda populations in China since 1974.

Date of survey	Estimated wild panda population
1974–7	2459
1985–8	1114
2003–4	1596
2014	1864

Discuss possible reasons why panda numbers have decreased and are now on the rise again, using recorded data where possible to support your comments. Suggest any other possible benefits from the rise in panda numbers.

> You will always be more successful in extended response questions if you plan your answer before you start writing.
>
> When you are asked to discuss, do not waffle. Identify the issues highlighted in the question and make very clear points so the examiner can see you have considered different sides of the question.
>
> In this question you need to think about
>
> - the causes of the decline in pandas
> - when it appeared to be halted
> - the current state of the population (using percentage increases taken from the data)
> - the sort of measures which can be taken to increase the numbers of a threatened species and any implications for other species.

....

....

....

....

....

....

....

....

....

....

....

....

....

.... **(6 marks)**

Formulae

1 Elements can be represented by symbols.

(a) Write down the symbol for potassium.

....

(1 mark)

(b) Write down the symbol for chlorine.

....

(1 mark)

(c) Write down the name of the element with the symbol He.

....

(1 mark)

(d) Write down the name of the element with the symbol S.

....

(1 mark)

2 Select the correct words below to complete the sentences.

atoms   **chlorine**   **compound**   **element**

copper   **mixture**   **molecules**

.... has the formula Cl_2.

This shows that it is an .... made up of ...., each one

containing two ....

(4 marks)

3 Which of the following formulae represent elements?

☐   **A** CO_2

☐   **B** Cl_2

☐   **C** O_2

☐   **D** $CuCl_2$

> • This question is worth two marks, so tick **two** boxes.
> • Remember, an element is made up of only one type of atom.

(2 marks)

4 Name the elements in the compound ethanol (C_2H_6O).

1. ....

2. ....

3. ....

(3 marks)

5 The compound sodium carbonate has the formula Na_2CO_3.
Deduce the number of atoms of each element:

sodium

2 ....

carbon

....

oxygen

....

(3 marks)

> 'Deduce' means use the information given to work out the answer.

Equations

 1 A student reacts together magnesium and copper chloride to produce magnesium chloride and copper. Write the word equation for this reaction.

magnesium + copper chloride → .... + ...   **(2 marks)**

> • Reactants (what reacts) are placed on the left side of an equation.
> • Products (what is made) are placed on the right.

 2 Write the word equation for the reaction between sodium and chlorine.

Guided

....   **(2 marks)**

3 A student heats solid calcium carbonate to form solid calcium oxide and carbon dioxide.

Add state symbols to complete the symbol equation for the reaction.

$CuCO_3(s)$ → CaO .... + CO_2 ....   **(3 marks)**

 4 Which state symbol is used to show that a substance is dissolved in water?
Tick **one** box.

Guided

☐ **A** (aq)

☐ **B** (l)

☐ **C** (s)

☐ **D** (g)   **(1 mark)**

 5 A student writes a symbol equation:

$Mg + HCl → MgCl_2 + H_2$

(a) Explain why the symbol equation is not balanced.

There is one hydrogen and one chlorine on the left side of the equation, but ......

....   **(2 marks)**

(b) Complete the symbol equation to balance it.

$Mg +$ .... $HCl → MgCl_2 + H_2$ **(1 mark)**

> • A balanced symbol equation has the same number of atoms on both sides of the equation (before the arrow and after it).
> • You can balance a symbol equation by writing a number **in front** of the formulae. You cannot change the small (subscript) numbers after the symbols in the formulae.

 6 Which of the following symbol equations is balanced? Tick **one** box.

Guided

☐ **A** $Mg + O_2 → MgO$

☐ **B** $Ca + HCl → + CaCl_2 + H_2$

☐ **C** $CaCO_3 + H_2SO_4 → CaSO_4 + CO_2 + H_2O$

☐ **D** $Mg(OH)_2 + HCl → MgCl_2 + H_2O$ **(1 mark)**

Hazards, risk and precautions

Practical skills

1 A student plans to heat a strip of magnesium ribbon in a Bunsen burner flame. She knows that the magnesium will give out a very bright white light.

(a) The image shows the magnesium container.
What does the hazard symbol mean?

.... **(1 mark)**

(b) State **two** hazards of carrying out this experiment.

1. The Bunsen burner will get hot, which ....

....

2. The magnesium will give out a bright light, which ....

.... **(2 marks)**

(c) State **two** precautions she should use to reduce the risk of harm.

1. ....

....

2. ....

.... **(2 marks)**

> • A precaution is a way of reducing the risks from a hazard.
> • Think of one precaution for each of the hazards you identified in part (b).

Guided

2 A scientist uses a concentrated acid that can cause burns to the skin.

(a) Choose the correct hazard to describe the acid. Tick **one** box.

☐ **A** irritant   ☐ **B** oxidising

☐ **C** toxic   ☐ **D** corrosive   **(1 mark)**

(b) Describe what the word 'risk' means.

....

....

.... **(2 marks)**

(c) Explain one precaution the scientist should use to reduce the risk of harm when using the acid.

....

....

.... **(2 marks)**

> When a question asks you to 'explain' you need to give a scientific reason for your answer.

Had a go ☐   Nearly there ☐   Nailed it! ☐

Atomic structure

1 Label the diagram of the atom.

proton

Choose from the words below:

electron   **nucleus**   **neutron**   ~~**proton**~~   **shell**   **(5 marks)**

2 For each statement, write down the atomic particle(s) it is describing.

> Guided

(a) Has a positive charge

   ....

(b) Has no charge

   ....

(c) Has a negative charge

   ....

(d) Is found in shells around the nucleus

   ....

(e) Has a mass of 1

   .... and ....

(f) Is found in the nucleus

   .... and ....   **(6 marks)**

3 Explain why atoms have no overall charge.

   Atoms have equal numbers of protons and electrons so ....

   ....   **(2 marks)**

4 The diameter of an atom is about 60 000 times larger than the diameter of its nucleus.
   A student wanted to make a model of an atom.

> Maths skills

   They wanted to use a lentil with a diameter of 2 mm to represent the nucleus.
   Calculate the diameter that they would need to use to represent the whole atom.
   Give your answer in metres.

   2 × 60 000 = ...

   ....   **(3 marks)**

   > There are 1000 mm in 1 m.
   > To convert mm into m you need to divide by 1000.

Isotopes

1 Complete the diagram below using a straight line to connect the term to its correct meaning.

Term	Meaning
Mass number	The number of protons (and electrons) in an atom
Atomic number	The total number of neutrons and protons in an atom
Relative atomic mass	The average mass of atoms of an element, taking into account all its different isotopes and their abundances

(3 marks)

2 An atom of lithium has a mass number of 7 and atomic number of 3.

(a) How many protons has it got?

3

(b) How many particles does it have in the nucleus?

....

(c) How many neutrons has it got?

....

(d) How many electrons does it have?

.... (4 marks)

3 What are isotopes? Tick **one** box.

☐ **A** atoms with the same number of protons and neutrons

☐ **B** atoms with the same number of protons, but a different number of neutrons

☐ **C** atoms with the same number of neutrons, but a different number of protons

☐ **D** atoms with the same number of neutrons, but a different number of electrons (1 mark)

4 Complete the table to show the number of neutrons, protons and electrons in each isotope.

Isotope	Number of protons	Number of neutrons	Number of electrons
Sodium-23	11	12	11
Oxygen-16			
Magnesium-26			
Chlorine-37			

(4 marks)

- Sodium-23 has the mass number 23.
- All isotopes of sodium have the same atomic number. This is 11 and can be found on the periodic table (you will have one in the exam and one is supplied in the back of this book).
- The atoms of all isotopes of a particular element will have the same number of protons and electrons.

Had a go ☐ Nearly there ☐ Nailed it! ☐

Mendeleev's table

Guided

1 Choose words from below to complete the sentences.

group **number** **row** **mass**

When Mendeleev was writing his periodic table, he arranged the elements in order of their atomic .... He moved them around so that elements with similar properties were in the same .... **(2 marks)**

2 This diagram shows part of Mendeleev's periodic table.
He wrote it in 1871.

Group

1	2	3	4	5	6	7
H						
Li	Be	B	C	N	O	F
Na	Mg	Al	Si	P	S	Cl
K Cu	Ca Zn	* *	Ti *	V As	Cr Se	Mn Br
Rb Ag	Sr Cd	Y In	Zr Sn	Nb Sb	Mo Te	* I

(a) State the number of the group he placed fluorine in.

.... **(1 mark)**

You can find out the symbol for fluorine by looking on a modern periodic table.

(b) Suggest why he put chlorine and fluorine in the same group.

.... **(1 mark)**

(c) Mendeleev chose not to place titanium (Ti) in group 3, but left a gap instead. Explain why.

He left gaps for elements that he predicted had not yet been discovered. He did not put titanium into group 3 because .... **(2 marks)**

This question is worth two marks. The first part has been done for you.

Guided

3 Give **one** similarity between Mendeleev's table and the modern periodic table.

....

.... **(1 mark)**

Guided

4 Which **two** ways are the modern periodic table different to Mendeleev's table?

☐ **A** Elements are now arranged by atomic mass

☐ **B** Elements are now arranged by atomic number

☐ **C** There are no gaps in the table

☐ **D** There are more gaps in the table **(2 marks)**

The periodic table

1 Select the correct words below to complete the sentences to explain how elements are arranged in the periodic table.

Guided

groups   mass   number   periods   properties   sizes

Elements are ordered across rows called .... in order of their atomic ....

Elements with similar .... are arranged in columns called .... **(4 marks)**

2 Use a copy of the periodic table to write the name of the element found in each position:

(a) Group 2, row 3 Magnesium

(b) Group 0, row 1 ....

(c) Group 7, row 4 ....   **(3 marks)**

3 The diagram shows an outline of the periodic table.
Some of the elements are represented by letters.

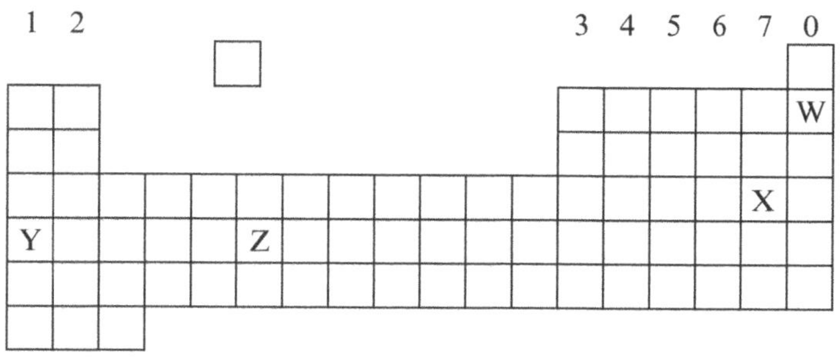

Write the letter(s) that represents:

(a) A non-metal element

W and ....   **(2 marks)**

(b) A metal element

....   **(2 marks)**

(c) The element whose atoms have the highest atomic number

....   **(1 mark)**

(d) The element whose atoms have the smallest number of protons

....   **(1 mark)**

> Look at how the elements are arranged by atomic number by looking at the periodic table at the end of this book.

4 On the periodic table in question 3, shade in a box that shows the position of an element that has similar properties to element W.

Guided

(1 mark)

Had a go ☐   Nearly there ☐   Nailed it! ☐

Electronic configurations

1 This diagram shows the electronic configuration of a chlorine atom.

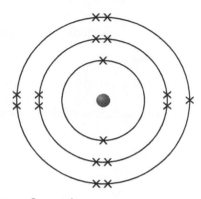

Write down its electronic configuration.

2 ....   **(1 mark)**

2 An oxygen atom has the electronic configuration 2,6.

Complete this diagram to show how its electrons are arranged.

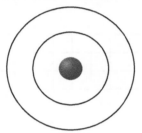

(2 marks)

3 Argon atoms have the electronic configuration 2,8,8.

Explain what this shows about argon's place on the periodic table.

It has three occupied electron shells so is in ....

It has eight electrons in its outer shell so is in ....   **(4 marks)**

> • The number of electron shells with electrons in them (occupied shells) is the same as the period the element is in.
> • The number of electrons in the outer shell is the same as the group the element is in.

4 The diagram shows the electronic configuration of an atom from an element.

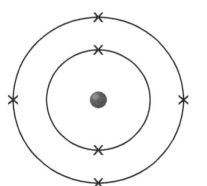

(a) State the period of the periodic table that the element is in.

....   **(1 mark)**

(b) State the group of the periodic table that the element is in.

4   **(1 mark)**

(c) Name the element the atom is from.

....   **(1 mark)**

> You can also work out the name of the element by counting its total number of electrons. This is its atomic number.

Ions

Guided

1 Which **two** statements about ions are true?

☐ **A** Metals form positive ions

☐ **B** Metals form negative ions

☐ **C** Atoms gain electrons to form negative ions

☐ **D** Atoms gain electrons to form positive ions **(2 marks)**

2 The diagram shows a sodium atom.

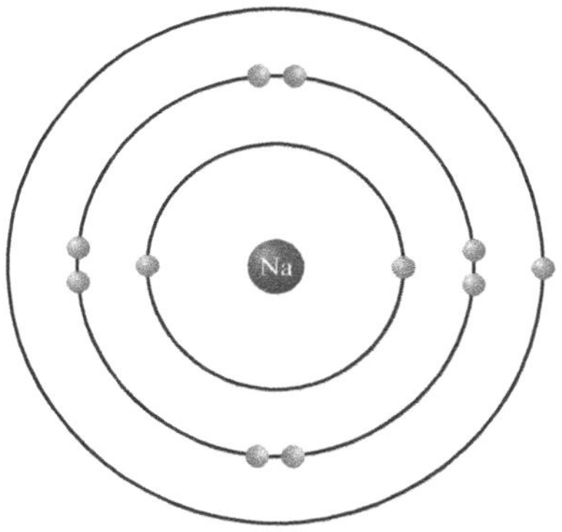

(a) Describe what happens when a sodium atom forms an ion.

It loses ....

.... **(1 mark)**

(b) Give the charge on the ion.

.... **(1 mark)**

(c) Explain why the ion has this charge.

The sodium atom has an equal number of positive .... and negative

.... so has no overall charge. When an ion is formed.....................

.... **(3 marks)**

3 Give the formula for ions formed by atoms of the following elements.

(a) Mg

.... **(1 mark)**

(b) S

.... **(1 mark)**

(c) Al

Al^{3+} **(1 mark)**

(d) Br

.... **(1 mark)**

> • You can work out how many electrons the atoms lose or gain by using the periodic table.
> • For example, group 1 metals always lose one electron. Group 7 elements always gain one electron.

4 Complete the table to show the number of protons and electrons in each ion.

Ion	Number of protons	Number of electrons
Li$^+$		
Cl$^-$		
Ca^{2+}	20	18
O^{2-}		

> Use the periodic table to find the atomic number of each element. This tells you the number of protons. Only the number of electrons changes when an atom forms an ion.

(4 marks)

Formulae of ionic compounds

1 Name the compounds shown by the formulae:

> You can use the periodic table to find out the name of elements from their symbol.

(a) LiCl

....

(b) LiBr

....

(c) MgO

....

(d) $CaCO_3$

.... carbonate

(e) $NaSO_4$

.... sulfate

(f) KOH

.... hydroxide

(g) $CuNO_3$

.... nitrate   **(7 marks)**

2 The formula of an iron(III) ion is Fe^{3+}. The formula of a carbonate ion is CO_3^{2-}.
   What is the formula of iron(III) carbonate? Tick **one** box.

☐ Guided ☒

☐ **A** $FeCO_3$

☐ **B** Fe_2CO_3

☐ **C** $Fe_3(CO_3)_2$

☐ **D** $Fe_2(CO_3)_3$ **(1 mark)**

3 Ions are charged particles.
   Some examples of ions are:

   Sodium: Na^+ Magnesium: Mg^{2+} Chloride: Cl^- Oxide: O^{2-}

   Write the formula for each of the following compounds:

   (a) Sodium chloride

   ....

   > • The charges on the ions must cancel each other out.
   > • A sodium ion has one positive charge, but an oxide ion has two negative charges.
   > • Two sodium ions are needed to balance out one oxide ion.

   (b) Sodium oxide

   Na_2 ....

   (c) Magnesium oxide

   ....

   (d) Magnesium chloride

   ....   **(4 marks)**

Properties of ionic compounds

1 State if each ion is an anion or cation.

| Metals form positive ions and non-metals form negative ions. |

(a) Na^+ *cation*

(b) O^{2-} ....

(c) A chlorine ion ....

(3 marks)

2 Which of these compounds are ionic? Tick **two** boxes.

☐ **A** carbon dioxide (CO_2)

☐ **B** potassium chloride (KCl)

☐ **C** sodium carbonate (Na_2CO_3)

☐ **D** methane (CH_4)

(2 marks)

3 Magnesium oxide (MgO) is an ionic compound.

(a) State the ions in magnesium oxide, with their charge.

| Remember that **opposite** charges **attract** and **like** charges **repel**. |

Mg^{2+} *and* ....

(2 marks)

(b) Explain how the ions are held together in magnesium oxide.

....

....

(2 marks)

(c) Complete the 2D diagram of magnesium oxide by writing in the ions.

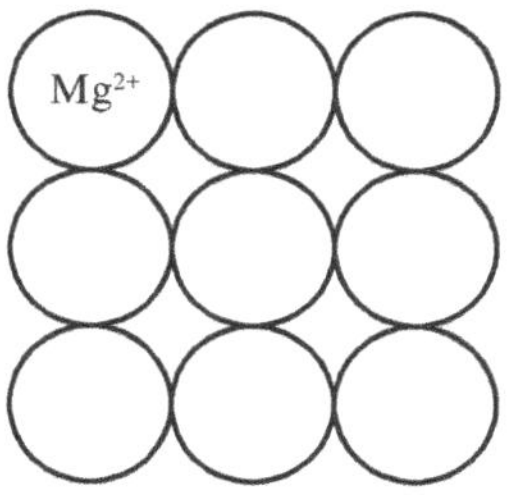

(1 mark)

(d) Magnesium oxide has a high melting point. Explain why.

The bonds between the ions are very strong ....

....

(2 marks)

4 A student carried out an experiment to test to see if lead bromide conducted electricity. They used the equipment shown in the diagram.

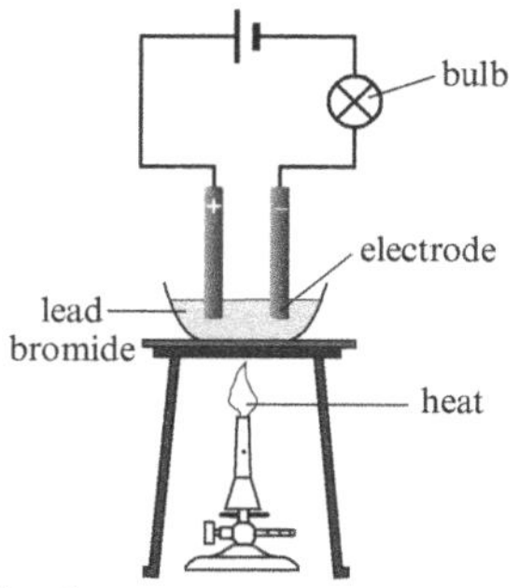

If the lead bromide conducts electricity, the bulb will light up.

Predict if the bulb will light up when the lead bromide is solid. Give a reason for your answer.

No, because ....

(2 marks)

(a) Predict if the bulb will light up when the lead bromide is melted.

....

....

(2 marks)

Covalent bonds

1 Draw a circle around the structures that contain covalent bonds between their atoms.

magnesium chloride   oxygen   copper   carbon dioxide

(2 marks)

2 The diagrams show two different molecules.

H – Cl   O = C = O

Hydrogen chloride   Carbon dioxide

Describe what the diagrams show about the covalent bonding in each molecule.

There is a single covalent bond between the atoms in hydrogen chloride ....

.... **(2 marks)**

3 Describe what a covalent bond is.

A shared pair of .... **(1 mark)**

4 In the space below draw the dot cross diagram to show the covalent bonds in:

(a) Water, H_2O.

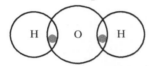

(2 marks)

> • The answer has been partly done for you – the atoms have been drawn,
>   showing the overlap and hydrogen's electrons have been added.
> • You just need to add the electrons in oxygen's outer shell. You can find
>   out the total number of electrons it has by looking up its atomic number
>   on the periodic table at the end of this book.

(b) Chlorine, Cl_2.

(2 marks)

5 The diameter of an atom is around 1×10^{-10} m.

The diameter of a simple molecule is around 1×10^{-9} m.

Calculate the difference in order of magnitude between the two structures.

$1 \times 10^{-9} \div 1 \times 10^{-10} =$ ....

.... **(2 marks)**

> If two numbers differ by one order of magnitude,
> one is about ten times larger than the other.
> If they differ by two orders of magnitude, they
> differ by a factor of about 100.

Simple molecular substances

1 Which of these substances exist as simple molecules? Tick **two** boxes.

    ☐   **A**   diamond

    ☐   **B**   oxygen

    ☐   **C**   ethane

    ☐   **D**   iron oxide

(2 marks)

2 The diagram shows the bonding in a sample of hydrogen gas.

(a) Choose the correct term from the list below to label bond Y.

covalent bond   **intermolecular force**   **ionic bond**

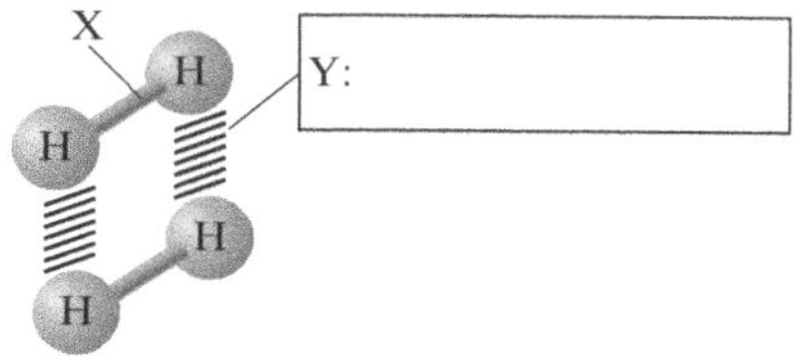

> Remember, strong covalent bonds exist between the atoms in simple molecules.

(1 mark)

(b) Give the letter of the bond, X or Y, which describes the bond that:

exists between atoms.

....

exists between molecules.

....

breaks when hydrogen boils.

....

is the strongest.

X

(4 marks)

3 Explain why simple molecules cannot conduct electricity.

....

....

(1 mark)

> Think about why melted or dissolved ionic compounds **can** conduct electricity. How are the structures of ionic compounds and simple molecules different?

4 Hydrogen chloride is made up of simple molecules.

Explain why it is a gas at room temperature.

The forces between the molecules are weak so ....

....

(2 marks)

Giant molecular substances

1   Silica is a compound found in sand. It has a giant molecular structure, as shown in the diagram.

Which properties does silica have? Tick **two** boxes.

☐   **A**   high melting point

☐   **B**   ability to conduct electricity when molten

☐   **C**   very hard

☐   **D**   soluble in water

silicon atom

oxygen atom

(2 marks)

> Think about what type of atoms make up graphite.

2   Graphite is also a giant molecular substance.

(a)   Explain why graphite is an element.

.... **(1 mark)**

(b)   Draw lines to match graphite's properties to a reason, based on its structure.

Property	Reason
Can conduct electricity	Strong covalent bonds between atoms
Feels slippery (layers slide over each other)	Delocalised electrons between layers are able to move
Solid at room temperature	Weak intermolecular forces between layers

(3 marks)

3   The diagram shows the structure of diamond.

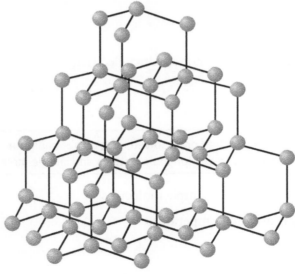

Use its structure to explain why diamond is used in cutting tools.

Each atom is bonded to three others by ....

....

.... **(3 marks)**

> Remember: covalent bonds are very strong and difficult to break.

Other large molecules

1 Poly(ethene) is an example of a substance that consists of large chains of molecules.
   What type of large molecule is poly(ethene)? Tick **one** box.

   ☐ **A** giant covalent

   ☐ **B** fullerene

   ☐ **C** metal

   ☐ **D** polymer **(1 mark)**

2 Buckminsterfullerene is a fullerene that has a ball structure.

   (a) What does its formula, C_{60}, tell you about it? Tick **two** boxes.

   ☐ **A** it contains only carbon atoms

   ☐ **B** it is a compound

   ☐ **C** each ball contains 60 atoms

   ☐ **D** each ball contains 60 molecules **(2 marks)**

Maths skills

   (b) The diameter of a Buckminsterfullerene ball is around 0.71 nm.

   Calculate the diameter in picometres (pm).

   1 nm = 1000 pm

   ....

   .... **(2 marks)**

3 Graphene is a fullerene.

   State one similarity and one difference between the structure of graphene and graphite.

   Similarity

   They both are formed of interlocking hexagonal rings of carbon atoms.

   Difference

   .... **(2 marks)**

4 Graphene can be rolled to form long tubes called carbon nanotubes.

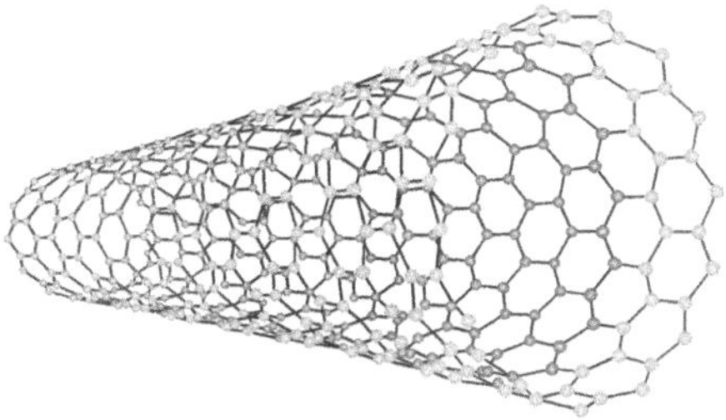

   A nanotube is shown in the diagram.

   These are used to strengthen golf clubs.

   Explain why the properties of carbon nanotubes make them suitable for this use.

   Carbon nanotubes are very strong because ....

   ....

   .... **(3 marks)**

Metals

1 The diagram shows the structure of metal.

   (a) Choose the correct terms below to label it.

delocalised electrons   **positive electrons**   **localised electrons**

positive atoms   **positive ions**

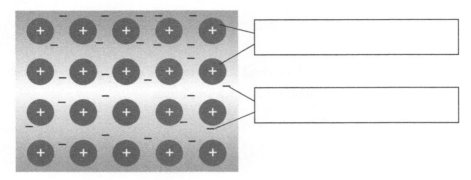

(2 marks)

   (b) Use the diagram to explain why metals can conduct electricity.

   ....

(1 mark)

2 Some properties of elements W, X, Y and Z are shown in the table below.
   Use the information to answer the questions below.

Element	Melting point in °C	Can it conduct electricity?	Appearance
W	−38.8	Yes	Shiny
X	−272.2	No	Dull
Y	1538	Yes	Shiny
Z	4000	Yes	Dull

   (a) Give the letters of the elements that are:

   metals

   ....

   non-metals.

   All metals are shiny and can conduct electricity.

   ....

(2 marks)

   (b) Mercury is a metal that is liquid at room temperature (20 °C).

   Which element is mercury? Give a reason for your answer.

   W because it has a melting point lower than 20 °C and ....

   ....

(3 marks)

   (c) Which letter could be graphite? Give a reason for your answer.

   ....

   ....

(3 marks)

Limitations of models

1 The diagram shows a model of a molecule.

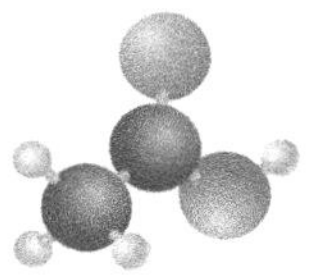

What type of model is it? Tick **one** box.

☐ **A** ball and stick

☐ **B** dot and cross

☐ **C** drawn structure

☐ **D** space-filling

(1 mark)

2 The diagram below shows a dot cross diagram for the molecule ethene.

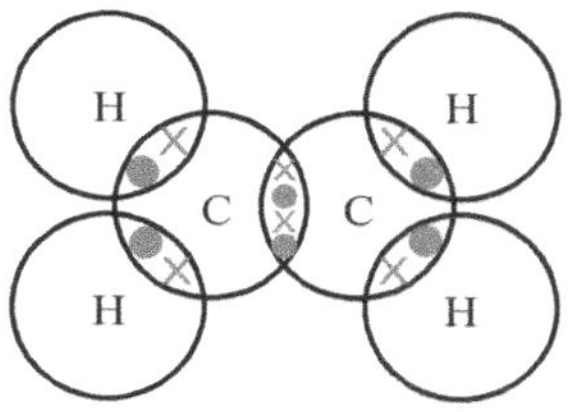

(a) In the space below, draw its structure, using lines to show the bonds between atoms.

H   H

  C   C

H   H

> • The letters to show each atom have been drawn for you.
> • You just need to add lines to show the bonds between them.
> • Remember: a single pair of shared electrons is a single bond. Two shared pairs of electrons are a double bond.

(2 marks)

(b) Give the structural formula of ethene.

....

(1 mark)

(c) Give the empirical formula of ethene.

....

(1 mark)

3 The diagram shows a space-filling model of ethene.

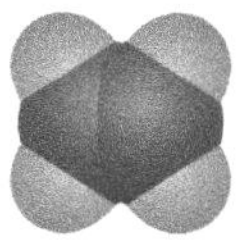

Describe one advantage and one disadvantage of this type of model over a dot and cross diagram.

Advantage

....

Disadvantage

....

(2 marks)

> Think about what each model shows you about ethene. Remember, the dot and cross diagram is 2D, but the space-filling model is showing a 3D structure.

Relative formula mass

Use the relative atomic masses, A_r, in the table below when you answer the questions.

Element	C	Cu	H	Mg	N	O
A_r	12	63.5	1	24	14	16

1 Draw lines to match the molecule to its relative formula mass.

molecule   relative formula mass

$$\begin{array}{c} H \\ | \\ H-C-H \\ | \\ H \end{array}$$

$$O=C=O$$

$$H-O-H$$

$$\begin{array}{c} H-N-H \\ | \\ H \end{array}$$

18

16

44

17

(4 marks)

2 Calculate the relative formula mass of:

(a) CuO

63.5 + 16 = ... **(1 mark)**

> Do not round the answer up to the nearest whole number.

(b) CO

.... **(1 mark)**

(c) NO_2

14 + (16 × 2) = ... **(1 mark)**

> You can type the calculation into your calculator using brackets or work out 16 × 2 first and then add it to 14.

3 Calculate the relative formula mass of:

(a) $MgCO_3$

24 + 12 + (16 × 3) = ... **(1 mark)**

(b) $Cu(OH)_2$

.... **(1 mark)**

> The brackets are used to show that there are two OHs – so two oxygen atoms and two hydrogen atoms.

(c) $Mg(NO_3)_2$

.... **(1 mark)**

Empirical formulae

Practical skills

1 Two students carried out a chemical reaction in their chemistry lesson. They took a small piece of magnesium metal and heated it inside a crucible using the equipment shown:

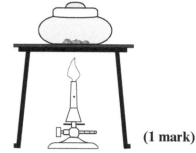

(a) The magnesium reacted with oxygen in the air to form a white powder, magnesium oxide.

Write the word equation for the reaction.

magnesium + ...   **(1 mark)**

(b) Suggest why they lifted the lid of the crucible a few times during the reaction.

....

....   **(2 marks)**

Maths skills

2 The students recorded the following masses throughout the experiment:

Mass 1 (crucible and lid) = 23.58 g

Mass 2 (crucible, lid and magnesium) = 23.82 g

Mass 3 (crucible, lid and magnesium oxide) = 23.98 g

(a) Calculate the mass of oxygen that reacted with the magnesium during the reaction.

23.98 − 23.82 = ...   **(2 marks)**

(b) Calculate the empirical formula of magnesium oxide using the results.

Mass of magnesium used = 23.82 − 23.58 = 0.24 g

Mass of oxygen used = ...

> Use your calculation from part (a).

Mg	O
$\frac{0.24}{24} = 0.01$	$\frac{............}{16} =$
$\frac{0.01}{............} =$	$\frac{............}{............} =$

> Divide the mass of each element by its A_r.

> Divide both numbers by the smallest number to find the ratio.

Empirical formula is ....   **(4 marks)**

Maths skills

3 The M_r of a compound is 30. Its empirical formula is CH_3.

Calculate its molecular formula.

$12 + (3 \times 1) =$ ....

> Calculate the M_r of the empirical formula.

$30 \div$ ....

> Divide the M_r given in the question by the M_r of the empirical formula.

molecular formula is ....   **(3 marks)**

> Multiply each number in the empirical formula by the answer.

Conservation of mass

1 A strip of copper is heated in air using a Bunsen burner.

(a) Write the word equation for the reaction.

copper + oxygen → .... **(1 mark)**

(b) What will happen to the mass of copper oxide as it is heated? Tick **one** box.

☐ **A** increase

☐ **B** stay the same

☐ **C** decrease

☐ **D** increase then decrease **(1 mark)**

> • A change in mass can be evidence that a chemical reaction has taken place.
> • If the mass increases then it suggests that reactants have chemically combined.
> • If the mass decreases then it suggests that a product has been formed that is a gas.

2 A student carries out a chemical reaction between colourless solutions. A solution containing 2.2 g of lead(II) nitrate was added to a solution containing 1.6 g of another reactant in a conical flask. They observe that a yellow solid is formed.

(a) Explain why their observation is evidence that a chemical change has taken place.

.... **(1 mark)**

Maths skills

(b) Calculate the total mass of reactants in the beaker after the reaction has taken place.

2.2 g + 1.6 g = ... **(1 mark)**

> During a chemical reaction, no atoms are lost or gained. The atoms in the reactant are just rearranged to form the products. This means that the mass of the reactants = mass of the products.

3 A science teacher heats 8.61 g of copper(II) carbonate powder, as shown in the diagram.

(a) The test tube will get hot.

Explain one precaution to control the risk of harm from this hazard.

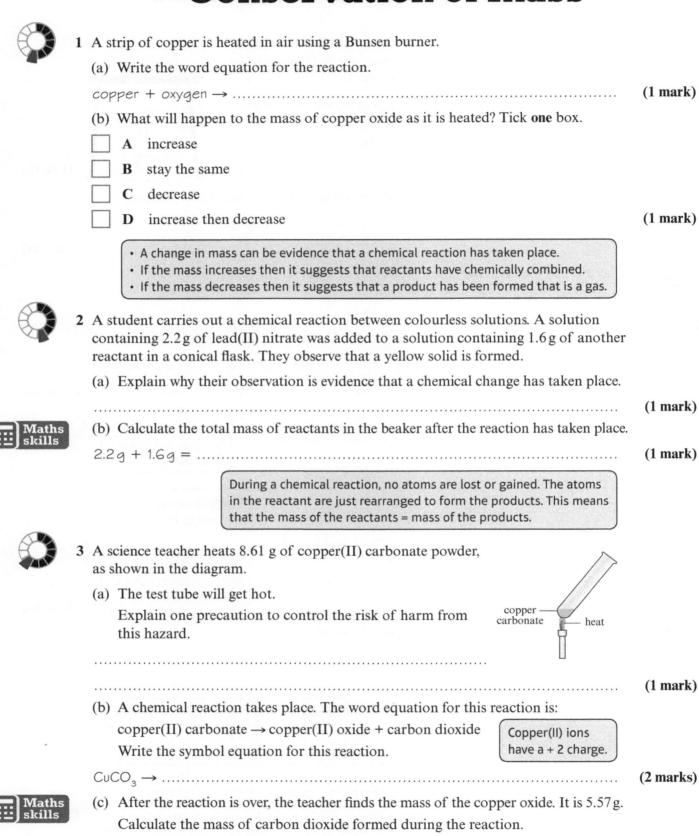

copper carbonate — heat

....

.... **(1 mark)**

(b) A chemical reaction takes place. The word equation for this reaction is:

copper(II) carbonate → copper(II) oxide + carbon dioxide

Write the symbol equation for this reaction.

> Copper(II) ions have a + 2 charge.

$CuCO_3$ → .... **(2 marks)**

Maths skills

(c) After the reaction is over, the teacher finds the mass of the copper oxide. It is 5.57 g. Calculate the mass of carbon dioxide formed during the reaction.

8.61 g – 5.57 g = ... **(1 mark)**

Concentration of solution

1 A scientist makes up some salt solutions.
Which solution is the most concentrated? Tick **one** box.

☐ **A** 5 g salt in 100 cm³ of water

☐ **B** 10 g salt in 250 cm³ of water

☐ **C** 15 g salt in 200 cm³ of water

☐ **D** 20 g salt in 250 cm³ of water   **(1 mark)**

2 Convert these volumes into dm³.

(a) 1000 cm³

....   **(1 mark)**

(b) 100 cm³

100/1000 = ...   **(1 mark)**

(c) 350 cm³

....   **(1 mark)**

> • 1000 cm³ = 1 dm³
> • So, to convert cm³ into dm³ divide by 1000.

3 Convert these volumes into cm³.

(a) 2.5 dm³

2.5 × 1000 = ...   **(1 mark)**

(b) 0.8 dm³

....   **(1 mark)**

(c) 0.05 dm³

....   **(1 mark)**

> • 1 dm³ = 1000 cm³
> • So, to convert dm³ into cm³ multiply by 1000.

4 10 g of copper sulfate is dissolved in 250 cm³ of water.
Calculate the concentration of the solution:

(a) in g cm⁻³

10 ÷ 250 = ...   **(1 mark)**

(b) in g dm⁻³

....   **(1 mark)**

> • The units for concentration can be g cm⁻³ (which can also be written as g/cm³) or g dm⁻³ (also written as g/dm³).
> • To calculate concentration, use this formula:
>   concentration = mass of solute/volume of solution

5 Calculate the mass of potassium chloride needed to make 2 dm³ of a solution with a concentration of 20 g dm⁻³.

....   **(1 mark)**

> You can rearrange the formula to make:
> • Mass of solute = concentration × volume of solution
> • Volume of solution = mass of solute/concentration

Had a go ☐   Nearly there ☐   Nailed it! ☐

Extended response – Types of substance

The table gives some information about the melting and boiling points of three covalent substances.

Substance	Melting point (°C)	Boiling point (°C)
Bromine	−7.2	58.8
Silicon dioxide	1710	2230
Oxygen	−218.4	−183.0

Compare the melting and boiling points for each substance.

> Describe the boiling and melting point for each substance – is it high or low? Then compare them. Which is the highest? Which is the lowest?

Give a reason for the differences, based on their structure and bonding.

> You might find it useful to plan out your answer first on scrap paper. Write out the headings of each section so you know what to include.
> • Covalent substances can be simple molecules or have giant structures.
> • First, remember which type each of the examples above is.
> • Then think about how they are bonded – how does this affect their melting and boiling points?
> • Discuss each substance in turn.
> This question is worth six marks so include as much information as you can to get maximum marks.

....

....

....

....

....

....

....

....

....

....

....

....

....

....

....

(6 marks)

States of matter

1 In which state(s) of matter are the particles always touching? Tick **one** box.

☐   **A**   solid and liquid

☐   **B**   solid only

☐   **C**   liquid and gas

☐   **D**   liquid only   **(1 mark)**

2 Name the change in state being described.

(a) A solid turning into a liquid.

....

(b) A gas turning into a liquid.

....

(c) A liquid turning into a gas.

....   **(3 marks)**

3 Describe the difference between a physical and chemical change.

In a chemical change ....

but in a physical change ....   **(1 mark)**

4 Solid carbon dioxide is also known as dry ice. When dry ice is heated, carbon dioxide gas is released.

(a) Name this change in state.

....   **(1 mark)**

(b) Explain how the movement and arrangement of particles changes during this change in state.

The particles move further apart so they are not touching and ....

....   **(2 marks)**

5 Ammonia has a melting point of −77.7 °C and a boiling point of −33.3 °C.

What state is ammonia at a temperature of:

(a) 50 °C?

....   **(1 mark)**

(b) −50 °C?

....

(c) −100 °C?

....

- At a temperature below its melting point a substance is a solid.   **(1 mark)**
- Between its melting and boiling point it is a liquid.
- Above its boiling point it is a gas.   **(1 mark)**

105

Pure substances and mixtures

1 Add ticks to the table to show if each substance is an element, compound or mixture.

Substance	Element	Compound	Mixture
Carbon	✓		
Carbon dioxide			
Air			
Helium			

(4 marks)

2 A bottle of mineral water contains water with minerals dissolved in it. The boiling point of the mineral water is not exactly 100 °C. Explain why.

> Is the water pure or a mixture?

....

.... **(2 marks)**

3 Substances can be elements, compounds or mixtures.

(a) Compare an element and a compound.

An element only contains one type of atom, but a compound ....

.... **(3 marks)**

(b) Choose words from below to complete the sentences.

compound   **element**   **mixture**   **pure**

Copper sulfate ($CuSO_4$) and water are both examples of a ....

When they are added together they form a .... **(2 marks)**

(c) After water and copper sulfate are added together it is easy to separate them. Explain why.

.... **(1 mark)**

4 A scientist cools a gas.

He measures its temperature at regular intervals until after it freezes.

The graph shows his results.

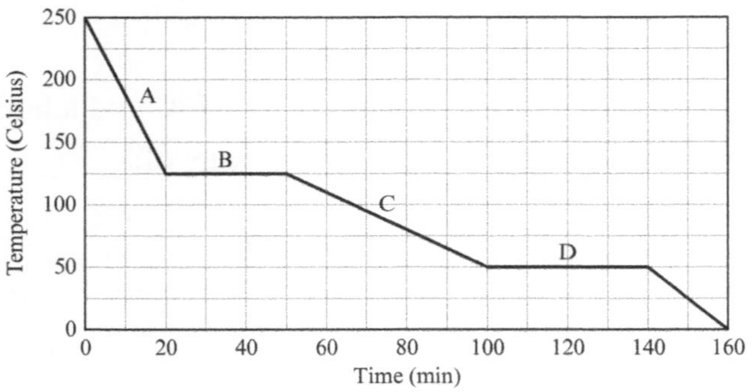

(a) During the cooling the substance sometimes exists in one state only.

During which time period on the graph is the substance a liquid? Tick **one** box. **(1 mark)**

☐ A   ☐ C

☐ B   ☐ D **(1 mark)**

(b) State the temperature that the substance freezes.

.... **(1 mark)**

(c) Is the substance pure or a mixture? Give a reason for your answer.

....

.... **(2 marks)**

Distillation

1 Methanol and ethanol are liquids that mix completely with each other.

   (a) What type of liquids are they? Tick **one** box.

   ☐ **A** insoluble

   ☐ **B** immiscible

   ☐ **C** miscible

   ☐ **D** mixtures   **(1 mark)**

   (b) Give the type of distillation that could be used to separate a mixture of methanol and ethanol.

   ....   **(1 mark)**

2 A student was asked to produce pure water from saltwater.

   The diagram shows the equipment they used.

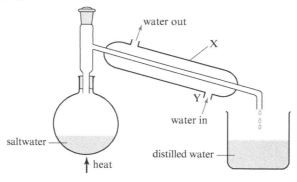

   (a) Describe the function of the piece of equipment labelled X.

   It is where condensation takes place and ....

   ....   **(2 marks)**

   (b) Explain why the cold water going in at point Y needs to be constantly flowing.

   ....

   ....   **(2 marks)**

   (c) Explain what happens to the concentration of the saltwater as it is heated.

   It increases because ....

   ....

   ....

   ....

   ....

   ....   **(3 marks)**

   (d) Suggest how the student could prove that the distilled water collected in the beaker is pure.

   ....

   ....   **(2 marks)**

   ┌───┐
   │ Pure water freezes at 0 °C and boils at 100 °C. │
   └───┘

Filtration and crystallisation

Practical skills

1 A student is asked to produce pure salt crystals from a mixture of salt and sand.

(a) They first add water to the mixture and stir.

Choose words from the list below to explain why they do this.

insoluble   **soluble**   **solution**   **solvent**

Salt is .... in water, but sand is ....

The salt dissolves to form a .... **(3 marks)**

(b) The student then filters the mixture.

Draw a labelled diagram of the equipment they should use in the space below.

(3 marks)

(c) Describe why they filter the mixture.

Explain how this separating technique works.

They filter the mixture to remove the ....

It works because there are small holes in the filter paper that ....

....

.... **(3 marks)**

(d) They are left with the liquid that passes through the filter paper. This is called the filtrate.

They heat the filtrate using the equipment shown.

— filtrate

— hot water

Describe the steps they should take to get pure salt crystals.

1. Heat the filtrate until it is saturated.

2. ....

3. .... **(3 marks)**

Practical skills This process is called crystallisation. The order of the method is: heat to form a saturated solution, cool, separate the crystals that form from the liquid.

Paper chromatography

Practical skills

1 Paper chromatography was used to find out which food colourings (A, B, C) were present in a sweet, X.

The diagram shows the equipment used.

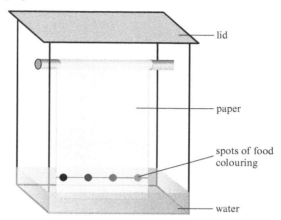

Choose labels from the diagram to answer the following questions.

(a) What is the mobile phase?

.... **(1 mark)**

(b) What is the stationary phase?

.... **(1 mark)**

(c) Name the solvent used.

water **(1 mark)**

(d) Give the function of the lid.

.... **(1 mark)**

2 The diagram shows the results.

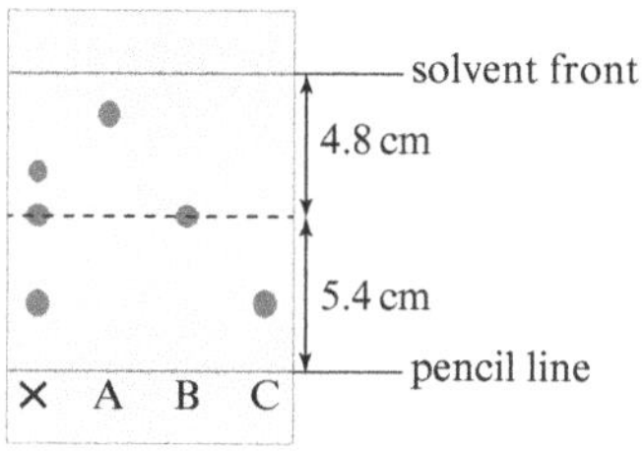

(a) Describe how the results show that X contains a mixture of food colourings.

.... **(1 mark)**

solvent front
4.8 cm
5.4 cm
pencil line
× A   B   C

(b) Explain what the results show about the food colourings in X.

It contains three food colourings: ....

.... **(2 marks)**

Maths skills

(c) Calculate the R_f value of the food colouring B.

$$R_f \text{ value} = \frac{\text{distance travelled by spot}}{\text{distance travelled by solvent}}$$

The distance travelled by the solvent is 5.4 cm + 4.8 cm = 10.2 cm. ....

The distance travelled by the spot is ....

.........../10.2 = ... **(3 marks)**

• You should give your answer to the same number of significant figures as the numbers in the question. So, for this question that is one significant figure.
• Remember, R_f values have no units.

109

Investigating inks

1 Ink is a mixture of coloured pigments dissolved in a solvent.

What method could be used to separate the solvent from the pigment? Tick **one** box.

☐ **A** chromatography

☐ **B** crystallisation

☐ **C** filtration

☐ **D** simple distillation

> Which method is used to separate **dissolved** solids from a solution?

(1 mark)

2 A student wanted to use paper chromatography to find out what inks are present in a waterproof pen.

This is the method they followed:

- Draw a pencil line near the bottom of the chromatography paper.
- Use the pen to add a small spot of ink to the line.
- Place the paper into a boiling tube containing a little solvent.
- Replace the bung and allow the solvent to travel through the paper.

(a) Explain why they used a pencil to draw the line and not a pen.

.... **(1 mark)**

(b) They chose the solvent propanone, not water. Explain why.

Waterproof pens are not soluble in water so propanone is used because ....

.... **(3 marks)**

(c) Propanone is flammable. Explain what the student should do in order to control the risk from this hazard.

.... **(1 mark)**

(d) The diagram shows part of the label on the bottle of propanone.

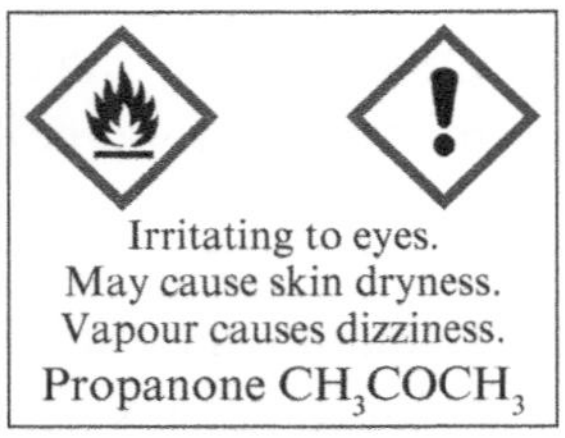

Explain why the student:

used the propanone in a fume cupboard ....

....

....

wore eye protection ....

....

....

Irritating to eyes.
May cause skin dryness.
Vapour causes dizziness.
Propanone CH_3COCH_3

(2 marks)

3 The results showed two spots of ink at 2.3 cm and 4.6 cm. The solvent reached 6.1 cm.

(a) Explain why one ink travelled further than the other.

Each ink is attracted to both the .... and stationary phase. The ink that

travelled further is more attracted to the .... phase than the other ink. **(2 marks)**

(b) Describe how they should calculate the R_f values of the inks.

....

.... **(1 mark)**

Drinking water

1 Water must be treated to make it potable.

(a) Describe what potable water is.

.... **(1 mark)**

(b) Which stage of water treatment is 2 on the diagram? Tick **one** box.

☐ **A** distillation

☐ **B** evaporation

☐ **C** filtration

☐ **D** sedimentation

(1 mark)

2 The final stage in water treatment is chlorination.

(a) Describe what happens during this stage.

.... is bubbled through the water. **(1 mark)**

(b) Explain why it is used.

.... **(2 marks)**

3 Aluminium sulfate can be added during water treatment. It forms aluminium hydroxide, which traps small solid particles suspended in the water.

The balanced equation for the reaction is.

$$Al_2(SO_4)_3(aq) + 6H_2O(l) \rightarrow 2Al(OH)_3(s) + 3H_2SO_4(aq)$$

(a) Name the solid formed in the reaction.

.... **(1 mark)**

(b) Complete the word equation for the reaction.

Aluminium hydroxide + ... → aluminium hydroxide + ... **(2 marks)**

4 The United Arab Emirates (UAE) is a country in the Middle East.

Rainfall is low so it has little freshwater.

It has a long coastline.

Temperatures are high for most of the year.

Evaluate the use of distillation to produce freshwater from seawater in the UAE.

Using distillation is a good idea because ....

....

....

Using distillation is not a good idea because ....

....

.... **(4 marks)**

> • The command word 'evaluate' means you need to describe both the advantages and disadvantages. You do not need to give a balanced number of advantages and disadvantages.
> • This question is worth four marks so you should write four separate points.

Extended response – Separating mixtures

A mixture contains salt, water and ethanol.

The information in the table shows some information about these substances.

Substance	Melting point (°C)	Boiling point (°C)	Is it soluble in water?	Is it soluble in ethanol?
Water	0	100	n/a	Yes
Sand	1713	2950	No	No
Ethanol	−144	78	Yes	n/a

Devise a method that can be used to separate the substances.

> The command word 'devise' means that you are being asked to plan or invent a procedure.

You should use the information in the table in your answer, and explain why you have suggested each step.

> Think about what separating techniques can be used.
> You have learned about simple distillation, fractional distillation, filtration, crystallisation and paper chromatography. You do not need to use them all to answer this question.

> How could you remove the sand?
> Then, think about how you could separate ethanol and water.

....

....

....

....

....

....

....

....

....

....

....

....

....

....

....

.... **(6 marks)**

Acids and alkalis

1 Add ticks to the boxes to show if each statement is describing acids or alkalis.

Statement	Acids	Alkalis
pH lower than 7		
pH higher than 7		
Are a source of hydroxide (OH^-) ions when in solution		
Are a source of hydrogen (H^+) ions when in solution		

(4 marks)

2 Complete the equations to show the ions present in solutions of acids and alkalis.

(a) $HCl(aq) \rightarrow$ ...... $(aq) + Cl^-(aq)$ **(1 mark)**

(b) .... $(aq) \rightarrow Na^+(aq) + OH^-(aq)$ **(1 mark)**

(c) $HNO_3(aq) \rightarrow$ .... $(aq) + NO_3^-(aq)$ **(2 marks)**

(d) $KOH(aq) \rightarrow$ .... $(aq) +$ .... (aq) **(2 marks)**

3 Three substances X, Y and Z were added to three different indicators.
The results are shown in the table.

Substance	Colour in universal indicator	Colour in methyl orange	Colour in litmus solution
X	red	red	red
Y	purple	yellow	
Z	green	orange	purple

(a) Which substance X, Y or Z has a pH of less than 7?

.... **(1 mark)**

(b) State the pH of substance Z.
Give a reason for your answer.

> The question is asking you to give an answer and then explain how the information in the table shows this is correct.

Substance Z has a pH of ....

The information shows this because .... **(2 marks)**

(c) What colour will substance Y go in litmus?

.... **(1 mark)**

4 Describe the advantages of using universal indicator rather than litmus solution to find the pH of a solution.

Litmus will only show if the solution is ...., ... or ....

Universal indicator ....

.... **(2 marks)**

113

Bases and alkalis

1 What **three** products are formed when a carbonate reacts with an acid?

1. Salt ....

2. ....

3. ....   **(3 marks)**

2 Complete the table to show the names of the salts produced when different acids and bases react.

Acid	Base		
	Sodium hydroxide	Potassium oxide	Copper carbonate
Hydrochloric acid	Sodium chloride		
Sulfuric acid		Potassium sulfate	
Nitric acid			Copper nitrate

(9 marks)

3 Calcium oxide (CaO) is a base.

(a) Calcium oxide is **not** an alkali.

Explain why.

.... **(1 mark)**

(b) Complete the word equation to show the reaction of calcium oxide and hydrochloric acid.

Calcium oxide + hydrochloric acid → .... + water   **(1 mark)**

4 A student adds magnesium to a test tube containing sulfuric acid.

(a) Balance the symbol equation for the reaction.

Mg(s) + HCl(aq) → $MgCl_2$(aq) + H_2(g)   **(1 mark)**

(b) The student observes that the piece of magnesium gets smaller during the reaction.

Explain why.

....

.... **(1 mark)**

> Take a look at the products of the reaction. Remember, the state symbol aq means that the substance is dissolved in water.

(c) The student adds a lighted splint to the top of the test tube.

Predict what they would observe.

Give a reason for your answer.

They would hear a ....

because the gas .... was produced in the reaction.   **(2 marks)**

Neutralisation

1 A student mixes together an acid and alkali.

(a) Which **two** products are made?

☐ **A**   Carbon dioxide

☐ **B**   Hydrogen

☐ **C**   Salt

☐ **D**   Water   **(2 marks)**

(b) Explain why this is a neutralisation reaction.

.... **(1 mark)**

2 A student was asked to investigate the change in pH of hydrochloric acid as a powdered base is added.

Practical skills

(a) The images (right) show the hazard symbols of two bases.
She chooses to use calcium hydroxide.
Suggest why.

calcium oxide   **(IRRITANT)** calcium hydroxide

Calcium oxide is corrosive, whereas calcium hydroxide is an ....

so .... **(2 marks)**

(b) Balance the symbol equation for the reaction between calcium hydroxide and hydrochloric acid.

$Ca(OH)_2$ + ...$HCl \rightarrow CaCl_2$ + ...H_2O **(2 marks)**

She carries out the investigation by following the method shown below:

• Add some dilute hydrochloric acid to the beaker.

• Measure and record the pH of the contents of the beaker.

• Add a small mass of calcium hydroxide powder, stir, and then measure and record the pH again. Repeat until the pH no longer changes.

(c) State one way she could measure the pH.

.... **(1 mark)**

(d) She gathers the results and plots them on a line graph.
Complete the graph by drawing the line of best fit.

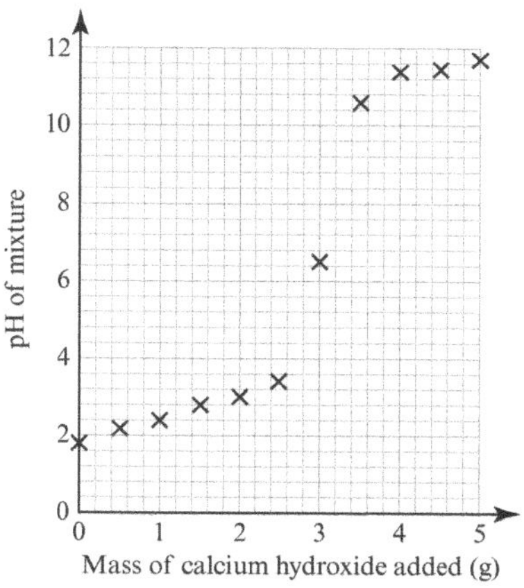

(1 mark)

(e) Use the line to work out the mass of calcium hydroxide needed to neutralise the acid.

....g   **(1 mark)**

> The acid is neutralised when the pH is 7.
> Draw a line from 7 on the y-axis until it meets the line of best fit.
> Then draw a line down from this point until it reaches the x-axis to find out the amount of calcium hydroxide that neutralised the acid.

Salts from insoluble bases

1 Which **two** reactants should be chosen to make the salt potassium sulfate in the school laboratory?

☐ **A** potassium

☐ **B** potassium carbonate

☐ **C** sulfur

☐ **D** sulfuric acid   **(2 marks)**

2 A student makes pure salt crystals by reacting copper oxide and sulfuric acid.

(a) Write the word equation for the reaction.

copper oxide + ...→ copper sulfate + ...   **(2 marks)**

They pour 25 cm³ of sulfuric acid into a beaker and heat it using a Bunsen burner.
They are careful not to boil the acid.
Explain why:

(b) They heat the acid.

To increase the rate of reaction between the acid and the copper oxide ....

....

They are careful not to boil the acid.

....   **(2 marks)**

(c) They add copper oxide powder to the sulfuric acid until the copper oxide is **in excess**.
Describe how they can tell when to stop adding the copper oxide.

....

....   **(1 mark)**

> **Practical skills**   If a reactant is in excess, some of it is left over when the reaction has finished.

(d) To separate the excess copper oxide the student lets the copper oxide settle to the bottom of the beaker and then carefully pours off the liquid.
Describe how they could improve their method.

Use filtration by ....

....

....   **(3 marks)**

(e) They pour the liquid into an evaporating dish.
Describe how they should form pure salt crystals.

Use a Bunsen burner to heat the mixture until ....

....

then ....   **(3 marks)**

Salts from soluble bases

1 Label the following pieces of equipment.

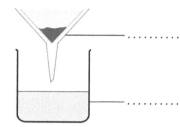

....

....

....

(3 marks)

2 Titration is used to react an acid with a known volume soluble base (alkali) to create a salt.

For each question, choose the correct measuring equipment used in titration from the list below.

beaker   burette   measuring cylinder   pipette

(a) This is filled with acid.

....

(1 mark)

(b) This is used to measure the volume of alkali.

....

(1 mark)

3 A student carries out a titration between hydrochloric acid and sodium hydroxide. They place 25 cm³ of sodium hydroxide into a conical flask and add a few drops of phenolphthalein.

(a) Phenolphthalein is different colours in different acidic and alkaline solutions. What is this type of chemical called?

....

(1 mark)

(b) What colour is phenolphthalein in the sodium hydroxide?

pink

(1 mark)

(c) The student adds acid a few drops at a time until neutralisation has occurred. Describe how they will know when this is.

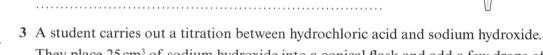

(1 mark)

4 Mira used a titration to find the volume of sulfuric acid needed to neutralise 25 cm³ of calcium hydroxide. The table shows her results.

(a) Calculate the titre for run two.

$30.85 - 15.45 =$ .... cm³

(2 marks)

Run	Volume of acid (cm³)		
	Initial	Final	Titre
Rough	0.00	17.50	17.50
1	0.00	15.45	15.45
2	15.45	30.85	
3	0.00	15.40	15.40

The titre is the volume of acid added to exactly neutralise the alkali:
titre = (final reading) – (initial reading)

(b) Calculate the mean titre from the concordant runs.

....

....

....

.... cm³ **(2 marks)**

Concordant titres are identical to each other or very close together (usually within 0.10 cm³).

Making insoluble salts

1 Put ticks in the table to show if each salt is soluble or insoluble.

Salt	Soluble	Insoluble
Sodium hydroxide		
Silver nitrate		
Lead sulfate		
Potassium carbonate		

(4 marks)

> There are some solubility rules you have to remember:
> • All common sodium, potassium and ammonium salts are soluble.
> • All nitrates are soluble.
> • Chlorides (apart from lead and silver) are soluble.
> • Sulfates (apart from lead, barium and calcium) are soluble.

Practical skills

2 Solutions of soluble salts can react to produce an insoluble salt, called a precipitate.

Write numbers in the table to put the steps to make an insoluble salt into the correct order.

Leave the salt to dry on the filter paper.	
Pour distilled water through the filter paper.	
Mix solutions of two substances that will form the insoluble salt.	1
Filter the mixture.	

(1 mark)

3 For each question below complete the word equation.

Circle any products that are precipitates.

(a) sodium hydroxide + copper chloride → copper hydroxide + sodium chloride   **(2 marks)**

(b) potassium sulfate + lead nitrate → .... + ...   **(2 marks)**

(c) calcium nitrate + sodium carbonate → .... + ...   **(2 marks)**

4 Choose suitable solutions as reactants to make the following insoluble salts:

(a) Calcium carbonate

calcium nitrate and ....   **(2 marks)**

(b) Silver chloride

....   **(2 marks)**

(c) Barium sulfate

....   **(2 marks)**

Extended response – Making salts

Describe how you would use solid sodium sulfate and solid calcium chloride to produce a pure, dry sample of calcium sulfate.

> Calcium sulfate is an insoluble salt. This means you will have to use a precipitation reaction. This involves mixing two solutions of soluble salts together.
> How will you turn solid sodium sulfate and solid calcium chloride into solutions?

You should mention the equipment and method you would use, and give reasons for why you would use them.

> It might help to divide up the method into sections:
> • Making the solutions
> • Carrying out the reaction
> • Purifying and drying the precipitate.

....
....
....
....
....
....
....
....
....
....
....
....
....
....
....
....
....
....
....
....
....
....   **(6 marks)**

119

Electrolysis

1 Complete the diagram below using a straight line to connect the term to its correct meaning.

Term	Meaning
Electrolysis	Negatively charged ion
Electrolyte	Positively charged ion
Cation	An ionic compound in the molten state or dissolved in water
Anion	A process where electricity is used to break down an ionic compound

(4 marks)

2 Use the words below to label the equipment used for electrolysis.

anode   d.c. supply   cathode   electrolyte

Guided

Practical skills

(4 marks)

3 A scientist carries out electrolysis of some molten ionic compounds.

(a) State what is meant by the term 'molten'.

.... **(1 mark)**

(b) Complete the table to show the products formed.

Electrolyte	Product formed at the cathode	Product formed at the anode
Copper chloride	Copper	Chlorine
Aluminium bromide		
Sodium oxide		

(3 marks)

> • When ionic compounds are molten the ions are free to move.
> • Positive ions move to the cathode.
> • Negative ions move to the anode.

Electrolysing solutions

1 Tick the boxes that show an object with a positive charge.

☐ **A** anion

☐ **B** anode

☐ **C** cathode

☐ **D** cation

(2 marks)

2 A student carried out electrolysis on sodium chloride solution (NaCl).

(a) State the ions present in the solution.

Cations	Na⁺	
Anions		OH⁻

(4 marks)

> A solution of an ionic compound contains:
> • cations and anions from the dissolved ionic compound, and
> • H^+ and OH^- ions from the water.

(b) Complete the sentences to describe what happens during electrolysis.

Positively charged ions move to the .... charged electrode (the ....)

where they .... electrons to form atoms.

.... charged ions move to the positively charged electrode (the ....)

where they .... electrons to form atoms.

(2 marks)

(c) Name the products formed at each electrode during the electrolysis of sodium chloride solution:

Negative ....

Positive ....

(2 marks)

> • At the negative electrode: hydrogen is produced, unless the compound contains ions from a metal less reactive than hydrogen. In that case, the metal is produced instead.
> • At the positive electrode: oxygen is produced (from OH^- ions) unless the compound contains halide ions (Cl^-, Br^- or I^-). In that case, halogens are produced instead.

3 For each solution, name the products formed at each electrode.

(a) Silver chloride

Negative silver

Positive chlorine

(2 marks)

(b) Magnesium sulfate

Negative ....

Positive ....

> Magnesium is more reactive than hydrogen.

(2 marks)

Investigating electrolysis

1 A student carried out electrolysis of copper sulfate solution using copper electrodes.

The equipment they used is shown below.

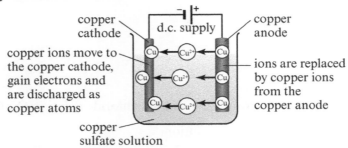

The student measures the mass of each electrode at the start of the investigation.

They use a current of 0.5 A and carry out electrolysis for 5 minutes.

They then measure the mass of the electrodes again.

Their results are shown in the table below.

Electrode	Mass at start (g)	Mass at end (g)	Change in mass (g)
Cathode	3.42	3.57	
Anode	4.95	4.77	−0.18

(a) Calculate the change in mass for each electrode. **(2 marks)**

(b) Explain why it is important that they dry the electrodes before they measure the mass at the end of the investigation.

To remove liquid on the electrodes, so ....

.... **(2 marks)**

(c) Explain the changes in mass for each electrode.

The mass of the anode decreased because copper atoms in the anode changed into

copper ions, which went into the solution.

The mass of the cathode ....

.... **(4 marks)**

(d) The change in mass of the cathode is less than expected. Suggest a reason for this.

.... **(1 mark)**

Practical skills Not all the copper ions formed from the anode will be transferred to the cathode. Think about why.

2 The student decides to repeat the experiment, but carries out the electrolysis for 7 minutes.

(a) Predict how their results will be different to the first investigation.

The changes in mass to both electrodes will be .... **(1 mark)**

(b) State one other independent variable they could investigate.

.... **(1 mark)**

Practical skills Think about what else they could change that would affect the change in mass of the electrodes.

Extended response – Electrolysis

Practical skills

A student carried out electrolysis of water using the equipment shown.

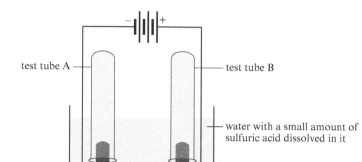

test tube A

test tube B

water with a small amount of sulfuric acid dissolved in it

They wrote down their observations:

- Observation 1: bubbles formed on each electrode and gas collected in both the test tubes.

- Observation 2: there was twice as much gas in test tube A compared with test tube B.

- Observation 3: when a lighted splint was added to the gas in test tube A, I heard a 'pop' noise.

Give an explanation for their observations.
Include the name of the product formed in each test tube.

> First of all, work out which electrode (positive or negative) is in which test tube. Then, start with the first observation and write down a scientific explanation for it. Make sure you include the names of the products.
> Next, do the same for the other two observations.
> Remember, the formula for water is H_2O.

....

....

....

....

....

....

....

....

....

....

....

....

....

.... **(6 marks)**

The reactivity series

1   Some metals react with water.

Complete the word and symbol equations for the reaction of potassium with water.

Potassium + water → .... + hydrogen

.... (s) + 2H$_2$O(l) → 2KOH(aq) + ...(g)   **(4 marks)**

2   Pieces of four different types of metal were added to cold water and to acid.

The table shows observations.

Metal	Observations when metal is added to water	Observations when metal is added to acid
A	Very slow bubbling	Vigorous bubbling
B	Vigorous bubbling	Not done
C	No bubbles formed	No bubbles formed
D	No bubbles formed	Slow bubbling

(a) Suggest why metal B was not added to acid.

It is very reactive so ....

....   **(3 marks)**

> 🧪 **Practical skills**   Think about health and safety considerations.

(b) Write the letters in order to show the reactivity of the metals from most to least reactive.

....

> Copper is an unreactive metal. It is below hydrogen on the reactivity series.

                                                                    (1 mark)

(c) Which metal (A, B, C or D) could be copper?
     Give a reason for your answer.

....

....   **(3 marks)**

3   Aaron adds a 2 cm-long piece of magnesium ribbon to a test tube full of dilute hydrochloric acid.

He observes that bubbles are slowly formed.

(a) Explain why bubbles form when magnesium is added to acid.

....   **(1 mark)**

(b) Explain why magnesium only bubbles **slowly**.

....   **(1 mark)**

> Where is magnesium in the reactivity series?

(c) Suggest **two** ways of increasing the rate of bubbling when magnesium is added to hydrochloric acid.

1. Increase the concentration of the acid

2. ....   **(2 marks)**

> You can increase a rate of reaction by changing concentration, surface area and temperature of reactants.

Metal displacement reactions

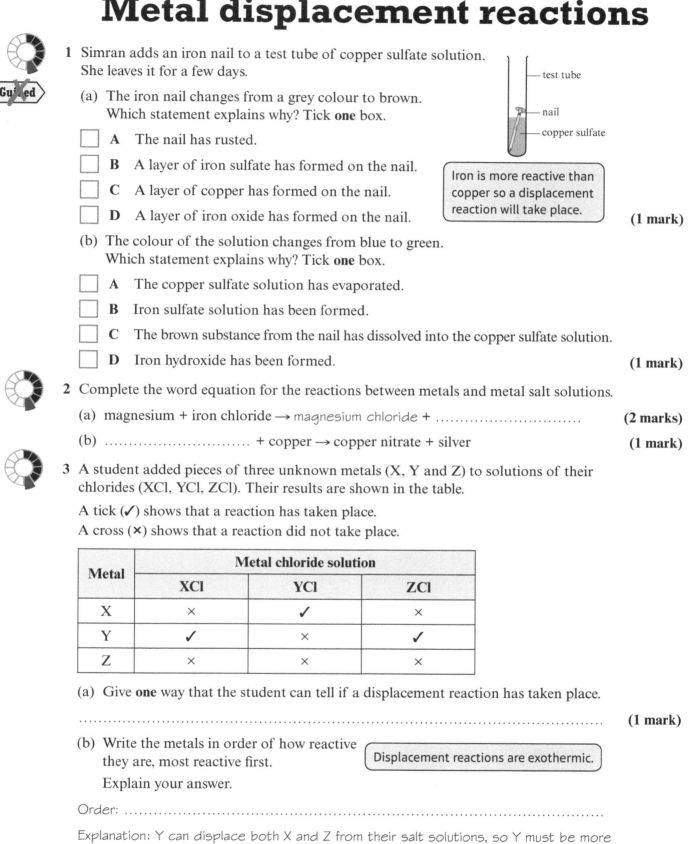

1   Simran adds an iron nail to a test tube of copper sulfate solution. She leaves it for a few days.

(a) The iron nail changes from a grey colour to brown. Which statement explains why? Tick **one** box.

☐   **A**   The nail has rusted.

☐   **B**   A layer of iron sulfate has formed on the nail.

☐   **C**   A layer of copper has formed on the nail.

☐   **D**   A layer of iron oxide has formed on the nail.

test tube

nail

copper sulfate

Iron is more reactive than copper so a displacement reaction will take place.

(1 mark)

(b) The colour of the solution changes from blue to green. Which statement explains why? Tick **one** box.

☐   **A**   The copper sulfate solution has evaporated.

☐   **B**   Iron sulfate solution has been formed.

☐   **C**   The brown substance from the nail has dissolved into the copper sulfate solution.

☐   **D**   Iron hydroxide has been formed.

(1 mark)

2   Complete the word equation for the reactions between metals and metal salt solutions.

(a) magnesium + iron chloride → magnesium chloride + ...   **(2 marks)**

(b) .... + copper → copper nitrate + silver   **(1 mark)**

3   A student added pieces of three unknown metals (X, Y and Z) to solutions of their chlorides (XCl, YCl, ZCl). Their results are shown in the table.

A tick (✓) shows that a reaction has taken place.

A cross (✗) shows that a reaction did not take place.

Metal	Metal chloride solution		
	XCl	**YCl**	**ZCl**
X	✗	✓	✗
Y	✓	✗	✓
Z	✗	✗	✗

(a) Give **one** way that the student can tell if a displacement reaction has taken place.

....   **(1 mark)**

(b) Write the metals in order of how reactive they are, most reactive first.

Explain your answer.

Displacement reactions are exothermic.

Order: ....

Explanation: Y can displace both X and Z from their salt solutions, so Y must be more

reactive than both X and Z.

X can displace ...., but not .... so ....

....

Z can ....   **(4 marks)**

Explaining metal reactivity

1 Cross out the incorrect word in each pair to complete the sentence.

The more reactive a metal is, the **more/~~less~~** easily it **gains/loses** electrons to form **positive/negative** ions.   **(3 marks)**

2 Put these metals in order according to their tendency to lose electrons. Start with the metal that has the highest tendency.

>Gu~~id~~ed>

aluminium   **gold**   **iron**   **sodium**

....

....

....

....

> You can use the reactivity series below to help you.

(1 mark)

3 Magnesium reacts with sulfuric acid.

(a) Use the reactivity series to explain why magnesium reacts with acid.

....

....

> Metals above hydrogen in the reactivity series will react with dilute acids.

potassium	most reactive
sodium	
calcium	
magnesium	
aluminium	
zinc	
iron	
(hydrogen)	
copper	
silver	
gold	least reactive

(1 mark)

(b) The symbol equation for the reaction is shown below.

$Mg(s) + H_2SO_4(aq) \rightarrow MgSO_4(aq) + H_2(g)$

Which **two** statements are true?

[✓] **A**   Magnesium atoms become magnesium ions

[ ] **B**   Magnesium ions become magnesium atoms

[ ] **C**   Hydrogen atoms become hydrogen ions

[ ] **D**   Hydrogen ions become hydrogen atoms

> Remember: ionic compounds contain ions.

(2 marks)

(c) Magnesium ions have a +2 charge.

What type of ions are they?

[ ] anions

[ ] cations   **(1 mark)**

(d) Deduce the charge on a sulfate ion.

....   **(1 mark)**

> Magnesium sulfate has no overall charge because the charges from the magnesium and sulfate ion cancel each other out.

Metal ores

1 Choose from the words in the list below to answer the questions.

iron ore   **sodium**   **platinum**   **zinc oxide**

(a) This metal can occur naturally.

....   **(1 mark)**

(b) A compound of a metal and non-metal.

....   **(1 mark)**

(c) A mixture of compounds.

....   **(1 mark)**

> • Reactive metals are naturally found combined with other elements in compounds.
> • Unreactive metals are not found as compounds, but may occur as alloys.

(c) An element that is always found naturally as a compound.

....   **(1 mark)**

2 Zinc ore contains the compound zinc oxide.

Zinc can be extracted from zinc oxide by reducing it.

(a) State what is meant by the term 'reduction'.

The loss of .... from a substance.   **(1 mark)**

(b) The reaction used is:

zinc oxide + carbon → zinc + carbon monoxide

State the substance that is:

Reduced

....

Oxidised

....   **(2 marks)**

3 Copper ore is found in a mine.

(a) It is economical to extract copper from copper ore only if it contains more than 1% copper.
Explain why.

It costs more to extract the ore than ....

....   **(1 mark)**

(b) Scientists test the ore.

They find that a piece of ore with a mass of 56 g contains 0.4 g of copper.

Calculate the percentage of the ore which is copper.

Give your answer to two significant figures.

(0.4/56) × 100 = ...   **(2 marks)**

> To work out the percentage you need to divide the mass of the copper by the total mass of the piece of ore and then multiply this number by 100.

(c) It might be economical to extract copper from this ore in the future.
Explain why.

In the future we may start to run out of copper so ....

....   **(2 marks)**

Iron and aluminium

1 Most metals are found naturally as compounds so need to be extracted.

Complete the table by putting the metals given below into the correct columns.

> You can use the reactivity series on page 126 to help you.

aluminium   gold   iron   potassium   silver   zinc

Extracted by electrolysis	Extracted by reduction	Does not need to be extracted – found pure
	Iron	

(3 marks)

> Metals below carbon in the reactivity series can be displaced from their compounds by carbon.

2 Iron is often found naturally as iron oxide.

(a) Electrolysis can be used to extract iron from iron oxide.

Explain why it is **not** used.

Electrolysis is very expensive to carry out because ....

.... **(2 marks)**

(b) Instead, iron oxide is heated with carbon in a blast furnace.

Complete the word equation to show one of the reactions that takes place.

Iron oxide + carbon → .... + ... **(2 marks)**

(c) Another of the reactions that takes place in the blast furnace is shown by the symbol equation below.

$Fe_2O_3(s) + 3CO (.........) \rightarrow ....Fe (.........) + 3CO_2(g)$

(i) Write in the missing number to balance the equation. **(1 mark)**

(ii) Write in the missing state symbols. **(2 marks)**

3 Aluminium is extracted from the compound aluminium oxide (Al_2O_3) by electrolysis.

(a) Explain why aluminium oxide has to be melted before it can be used as the electrolyte.

When aluminium is melted its ions are free to move to the .... **(2 marks)**

(b) Predict the products formed at each electrode:

Anode

....

Cathode

....

> The anode is positively charged and the cathode is negatively charged.

(2 marks)

(c) The anodes are made of graphite (carbon).

Explain why they have to be replaced every few weeks.

.... **(1 mark)**

Recycling metals

1 Harry puts his empty aluminium drinks can into a recycling bin. The contents of the bin are transported to a recycling centre.

(a) Describe what will happen to the aluminium can to recycle it.

It will be melted and then .... **(2 marks)**

(b) Which **two** are advantages of recycling metals?

☐ **A** It uses up a lot of energy

☐ **B** It is less expensive than extracting metals from their ores

☐ **C** It will help metal ores to last longer

☐ **D** Metals can be melted down   **(2 marks)**

2 Different amounts of energy are saved by recycling metals compared with extracting them from ores.

Metal	Percentage energy saved
Aluminium	94
Copper	86
Iron and steel	70

Recycling which metal saves the most energy?

....

Explain why.

If you recycle a metal it means that less of it has to be extracted from its ores.

Extracting the metal .... from its ores requires a lot of energy because

.... **(3 marks)**

3 If more metals are recycled then fewer quarries and mines are needed.

Describe **one** advantage and **one** disadvantage of this.

Advantage

....

....

....

....

Disadvantage

....

....

....

.... **(2 marks)**

In quarries and mines, rocks are dug up out of the ground. Think about how this affects the environment. Quarries and mines provide jobs for many people.

Life-cycle assessments

1 A life-cycle assessment (LCA) has four stages.

(a) Use the labels below to write the stages of an LCA onto the correct place on the diagram.

using the product   **disposing of the product**

obtaining raw materials   **manufacturing the product**

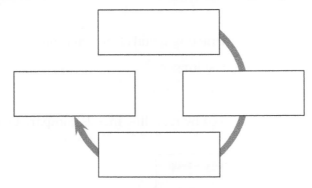

(1 mark)

(b) At the end of its life, some products can be recycled.

Draw an arrow onto the diagram to represent recycling.   **(1 mark)**

2 The table shows information about plastic and paper bags.

	Paper bag	Plastic bag
Raw materials	Wood	Crude oil
Energy used in manufacture	Medium	High
Transport	Take up a lot of space	Take up little space
Use during lifetime	Not normally reused	Can be reused many times
Disposal	Easily recycled	Not easily recycled – usually taken to landfill

(a) Which type of bag is made from a finite resource?

....   **(1 mark)**

(b) Explain why the transport of paper bags creates more pollution than the transport of plastic bags.

They take up more space so ....

....   **(2 marks)**

(c) Describe **two** reasons why paper bags could be considered better for the environment than plastic bags.

....

....

....

....   **(2 marks)**

> The question asks you to describe. You should add more detail than just stating the reasons.

The Haber process

1 (a) A student sees this symbol equation in a text book:

$NH_4Cl(s) \rightleftharpoons NH_3(g) + HCl(g)$

State what the symbol $\rightleftharpoons$ means.

.... **(1 mark)**

(b) What **two** things does this show about the reaction?

☐ **A**   The products break down to form the reactant

☐ **B**   The reactants join to form the product

☐ **C**   The products join to form the reactant

☐ **D**   The reactant breaks down to form the products **(2 marks)**

2 Which **two** statements about dynamic equilibrium are correct?

☐ **A**   It only takes place in an open system

☐ **B**   It only takes place in a closed system

☐ **C**   At equilibrium the amounts of both reactants and products are the same

☐ **D**   At equilibrium the rate of forward and back reactions are the same **(2 marks)**

3 The equation below shows the reaction in the Haber process.

$3H_2 + N_2 \rightleftharpoons 2NH_3$

(a) State the **two** reactants in the Haber process.

Hydrogen and .... **(2 marks)**

(b) State the product of the Haber process.

.... **(1 mark)**

(c) List the conditions used in the Haber process:

Catalyst

....

Temperature

....°C

Pressure

.... atmospheres **(3 marks)**

(d) Explain why a catalyst is used.

To increase the rate of reaction so ....

.... **(2 marks)**

> In this question you are asked to 'explain' so just writing what a catalyst does is not enough for the two marks. You also need to say **why** this is important.

(e) Explain why the product is cooled and removed as soon as it is made.

....

....

> In a reversible reaction the product will break down to form the reactants.

.... **(2 marks)**

Extended response – Reactivity of metals

Saffia is asked to identify an unknown metal, X.

She carries out a number of tests, as described in the table.

Test	Observations
1 Add X to water	No change
2 Add X to dilute hydrochloric acid	Bubbles form
3 Add X to a solution of iron chloride	A slight increase in temperature; colour change
4 Add X to aluminium chloride	No change

Identify what **two** metals X could be. Use the reactivity series to help you.

Use the results from the tests to justify your answer.

> • Go through the results of each test and use the observations to cross out metals in the reactivity table that X cannot be. For example, it does not react with water so it cannot be potassium, sodium or calcium.
> • If there was no change then a reaction did not take place.
> • Explain how the results from the tests are evidence for your answer.

potassium	most reactive
sodium	
calcium	
magnesium	
aluminium	
zinc	
iron	
(hydrogen)	
copper	
silver	
gold	least reactive

....
....
....
....
....
....
....
....
....
....
....
....
....
....
....
....
....

(6 marks)

The alkali metals

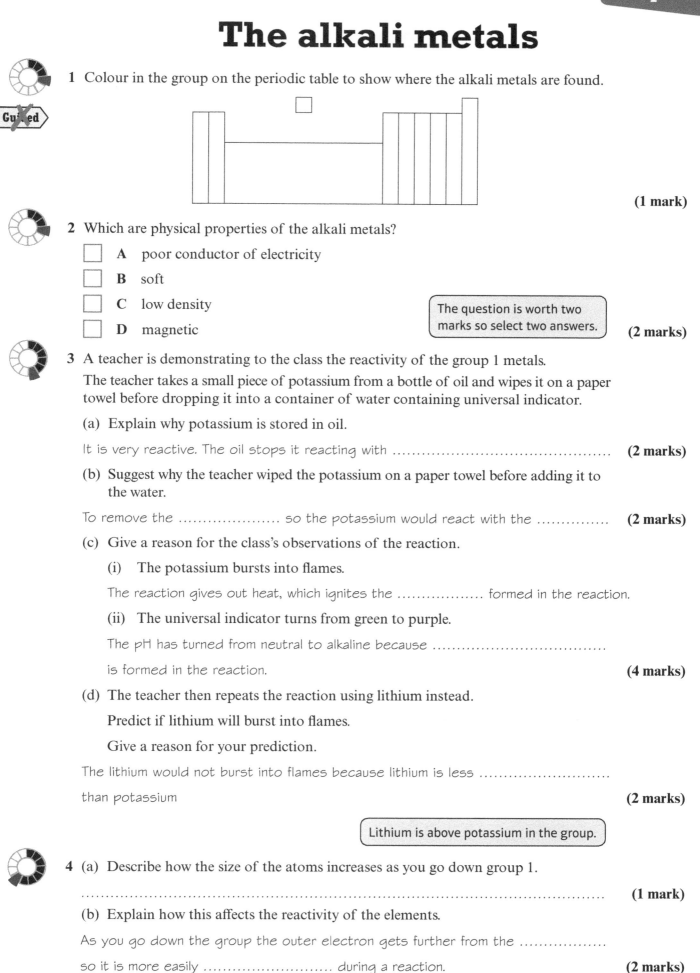

1 Colour in the group on the periodic table to show where the alkali metals are found.

(1 mark)

2 Which are physical properties of the alkali metals?

☐ **A** poor conductor of electricity

☐ **B** soft

☐ **C** low density

☐ **D** magnetic

> The question is worth two marks so select two answers.

(2 marks)

3 A teacher is demonstrating to the class the reactivity of the group 1 metals.

The teacher takes a small piece of potassium from a bottle of oil and wipes it on a paper towel before dropping it into a container of water containing universal indicator.

(a) Explain why potassium is stored in oil.

It is very reactive. The oil stops it reacting with .... **(2 marks)**

(b) Suggest why the teacher wiped the potassium on a paper towel before adding it to the water.

To remove the .... so the potassium would react with the .... **(2 marks)**

(c) Give a reason for the class's observations of the reaction.

(i) The potassium bursts into flames.

The reaction gives out heat, which ignites the .... formed in the reaction.

(ii) The universal indicator turns from green to purple.

The pH has turned from neutral to alkaline because ....

is formed in the reaction. **(4 marks)**

(d) The teacher then repeats the reaction using lithium instead.

Predict if lithium will burst into flames.

Give a reason for your prediction.

The lithium would not burst into flames because lithium is less ....

than potassium **(2 marks)**

> Lithium is above potassium in the group.

4 (a) Describe how the size of the atoms increases as you go down group 1.

.... **(1 mark)**

(b) Explain how this affects the reactivity of the elements.

As you go down the group the outer electron gets further from the ....

so it is more easily .... during a reaction. **(2 marks)**

The halogens

1 In which group in the periodic table are the halogens found?

.... **(1 mark)**

2 Complete the table to show information about the halogens.

Name	Formula	State at room temperature	Colour
Fluorine	F_2	Gas	
Chlorine		Gas	Yellow-green
Bromine	Br_2		Red-brown
	I_2	Solid	Grey

(4 marks)

3 The table shows the boiling points of the halogens.

Halogen	Boiling point (°C)
Fluorine	−188
Chlorine	−35
Bromine	59
Iodine	184

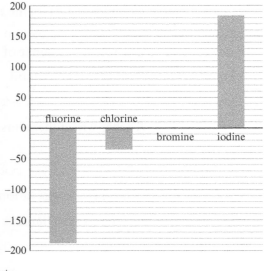

(a) The data is shown on a bar chart.

Complete the bar chart.

> You need to write in the axes titles as well as draw the missing bar.
> Remember to use a ruler to draw the bar.

(3 marks)

(b) Describe the pattern shown in the chart.

Give a reason for this.

As you go down the group the boiling point ....

....

This is because the intermolecular forces between the molecules get ....

so .... heat energy is needed to overcome them.   **(3 marks)**

(c) Astatine is a halogen found below iodine in the periodic table.

Use the data to predict the boiling point of astatine.

....

.... **(1 mark)**

Reactions of halogens

1 The gas hydrogen bromide is dissolved in water to form a solution.
   Predict the pH of the solution.

   ☐ **A** 3
   ☐ **B** 6
   ☐ **C** 8
   ☐ **D** 10

> Hydrochloric acid is formed by dissolving hydrogen chloride gas in water.
> You can use this information to answer the question.

(1 mark)

2 A teacher places a piece of sodium into a container full of chlorine.
   The sodium bursts into an orange flame and a white powder is produced.

   (a) Write the word equation for this reaction.

   sodium + chlorine → ....   **(2 marks)**

   (b) Name the product formed when fluorine reacts with sodium.

   ....   **(1 mark)**

   (c) Explain why the teacher cannot carry out this reaction in the classroom.

   Fluorine is more reactive than chlorine so ....

   ....   **(3 marks)**

3 When halogens react with metals they form halide ions.

   (a) Give the charge on a halide ion.

   ....   **(1 mark)**

   (b) Explain why halide ions have this charge.

   Halogen atoms have .... electrons in their outer shell.

   When they react with metals they gain .... electron to complete the shell.   **(2 marks)**

4 The diagrams show atoms of chlorine and fluorine.
   Use them to explain why fluorine is more reactive than chlorine.

   A fluorine atom is ....

   than a chlorine atom, so its outer shell is

   .... to the nucleus.

   The force of attraction between the outer

   shell and the nucleus is ....

   so fluorine gains an electron .... easily.

   (4 marks)

fluorine 2,7

chlorine 2,8,7

Halogen displacement reactions

1   Complete the definition of a halogen displacement reaction.

A reaction where a .... reactive halogen will displace a

.... reactive halogen from its compound.   **(2 marks)**

2   Complete the following word equations. If a reaction does not take place write 'no reaction'.

(a)   chlorine + potassium bromide → ....

(b)   sodium chloride + bromine → ....

(c)   bromine + sodium iodide → ....

(d)   iodine + potassium chloride → ....   **(4 marks)**

3   A student reacts chlorine solution with sodium bromide solution.

(a)   Explain why dilute solutions of halogens are used instead of the pure halogen.

....   **(1 mark)**

(b)   The word equation for the reaction is:

chlorine + sodium bromide → sodium chloride + bromine

> All the substances in the reaction are solutions.

Balance the equation for this reaction. Include state symbols.

Cl_2 (......) + ... NaBr(......) → .... NaCl(......) + Br_2 (.........)   **(2 marks)**

(c)   Describe what the student would see.

Give a reason for your answer.

The mixture would get darker because .... is made   **(2 marks)**

4   A student wanted to identify the halide ions present in three unknown solutions.

She added halogens to the unknown solutions. The table shows her results. A tick (✓) shows that a displacement reaction happened.

Halogen added	Unknown solution		
	A	B	C
Bromine	✗	✓	✗
Iodine	✗	✗	✗
Chlorine	✓	✓	✗

(a)   Which solution contained chloride ions? ....

Give a reason for your answer.

....   **(2 marks)**

(b)   Which solution contained bromide ions? ....

Give a reason for your answer.

....   **(2 marks)**

The noble gases

1 Complete the sentences about the noble gases.

(a) The noble gases are located in the periodic table in group .... **(1 mark)**

(b) The noble gases exist as atoms with .... electrons

in their outer shell.

> The noble gases have full outer shells of electrons. This is why they are unreactive.

(2 marks)

2 Complete the diagram below using straight lines to connect the noble gas to its use and a reason why it has this use.

> Guided

Noble gas	Use	Reason it has this use
Helium	Shield gas in welding	Denser than air
Argon	To fill filament lamps	Density lower than air
Krypton	To fill airships	Unreactive

(3 marks)

3 The data in the table shows the density of some of the noble gases.

Noble gas	Density (g dm^{-3})
Helium	0.18
Neon	0.90
Argon	1.78
Krypton	
Xenon	5.85

(a) Describe the trend in density.

As you go down the group the density .... **(1 mark)**

(b) Calculate the mass of 5 dm^3 of argon.

....

.... g **(2 marks)**

> The density in the table shows the mass of **1 dm^3** of each gas.

(c) Estimate the density of krypton.

....

.... g dm^{-3} **(1 mark)**

4 Complete this diagram to show how the electrons are arranged in a neon atom.

> Use the periodic table to find the atomic number of neon

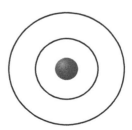

(2 marks)

Extended response – Groups

Cody carries out some reactions between halide salt solutions and some unknown halogen solutions.

The table shows his results.

A tick shows that the mixture got darker.

Unknown halogen	Halide salt solution		
	Potassium chloride	Potassium bromide	Potassium iodide
X	×	×	✓
Y	×	✓	✓
Z	×	×	×

Identify the unknown halogens, X, Y and Z, and explain how you identified them.

> This question is about halogen displacement reactions.
> If a displacement takes place, the mixture gets darker.

Use what you know about the electronic configuration of the halogens to explain the pattern in these results.

> The halogens are in group 7.
> The size of the atoms gets bigger as you go down the group.

....

....

....

....

....

....

....

....

....

....

....

....

....

....

....   **(6 marks)**

Rates of reaction

1 Add words to the gaps to complete the sentences.

Guided

For a reaction to happen the .... particles must collide with

each other and the collisions must have enough ....

The .... energy of a reaction is the minimum energy

needed by reactant particles for a reaction to happen.   **(3 marks)**

2 The table shows some reactions. Give the correct order in their rate by writing the numbers 1 to 3 in the correct row, where 1 has the slowest rate of reaction.

Guided

Reaction	Rate of reaction
Lithium reacting with water	
Iron rusting	
Explosion between hydrogen and oxygen	

(3 marks)

3 Niamh reacted pieces of zinc with hydrochloric acid.

She observed bubbles being produced slowly.

Give **three** ways that she could increase the rate of this reaction.

1. Increase the concentration of acid ....

2. ....

3. ....   **(3 marks)**

4 The graph shows the results of an investigation into the effect of changing the size of calcium carbonate chips on the rate of reaction with dilute hydrochloric acid.

Draw a line on the graph to show the results using the same mass of powdered calcium carbonate.

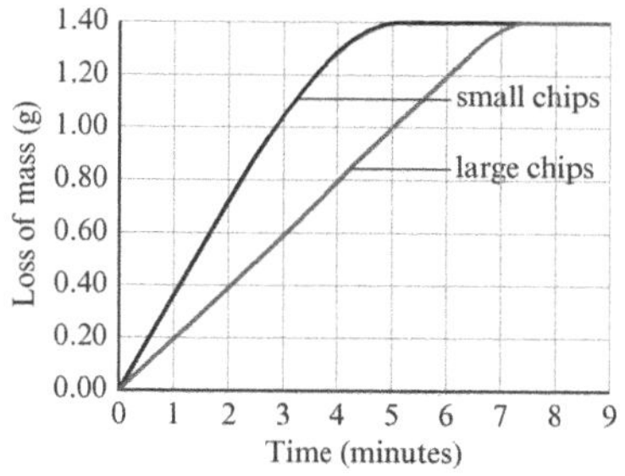

> The faster the rate of reaction, the more quickly mass will be lost.

Graph: Loss of mass (g) on y-axis (0.00 to 1.40), Time (minutes) on x-axis (0 to 9), showing curves labelled "small chips" and "large chips".

(2 marks)

5 The symbol equation shows the reaction between ammonia and hydrogen chloride.

$$NH_3(g) + HCl(g) \rightarrow NH_4Cl(s)$$

(a) State how increasing the pressure will affect the rate of the reaction.

Increasing the pressure will .... the rate of the reaction.   **(1 mark)**

> The command word 'state' asks you to write down simple information – there is no need to give reasons.

(b) Explain why this happens, using particle theory.

Increasing the pressure will push the particles of reactant together so ....

....   **(2 marks)**

> The command word 'explain' asks you to say how or why something happens.

Investigating rates

1 A student investigates how a variable affects the rate of reaction between marble chips (calcium carbonate) and hydrochloric acid.

They add marble chips of different sizes to the acid and measure the change in mass. The diagram shows the equipment they use.

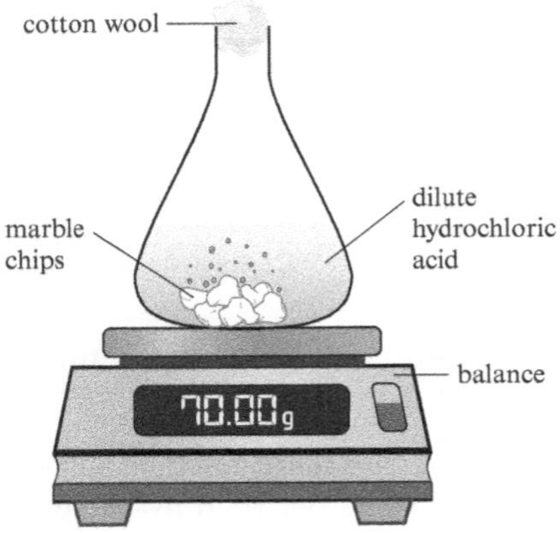

(a) Give the function of the cotton wool.

To stop the .... spraying out,

but to allow the .... to escape.

(2 marks)

(b) Name the independent and dependent variable they use.

Independent variable: ....

....

Dependent variable: ....

.... **(2 marks)**

(c) State **two** control variables they would have used in order to get valid results.

1. ....

2. .... **(2 marks)**

cotton wool

marble chips

dilute hydrochloric acid

balance

`70.00 g`

> The independent variable is what they change during the investigation. The dependent variable is what changes as a result and is what they measure or observe.

The table shows their results.

Time (minutes)	Mass loss (g)		
	Large marble chips	Medium marble chips	Small marble chips
0	0	0	0
5	3.4	3.6	3.8
10	3.9	3.9	4.0
15	4.0	4.0	4.0

(d) Describe how they calculated mass loss.

.... **(1 mark)**

(e) Calculate the rate of reaction for the large marble chips after 5 minutes.

Use the formula:

rate of reaction = change in mass/chosen time

3.4/5 = ... g/min   **(2 marks)**

(f) Explain how the size of the marble chip affected the rate of reaction.

The smaller the marble chip the .... the rate of reaction.

This is because ....

....

.... **(3 marks)**

> Changing the size of the marble chip affects the surface area to volume ratio.

Exam skills – Rates of reaction

1 A student reacts magnesium ribbon with dilute hydrochloric acid. They measure the volume of hydrogen produced.

(a) Which piece of equipment could they use to measure the volume of hydrogen? Tick **one** box.

☐ **A** balance

☐ **B** test tube

☐ **C** gas syringe

☐ **D** burette   **(1 mark)**

(b) The table shows their results.

Time (seconds)	0	10	20	30	40	50	60
Volume of gas collected (cm³)	0	12.4	20.6	32.7	38.0	40.0	40.0

Plot the results on the grid below.

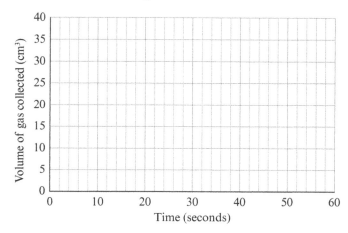

Plot the points using crosses and then draw a line of best fit.

(3 marks)

(c) Use the graph to determine when the reaction finishes. Explain how you worked out your answer.

The reaction finished after .... seconds. The graph shows this

because ....   **(3 marks)**

(d) The student repeats the experiment. They use all the same conditions except that they use a lower temperature of dilute acid.

On the same grid, sketch a line to predict the results.   **(2 marks)**

> • Draw a freehand line on the same grid. You do not have to draw the individual points.
> • Remember, if the same conditions were used then the same volume of gas will eventually be produced.

Heat energy changes

1 Which **two** statements are describing exothermic reactions?

☐   **A**   Heat energy is given out

☐   **B**   Heat energy is taken in

☐   **C**   The reaction mixture or surroundings increase in temperature

☐   **D**   The reaction mixture or surroundings decrease in temperature   **(2 marks)**

2 A student investigates reactions to see if they are exothermic or endothermic. The diagram shows the equipment they use.

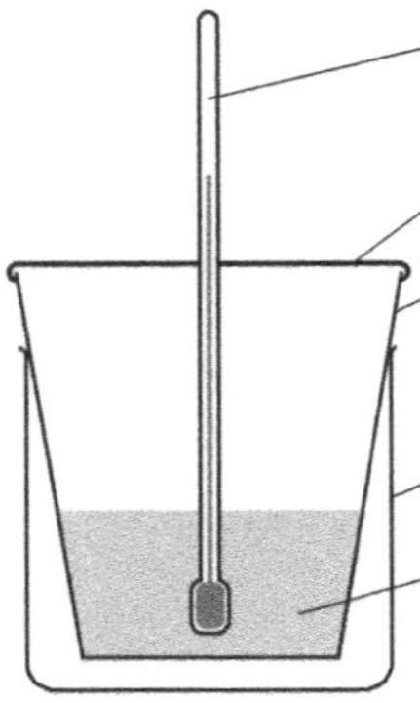

(a) Explain why a polystyrene cup is used.

Polystyrene is an insulator of heat. It is used because

....

....

                                         (2 marks)

thermometer

lid with hole

polystyrene cup

beaker for support

reaction mixture

They carry out the reactions. The table shows their results.

Reaction	Temperature at start (°C)	Temperature at end (°C)	Temperature change (°C)
A	21.2	45.6	24.4
B	21.4	16.4	−5.0
C	21.2	12.9	

> Remember to include the unit if it has not been given to you.

(b) Calculate the temperature change for reaction C.

12.9 − 21.2 = ... **(2 marks)**

(c) Which reaction(s), A, B or C:

     is an endothermic reaction? ....

     is an exothermic reaction? ....

     could be a neutralisation reaction? ....

3 During the combustion of methane, methane reacts with oxygen to form carbon dioxide and water.

> Combustion is another word for burning.

(a) Is the combustion of methane an endothermic or exothermic reaction?

.... **(1 mark)**

(b) Suggest a reason for this, based on bonds and energy.

The energy needed to break the bonds in .... and

.... is less than the energy released

when bonds are formed in .... and

.... **(2 marks)**

> • Bond-breaking is endothermic (energy is needed).
> • Bond-making is exothermic (energy is released).

Reaction profiles

1   Energy profile diagrams model the energy changes that happen during reactions.

   This energy profile diagram shows an endothermic reaction.

   Complete it by drawing a line to represent the products.

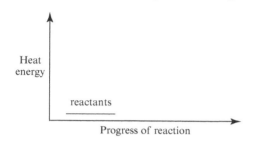

> In an endothermic reaction the products have a higher energy level than the reactants.

(1 mark)

2   The diagram shows an energy profile.

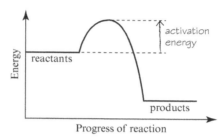

   (a) Draw on a labelled arrow to show the **activation energy**.   **(1 mark)**

   (b) Draw on a labelled arrow to show the **overall energy change**.   **(1 mark)**

3   Hydrogen peroxide breaks down in a reaction to form water and oxygen.

   $2H_2O_2(l) \rightarrow 2H_2O(l) + O_2(g)$

   The energy profile diagram for the reaction is shown below.

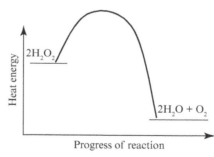

   (a) State if the reaction is exothermic or endothermic.

      Describe how the energy profile shows this.

      The reaction is .... The diagram shows this because

      the energy level of the reactants is .... than the energy level

      of the ....   **(2 marks)**

   (b) Manganese(IV) oxide can be used as a catalyst in this reaction.

      Draw a line on the energy profile diagram to show the reaction when manganese(IV) oxide is used.   **(1 mark)**

Crude oil

1 What type of substance is crude oil? Tick **one** box.

> Crude oil contains many different molecules.

☐ **A** alloy

☐ **B** element

☐ **C** compound

☐ **D** mixture   **(1 mark)**

2 Crude oil is a finite resource.

This means that supplies on Earth could soon run out.

Explain why.

New crude oil takes .... of years to form.   **(1 mark)**

3 Which **two** molecules could be found in crude oil?

☑ **A** CH_4

☐ **B** CO_2

☐ **C** C_2H_5OH

☐ **D** C_2H_6 **(2 marks)**

4 The diagram shows the structure of a compound in crude oil.

Give its formula

> Count the number of Cs and Hs

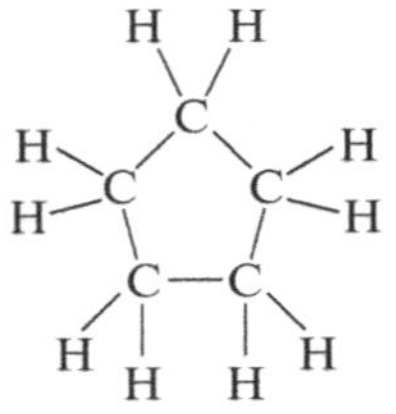

....   **(1 mark)**

5 The diagram represents a molecule found in crude oil.

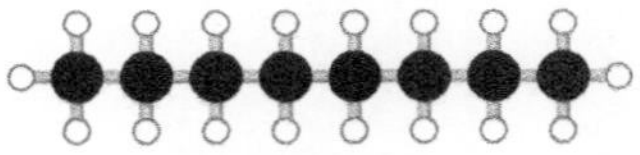

The black circles represent carbon atoms.

State what the white circles represent.

Give a reason for your answer.

> The compounds in crude oil are hydrocarbons.

....

....   **(2 marks)**

6 Give **two** important uses for the molecules in crude oil.

1. As a starting material for industrial chemical processes

2. ....   **(2 marks)**

Fractional distillation

1 Crude oil is separated into mixtures called fractions by fractional distillation. The diagram shows a fractionating column with the names of the fractions.

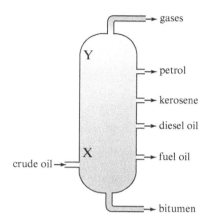

(a) Draw straight lines to connect the fraction to its use.

Fraction		Use
Petrol		Fuel for aircraft
Kerosene		Surface roads and roofs
Fuel oil		Fuel for cars
Bitumen		Burned in some power stations

(4 marks)

(b) At which point on the column (X or Y) is the temperature hottest?

.... **(1 mark)**

(c) Which fraction on the diagram:

has the lowest boiling point?

....

is the most viscous?

Bitumen

is the easiest **liquid** to ignite?

.... **(3 marks)**

2 Explain the relationship between the length of the hydrocarbon molecule and the boiling point.

The longer the molecule, the .... the boiling point because

the strength of the intermolecular forces between the molecules ....

.... so more .... must be transferred to

overcome them.

(3 marks)

As you go up the column the:
length of the molecules, boiling
point and viscosity decreases,
ease of ignition increases.

145

Alkanes

1 Which **two** molecules are alkanes?

  ☐ **A** C_4H_8

  ☑ **B** C_2H_6

  ☐ **C** C_5H_{12}

  ☐ **D** CH_2CH_2 **(2 marks)**

2 Alkanes belong to a homologous series.

Which **two** statements about homologous series are correct?

> Guided

  ☐ **A**   They have similar chemical properties

  ☐ **B**   They have similar physical properties

  ☐ **C**   They show a trend in chemical properties

  ☐ **D**   They show a trend in physical properties   **(2 marks)**

3 Complete the table to show information about the first three alkanes in the series.

> Guided

Name	Formula	Structure
	CH_4	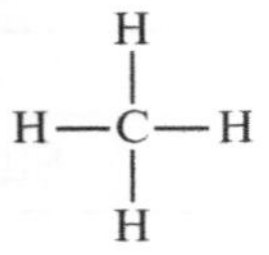 H—C—H with H above and H below (methane structure)
Ethane	C_2H_6	
Propane		

     (4 marks)

4 The general formula for the alkanes is C_nH_{2n+2}

Give the formula of the alkane that contains 20 carbon atoms.

C_{20} ....   **(1 mark)**

> To calculate the number of hydrogen atoms you need to multiply the number of carbon atoms by 2 and then add 2.

Incomplete combustion

1 Which is a reactant of combustion? Tick **one** box.

☐ **A** carbon dioxide

☐ **B** carbon monoxide

☐ **C** oxygen

☐ **D** water

(1 mark)

2 Complete the table by placing a tick (✔) into each correct box to show the products formed in each type of combustion.

Product	Complete combustion	Incomplete combustion
Carbon		✔
Carbon monoxide		✔
Carbon dioxide		
Water		

(4 marks)

3 The flame in a gas boiler should be blue.

If the flame is orange and soot is formed then this is a sign there is a fault.

(a) Explain what the fault is.

.... combustion is taking place because the supply

of oxygen is ....

(2 marks)

(b) Carbon monoxide will also be formed. Explain why this gas is toxic.

Carbon monoxide attaches to the .... in red blood

cells, reducing the amount of .... being carried

around the body.

(2 marks)

4 When you turn on a Bunsen burner you should make sure the air hole is closed. This produces the safety flame.

The heating flame is produced by opening the air hole.

(a) What type of combustion produces the heating flame?

....

(1 mark)

> Opening the air hole will allow more oxygen to enter.

(b) Explain why the heating flame is hotter than the safety flame.

....

....

(2 marks)

> Complete combustion gives out more energy than incomplete combustion.

147

Acid rain

1 Complete the diagram below using labels from the box.

| acid rain | power station | rain cloud | acidic gases | distant city |

wind

distant city

(5 marks)

2 Which **two** produce sulfur dioxide?

> Guided

☐ **A** Car engines

☒ **B** Rainwater

☐ **C** Power stations

☐ **D** Trees

(2 marks)

3 List **two** ways that acid rain can damage the environment.

1. Damages trees

2. .... **(2 marks)**

4 Hydrocarbon fuels may contain sulfur compounds as impurities.

Complete the word and symbol equations to show what happens when the sulfur in the fuels burns.

sulfur + ... → sulfur dioxide

...........(s) + O_2(g) → SO_2 (g)

> Sulfur dioxide is a non-metal oxide, so it will dissolve in water to form an acidic solution.

(3 marks)

5 Explain how burning fuels can produce acid rain.

> Guided

.... **(1 mark)**

6 Nitrogen oxides can also form acid rain.

They form when nitrogen and oxygen react together at high temperatures.

> Guided

(a) Balance the equation for the reaction that produces nitric oxide.

N_2(g) + O_2(g) → .... NO(g)

(1 mark)

(b) Name **one** place where this reaction takes place.

.... **(1 mark)**

Choosing fuels

1 Fossil fuels are useful resources.

(a) Name the fossil fuel used:

in cars

....

in some cars and trains

....

in large ships.

....   **(3 marks)**

(b) Name the raw material that these fossil fuels are obtained from.

....   **(1 mark)**

(c) Explain why fossil fuels are described as being **non-renewable**.

They are being used up faster than..   **(1 mark)**

2 Which **two** are features of a good fuel?

☐ **A** A liquid at room temperature

☐ **B** Easy to ignite

☐ **C** A high amount of energy per kilogram

☐ **D** Produces soot when burnt   **(2 marks)**

3 Hydrogen can be used as a fuel in cars.

In the engine, hydrogen reacts with oxygen to produce water.

(a) Balance the symbol equation for this reaction.

.... H_2 + O_2 → .... H_2O **(2 marks)**

(b) Describe one environmental advantage of using hydrogen as a fuel in cars, rather than petrol.

Burning hydrogen produces only....................................., burning petrol produces

....   **(2 marks)**

> Remember to compare the two fuels in your answer.

4 Hydrogen can be produced by the electrolysis of water.

Explain how this method may use non-renewable fuels.

Electrolysis uses electricity, which may be produced by ....

....   **(2 marks)**

> Fossil fuels, such as gas, coal and fuel oil, are used in some power stations.

Cracking

1 Write words in the gaps to complete the sentence.

Cracking is a process where long .... are broken down into ....

alkanes and .... **(3 marks)**

2 The hydrocarbon with the formula $C_{12}H_{26}$ is found in the kerosene fraction. It is cracked to produce other hydrocarbons.

(a) Which **two** hydrocarbons could be produced in this reaction?

☐ **A** C_2H_6

☐ **B** C_4H_8

☐ **C** C_8H_{18}

☐ **D** $C_{10}H_{22}$ **(2 marks)**

(b) Explain why cracking is carried out on this hydrocarbon.

It produces shorter alkanes that are more useful as fuels and ....

.... **(2 marks)**

> There are two products of cracking: shorter alkanes and alkenes. Think about what each of these is used for.

3 The diagram shows the equipment used to carry out cracking in the laboratory.

Practical
skills

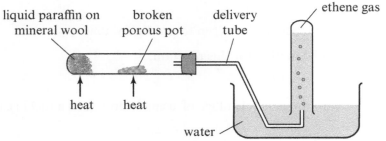

(a) Use the labels on the diagram to name:

The reactant

....

The product formed

.... **(2 marks)**

(b) Give the function of the broken porous pot.

.... **(1 mark)**

Extended response – Fuels

Hydrogen can be used as a fuel in cars, instead of petrol.
Read the following information.

- Compressed hydrogen has 143 megajoules of energy per kilogram, but only
  5.6 megajoules per litre. Petrol has 47.2 megajoules of energy per kilogram, but
  34 megajoules per litre.

- Burning hydrogen produces only water.

- Hydrogen requires unique storage conditions. In its gaseous form, enough hydrogen
  cannot be stored to make it of practical use and it is also exceptionally flammable.
  In liquid form, hydrogen is much less explosive. However, creating liquid hydrogen
  requires cooling it to very low temperatures or compressing it.

> Read through the information carefully. You can underline or highlight important points.

Use this information, plus your own knowledge, to evaluate the advantages and
disadvantages of using hydrogen, rather than petrol, as a fuel in cars.

> The command word 'evaluate' means you need to use information
> to make a judgement or to justify your answer in some way.

....
....
....
....
....
....
....
....
....
....
....
....
....
....
....
....
....
....
....
....

(6 marks)

The early atmosphere

1 What first produced the gases in the Earth's early atmosphere? Tick **one** box.

☐   **A**   animals

☐   **B**   plants

☐   **C**   oceans

☐   **D**   volcanoes

(1 mark)

2 Which **two** statements about the Earth's early atmosphere are correct?

☐   **A**   It contained little carbon dioxide

☑   **B**   It contained little oxygen

☐   **C**   It contained a lot of carbon dioxide

☐   **D**   It contained a lot of oxygen

(2 marks)

3 Changes took place to change the composition of gases in the Earth's atmosphere.

(a) The table shows the stages in the development of today's atmosphere.

Add a number to each box to order the processes from 1 (first) to 4 (last).

Event	Order
Plant life evolves in the oceans	
Oxygen builds up in the atmosphere	
The Earth cools and oceans form	
Oxygen builds up in the oceans	

(1 mark)

(b) Name the process that increased the levels of oxygen in the early atmosphere.

....

(1 mark)

(c) Explain why the Earth cooling resulted in oceans forming.

.... **(2 marks)**

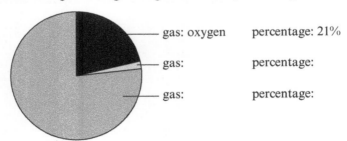

The early atmosphere contained water vapour.

4 The pie chart shows the percentages of gases in today's atmosphere.

— gas: oxygen   percentage: 21%

— gas: percentage:

— gas: percentage:

Next to each line, write the correct gas and its percentage. Use the labels below to do this.

nitrogen   **oxygen**   **other gases**

1%   **21%**   **78%**   **(3 marks)**

Greenhouse effect

1 Which **two** gases are greenhouse gases?

- [✓] **A** carbon dioxide
- [ ] **B** methane
- [ ] **C** nitrogen
- [ ] **D** oxygen **(2 marks)**

2 The diagram shows how the greenhouse effect takes place.
Write the labels into the correct boxes.

heat radiated away from the Earth   **energy from the Sun**

gases absorb heat   **gases release energy**

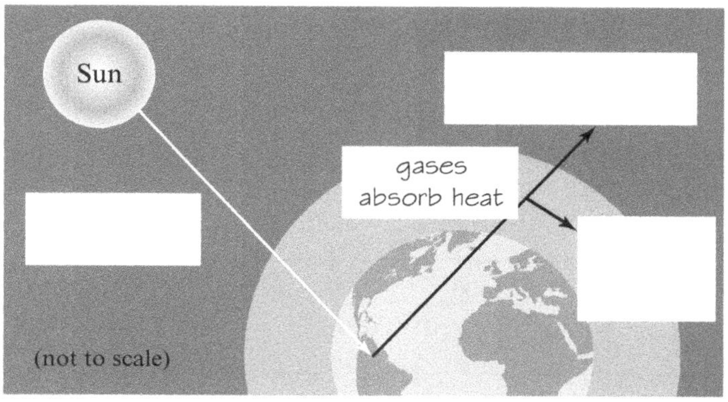

Sun

gases absorb heat

(not to scale)

(4 marks)

3 The percentage of carbon dioxide in the atmosphere is rising.

(a) Give a reason for this change. Explain your answer.

Carbon dioxide is produced when fossil fuels burn ....

.... **(2 marks)**

(b) Explain how an increase in carbon dioxide causes global warming.

....

.... **(2 marks)**

> Remember, carbon dioxide is a greenhouse gas.

(c) Give **two** environmental impacts of global warming.

1. ....

2. .... **(2 marks)**

Extended response – Atmospheric science

Most scientists agree that human activity is causing climate change.

One source of evidence to support this theory are measurements taken over time.

> Think about how valid these measurements are: do they reflect changes on all parts of the Earth? How accurate are measurements that were taken in the past?

The graph shows some of these measurements.

Evaluate the graph as evidence that climate change is caused by human activity.

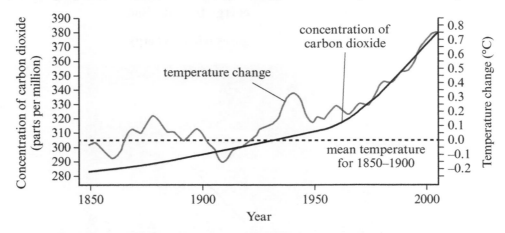

> • Describe what the graph shows – are there any **correlations**? For instance, do the patterns of the data relate/have a meaningful connection?
> • Give an explanation for any correlations.
> • Provide more than one point of view – why might the graph **not** be good evidence?
> • Make a final judgement; make sure you use evidence from the graph to support it.

....

....

....

....

....

....

....

....

....

....

....

....

....

.... **(6 marks)**

Key concepts

1 Force is calculated from the equation: $F = m \times a$, where F is force, m is mass, and a is acceleration. Rearrange the equation to calculate

(a) mass

.... **(1 mark)**

(b) acceleration

.... **(1 mark)**

2 Match up the name of the quantity with its SI unit.

length   kg

mass   K

weight   m

temperature   N   **(1 mark)**

3 Convert the following quantities:

(a) 50 000 Hz into kHz.

$\frac{50\,000}{1000}$ = ... kHz .... **(1 mark)**

(b) 400 cm into m.

.... **(1 mark)**

4 A scientist finds that the frequency of a wave is 354.03 Hz.

State how many significant figures this result is given in.

.... **(1 mark)**

> The number of significant figures is the number of non-zero digits or zeros between non-zero digits.

5 Convert the numbers to the given number of significant figures:

(a) 24 575 to three significant figures.

24 600   **(1 mark)**

(b) 3.56000 to three significant figures.

.... **(1 mark)**

6 Convert the numbers to standard form.

(a) 456

4.56×10^2 **(1 mark)**

> Standard form is given as $A \times 10^B$, where A is a number between 1 and 10, and B is a whole, positive or negative number.

(b) 10 300 .... **(1 mark)**

(c) 0.00345 3.45×10^{-3} **(1 mark)**

(d) 0.03523 to two significant figures .... **(1 mark)**

(e) 429 356 to three significant figures .... **(1 mark)**

Scalars and vectors

1 (a) Explain the difference between scalars and vectors.

A scalar quantity only has magnitude, whereas a vector has ....

.... **(2 marks)**

(b) Give **one** example of a scalar quantity and one example of a vector quantity.

....

.... **(2 marks)**

2 State whether acceleration is a scalar or vector quantity, and explain why.

....

....

.... **(3 marks)**

3 Explain the difference between speed and velocity.

Speed is a scalar quantity as it only has a magnitude. Velocity is ....

....

.... **(2 marks)**

4 A bicycle is moving along with a pushing force of 500 N.

(a) State the magnitude of the force acting backwards when the cyclist is travelling at a constant velocity. Explain your answer.

At constant velocity the resultant force is zero (i.e. the magnitude of the forwards

and backwards forces are equal), so the magnitude of the backwards force is ...... **(2 marks)**

> The forward and backward force are pointing in the opposite direction, so one of the forces is given a minus sign to show this. Either write 'backwards force of 500 N' or use a minus sign to show that it is a backwards force.

(b) State the resultant force when the cyclist is moving at constant speed.

.... **(1 mark)**

5 A scout is walking at 3 miles per hour (mph) to the north, through the woods.

(a) State whether this information gives you a scalar or vector quantity.

3 mph to the north is a ...... quantity because there is a magnitude and a direction. **(1 mark)**

(b) The scout now turns around and goes back the same way at the same speed. State the velocity of the scout now.

.... **(1 mark)**

6 Explain the difference between mass and weight. In your answer you should also consider whether they are vectors or scalars.

Mass is related to the number of particles in an object and is given in kg. Since it

only has magnitude, it is scalar. ....

Weight is ....

.... **(4 marks)**

Speed, distance and time

1 State the equation to calculate speed.

Guided

.... **(1 mark)**

2 The distance–time graph shows the journey of a
child walking to the local playground.

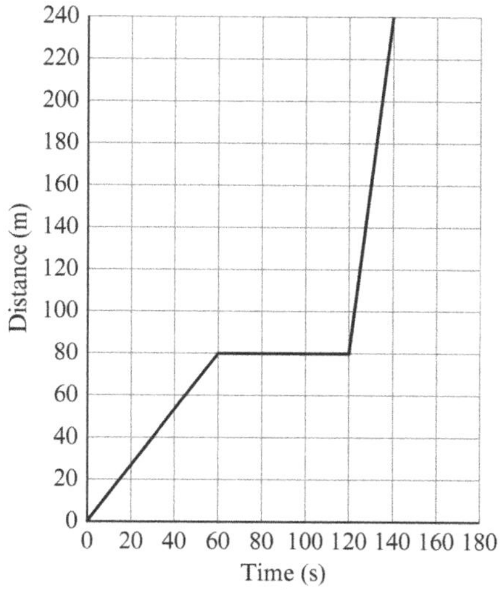

(a) State the time interval(s) in which is the
student moving.

The student is moving between 0 and 60s,

and 120s and 140s.

(2 marks)

(b) State in which time interval the student is
moving the fastest and explain how you know.

The fastest movement is between 120s and

140s because ....

....

(2 marks)

(c) Calculate the average speed of the child. Give your answer to two significant figures.

....

.... **(2 marks)**

> The average speed is the final distance divided by
> the time it took (provided the graph starts at 0!).

(d) Calculate the distance travelled by the child between 0 min and 1 min.

....

.... **(1 mark)**

> In a distance–time graph, the distance is given on the *y*-axis.
> You don't have to calculate the area under the curve.

3 A racing car was waiting at the start line on a race track. At the start signal it
accelerated from stationary at $5\,\text{m/s}^2$ in 10 s. What speed was it travelling at by the
end of this time?

Acceleration = $5\,\text{m/s}^2$, initial velocity = 0 m/s, time = 10s, $a = \frac{v-u}{t}$, so

$v - u = at =$,.. **(2 marks)**

4 A bus travels a distance of 100 km in 2 hours. Calculate the average speed of the bus.
Give your answer in m/s to two significant figures.

Distance = 100 km = 100 000 m, time = 2 h = ...

.... **(2 marks)**

Equations of motion

1 The list includes **three** quantities that are required to work out acceleration in one equation.

  (a) Which quantity is **not** required in this equation? Tick **one** box.

  ☐ **A** initial velocity   ☐ **C** force

  ☐ **B** time   ☐ **D** final velocity   **(1 mark)**

  (b) Give the equation linking the quantity you ticked in (a) to acceleration.

  $F = ma$, where F is force (in Newtons, N), m is mass (in kilograms, kg) and a is

  acceleration (in m/s²) ....   **(1 mark)**

2 A dog accelerates from 2.0 m/s to 8.0 m/s in 1.0 s. Calculate the dog's acceleration.

  $v = 8.0$ m/s, $u = 2.0$ m/s, $t = 1.0$ s, $a = \frac{v-u}{t}$ ....   **(2 marks)**

3 Jack drives his new car along a straight, level road at a constant speed of 10 m/s. He then accelerates the car to 21 m/s in 4 seconds. Describe the change of the horizontal forces that act on the car during the first two seconds of the acceleration.

  The driving force increases and air resistance ....

  ....

  ....   **(3 marks)**

4 A cat gets to its final velocity of 5 m/s over a distance of 100 m. Calculate its acceleration and give your value to two significant figures.

  ....

  ....

  ....   **(2 marks)**

> For this type of question you can use the equation: $v^2 - u^2 = 2ax$

5 A fit cyclist is going to the shops in a mountain area. She is initially going at a velocity of 1 m/s, but then accelerates at a rate of 1.5 m/s² over a distance of 500 m down a mountain. Calculate the final velocity of the cyclist and give your answer to two significant figures.

  Initial velocity = 1 m/s, acceleration = 1.5 m/s², distance = 500 m. $v^2 - u^2 = 2ax$

  $v^2 = 2ax + u^2 = 2 \times 1.5$ m/s² $\times 500$ m $+ (1$ m/s$)^2 =$ ....

  ....   **(3 marks)**

> Don't forget to take the square root when working out v.

6 A car is leaving a car park driving at 2 m/s. It then accelerates at 2 m/s² to a final velocity of 13 m/s. Calculate the distance it took to get to the final velocity.

  Initial velocity = 2 m/s, final velocity = 13 m/s, acceleration = 2 m/s². $v^2 - u^2 = 2ax$

  ....   **(3 marks)**

> Rearrange the equation to calculate distance.

Velocity/time graphs

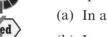

1 Complete the sentences below.

(a) In a velocity/time graph, the slope (gradient) shows .... **(1 mark)**

(b) In a velocity/time graph, the distance is represented by .... **(1 mark)**

(c) In a velocity/time graph, a horizontal line represents .... **(1 mark)**

2 The velocity/time graph below shows how the velocity of a train changes along a track.

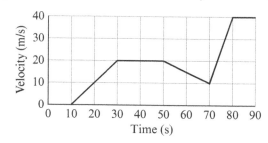

(a) State what the train is doing in the first 10 seconds. Explain your answer.

The velocity is zero and there is a horizontal line on the graph. This shows that the

train is stationary. **(2 marks)**

(b) The train is accelerating between 10 and 30 seconds, and again between 70 and 80 seconds.

Explain in which section the acceleration was higher.

In the second section (70 – 80 s) the line is ....

....

.... **(2 marks)**

(c) Calculate the deceleration of the train between 50 and 70 seconds.

Velocity = (20 – 10) m/s, time = (70 – 50) s ....

....

.... **(2 marks)**

> Deceleration is negative acceleration (i.e. slowing down instead of speeding up). If the question asks you to work out the acceleration for an object slowing down, you need to put a '−' in front of your result. In this case, the question asks about deceleration, so you don't need to put a '−' in.

(d) What is the distance travelled by the train between 70 and 90 seconds?

Distance travelled between 70 and 80 s: $\frac{1}{2}$ × (40 – 10) × (80 – 70) = ...

Distance travelled between 80 and 90 s: 40 × 10 = ...

Total distance travelled: .... **(3 marks)**

159

Determining speed

Practical skills

1 Describe how you would measure the average speed of a car rolling down a slope.

Set up a ramp and measure the distance that the car will be going. ....

....

.... **(3 marks)**

Guided

2 Compare the speed of walking and running, stating approximate values.

....

.... **(2 marks)**

Maths skills

3 Seagulls can fly at a speed of about 11 m/s. How far would a seagull fly in 2 min at this speed? Give your answer in km and to two significant figures.

Speed = 11 m/s, time = 2 min = 2 × 60 s = 120 s. $v = \frac{x}{t}$, so $x = vt$ = ...

.... **(2 marks)**

Maths skills

4 A snail moves a distance of 5 m in 8 min.

(a) Calculate its average speed in m/s.

.... **(3 marks)**

Maths skills

(b) The snail stopped for 3 min to nibble on a strawberry, increasing the overall time it took to move 5 m to 11 min. Explain how this would affect the average speed of the snail.

The equation for speed is .... If the time taken to cover the same

distance increases .... **(2 marks)**

> If you are not sure about this question compare what you get when you calculate:
> 1 ÷ 2 = 0.5 with what you get when you calculate: 1 ÷ 4 = 0.25.

Maths skills

5 The typical walking speed is approximately 1.5 m/s. How long would it take a person to walk 2 km? Give your answer in minutes, to two significant figures.

v = 1.5 m/s, x = 2 km = 2000 m. $v = \frac{x}{t}$, so $t = \frac{x}{v}$

.... **(2 marks)**

> To work out time, you could use a triangle like this one, and cover up time with your thumb: $\frac{x}{v \times t}$

Newton's first law

1 State Newton's first law.

Newton's first law states that if the forces on an object are balanced, the object

will either stay at rest or ....

.... **(3 marks)**

2 Jamie is pushing a box with a forwards force of 30 N. The frictional force acting on the box is 10 N.

(a) Sketch a diagram to show the forces acting on the box. Label the forces and their values on your diagram.

> Make sure you follow the instructions carefully, and label the arrows with the name of the force and the value of each force.

(2 marks)

(b) Ignoring any other forces acting on the box, state if the forces are balanced.

.... **(1 mark)**

(c) Calculate the resultant force on the box.

30N – 10N = ...

.... **(1 mark)**

3 Explain how an object can be at rest yet have two forces acting on it.

The resultant force on an object at rest is zero. Therefore, if two forces are acting

on the object, the forces ....

....

....

.... **(3 marks)**

4 A space rocket travelling at constant speed experiences a force at an angle from a small piece of rock travelling through space. Explain what will happen to the space rocket.

....

....

....

.... **(3 marks)**

> In a question like this it is a good idea to start off with a definition or simple statement, and then explain what happens to the rocket.

Newton's second law

1   Which equation describes Newton's second law of motion? Tick **one** box.

☐   **A** $F = \frac{m}{a}$ ☐   **C** $F = ma$

☐   **B** $F = \frac{a}{m}$ ☐   **D** $F = \frac{1}{2}ma^2$ **(1 mark)**

2   Describe what happens when an unbalanced force is acting on an object.

When an unbalanced force is acting on an object, the object will accelerate.   **(1 mark)**

3   A cat has a mass of 4 kg. When it sees a mouse, it suddenly accelerates from 0 m/s^2 to 5 m/s^2.

Calculate the force the cat is exerting with its legs.

Mass (m) = 4 kg. Acceleration (a) = 5 m/s^2 $F = ma =$ ....

....   **(3 marks)**

4   A plane is flying across an ocean into a strong wind. The plane flies at constant speed. Explain how the strong wind affects the forces acting on the plane.

....

....

....

....   **(3 marks)**

5   The acceleration of a motorbike is 15 m/s^2. The motorbike experiences a resultant force of 3750 N.

(a)   What is its mass?

Acceleration (a) = 15 m/s^2. Force (F) = 3750 N. $F = ma$ ....

....   **(3 marks)**

> $F = ma$. You can convert this to a triangle to help you quickly rearrange the equation for mass: $\frac{F}{m \times a}$

(b)   The motorbike is driving at a velocity of 10 m/s. Calculate the time it took to get to this speed, from rest, with an acceleration of 15 m/s^2. Give your answer to two significant figures.

Acceleration (a) = 15 m/s^2. Velocity (v) = 10 m/s. $a = \frac{\Delta v}{t}$, $t = \frac{\Delta v}{a} =$ ....

....   **(3 marks)**

Weight and mass

1 Tick **three** characteristics of weight.

☐ vector   ☐ scalar

☐ measured in N   ☐ measured in kg   **(1 mark)**

☐ has magnitude

2 Your physics teacher has a mass of 65 kg.

(a) State the mass of the teacher on the Moon. Gravitational field strength (g) on the Moon is 1.6 N/kg.

The mass stays the same, regardless of where you are, so the mass of the teacher

on the Moon is 65 kg.   **(1 mark)**

(b) Calculate what the teacher's weight would be on Jupiter. (g on Jupiter is 26 N/kg).

Mass = 65 kg, g = 26 N/kg. $W = mg$

.... **(2 marks)**

(c) His weight on Neptune would be 725 N. Calculate the gravitational field strength of Neptune.

> The equation to use is $W = mg$. If you find rearranging equations difficult, you could use the triangle: $\frac{W}{m \times g}$.

.... **(2 marks)**

3 A student is setting up an experiment to measure the weight of a set of objects of known mass.

(a) State the independent and dependent variables of the experiment.

The independent variable is the mass of the objects, the dependent variable is ... **(2 marks)**

....

(b) After collecting the data, the student wants to plot a graph of weight against mass. Describe the graph she would expect to see.

....

.... **(2 marks)**

4 An average house has a mass of approximately 55 000 kg.

(a) If it was possible to put a house on Mercury, the weight of this house would be 198 000 N. Calculate the gravitational field strength on Mercury.

.... **(2 marks)**

(b) Explain how weight is a force.

Weight is the gravitational force between the object and the Earth. It is given by

the equation $W = mg$.   **(2 marks)**

5 Explain how the weight of an object would differ on the Earth (g = 10 N/kg), Jupiter (g = 26 N/kg) and a neutron star (g = 10^{12} N/kg).

The weight of the object on the Earth would be smallest because ....

It would be highest on .... because........................ **(4 marks)**

Force and acceleration

1 Calculate the force required to accelerate a hammer by 5 m/s². The mass of the hammer is 450 g.

Acceleration = 5 m/s², mass = 450 g = 0.450 kg. $F = ma$

.... **(2 marks)**

2 The brakes of a car are applied with a force of 400 N. The deceleration of the car is 0.4 m/s². Calculate the mass of the car.

Force = 400 N, acceleration = 0.4 m/s². $F = ma$, so $m = F/a$ ....

.... **(2 marks)**

> Use this triangle to help you rearrange equations: $\frac{F}{ma}$.

3 A force of 400 kN is acting on an object of mass 2000 kg. What is its acceleration?

....

.... **(3 marks)**

4 A skydiver is jumping out of a plane.

(a) The mass of the skydiver is 70 kg. Calculate the weight of the skydiver on Earth. ($g = 10$ N/kg)

....

.... **(2 marks)**

(b) Explain why the weight of the skydiver does not change during the fall from the plane.

Weight is dependent on the mass and the gravitational field strength. ....

....

.... **(2 marks)**

> Think about how the variables in the equation for weight are affected by the fall. Will any of them change?

(c) Explain how the resultant force changes as the skydiver falls, before she opens her parachute.

At first there will be a large unbalanced downward force, because air resistance is not

very high just after jumping out of the plane. As the skydiver speeds up, ...

....

....

Finally, air resistance and weight. ....

....

....

....

.... **(5 marks)**

Newton's third law

1 State Newton's third law.

For every action force ....

.... **(1 mark)**

2 A book lying on a desk has a weight of 20 N. Calculate the force exerted by the desk on the book.

Newton's third law states that for every action force ....

.... The force exerted by the

desk on the book must therefore be .... **(2 marks)**

3 Give an everyday observation which explains why we know that Newton's law is correct.

Guided

....

....

.... **(1 mark)**

4 Identify **two** action-reaction pairs in the picture.

The squirrel is sitting on the ground, and the ground is pushing back with an equal and opposite force.

....

....

....

.... **(2 marks)**

> For every force there is a reaction force which is equal in size and acting in the opposite direction.

5 Explain, using everyday examples, why Newton's third law applies to everyone all the time.

Guided

....

....

....

....

.... **(3 marks)**

Human reaction time

1 State what is meant by human reaction time.

Human reaction time is the time it takes for a person to react to a stimulus. **(1 mark)**

2 Tick the relevant boxes to show which of these affect human reaction time.

Guided

☐ being tired   ☐ age

☐ rain   ☐ caffeine

☐ distractions   ☐ alcohol   **(1 mark)**

3 Describe an experiment to measure human reaction time.

Person 1 holds a metre ruler and person 2 puts their index finger and thumb around

it at 0 cm, leaving a gap. Person 1 lets go of the ruler. ....

....

....

....

.... **(5 marks)**

> What would you do with the data? Be clear about how your results will give the reaction time.

4 A car is driving along at 10 m/s. Suddenly, a deer runs into the road 50 m in front of the car. The driver has a reaction time of 0.25 s. Calculate the thinking distance.

Speed = 10 m/s, time = 0.25 s. $v = \frac{x}{t}$, $x = vt$ ....

.... **(2 marks)**

5 Ruby and Sam are carrying out an experiment to work out Ruby's reaction time, using a metre ruler. They carry out the experiment five times. The table below gives their results.

(a) Calculate the mean of their data.

Distance the ruler dropped (m)
0.25
0.28
0.29
0.27
0.26

.... **(1 mark)**

(b) Calculate Ruby's reaction time and give your answer to two significant figures. The equation to calculate reaction time is: $t = \sqrt{(2x / g)}$.

gravitational field strength = 10 m/s^2, $t = \sqrt{\frac{2x}{g}}$ = ...

.... **(2 marks)**

(c) Compare Ruby's reaction time to a typical person.

A typical person has a reaction time between 0.2 and 0.25 s. Ruby's reaction time

....

.... **(2 marks)**

Stopping distance

1   Define braking distance.

The braking distance is the distance a car travels once the brakes have been

applied.
     (1 mark)

2   Match up the factors with the distance they affect. You can use each factor once, twice, or not at all. The first one has been done for you.

| Tiredness |
| Amount of friction between the tyres and the road |
| Alcohol and drugs |
| The colour of the driver's car |
| Conditions of the brakes |
| Mass of the car |
| Distraction |

Thinking distance   Braking distance

     (2 marks)

3   Compare the stopping distance of a car moving at 5 m/s to that of a car moving at 15 m/s.

Guided

....

....

....

....   **(2 marks)**

4   A man is driving along a country lane at 10 m/s. He sees a fox in the middle of the lane at a distance of 20 m. His reaction time is 0.3 s and his braking distance at this speed is 14 m. Calculate his stopping distance and comment on whether or not he can stop in time.

> Work out the thinking distance first using $d = vt$. Then work out the total stopping distance.

....   **(3 marks)**

5   Explain why and how wet road conditions affect the stopping distance.

Guided

....

....

....

....

....   **(3 marks)**

Extended response – Motion and forces

1   Use **two** examples to explain the difference between scalars and vectors.

> You will be more successful in extended response questions if you plan your answer before you start writing.
>
> Start off with a more general sentence to define the two keywords the question asks about. Then choose two examples and apply your definition, describing what makes each example a vector or a scalar.

....

....

....

....

....

....

....

....

....

....

....

....

....

....

....

....

....

....

....

....

....

....

....

....

....   **(6 marks)**

Energy stores and transfers

1 Name **two** energy stores.

1. ....

2. .... **(2 marks)**

2 Explain what a closed system is and how a closed system affects energy transfers.

A closed system is a system where no matter can get in or out, but energy can

flow in and out. **(2 marks)**

3 Name **one** way in which energy can be transferred and give an example.

....

....

.... **(2 marks)**

> Energy can be transferred in four ways: mechanically (a force moving something through a distance), electrically (using an electric current), thermally (because there is a temperature difference), and by radiation (by waves, for example, light or sound).

4 Energy is transferred in a torch.

(a) Draw a flow diagram to show the energy transfer from a battery to the light bulb in the torch.

(4 marks)

> In a flow diagram you need to show the store, the transfer that occurs along the arrow and the types of energy the stored energy is transferred into.

(b) Explain, using the example of the torch, the law of conservation of energy.

The law of conservation of energy states that ....

In the torch, the total energy is .... **(2 marks)**

5 A car is moving along at high speed. Draw a flow diagram to fully show the energy transfers.

(6 marks)

Efficient heat transfer

1 Describe how unwanted thermal energy transfers in a house can be prevented. Give two examples.

Thermal insulation can be put in to avoid heat loss by conduction from a house.

Examples of thermal insulation in a house are: double glazing and ....

.... **(3 marks)**

2

There are two houses at the end of High Road, as shown in the diagram. Explain, giving reasons, which house will have the higher heating bill in winter.

The house on the right will have the higher heating bill. This is because it has no

additional insulation in the cavity wall and ....

....

....

.... **(3 marks)**

3 A house has a total energy input of 600 kWh per m² a year. 175 kWh per m² a year are used to heat the house and make hot water. 270 kWh per m² a year are transferred through the walls and windows of the house with a further 30 kWh per m² a year transferred through ventilation. 125 kWh per m² a year are transferred through the roof and floor.

(a) Draw a Sankey diagram to show the energy transfers.

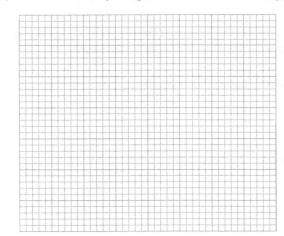

> A Sankey diagram shows the energy transfers in a visual way. The useful energy is usually shown horizontally with the total energy input. The wasted energies usually fork off pointing downwards. The widths of the arrows show how much energy is transferred.

(5 marks)

(b) Calculate the efficiency of the house. Give your answer to three significant figures.

Useful energy out = 175; total energy in = 600.

.... **(2 marks)**

Energy resources

1 List **three** renewable energy resources.

> Guided

    1. ....

    2. ....

    3. .... **(3 marks)**

2 Petrol is a non-renewable energy resource. Explain what this means.

Non-renewable energy resources will eventually run out because ....

.... **(2 marks)**

3 Wind turbines are often placed in estuaries or out at sea.

  (a) State if wind turbines are a renewable or non-renewable energy resource and name the energy resource they use.

    Wind turbines use wind energy, so they make use of a renewable energy resource.

  (b) Explain why wind turbines are often placed on plains or out at sea.

    ....

    ....

    .... **(3 marks)**

> Think about what wind turbines need and connect this to the locations they are often built in.

4 There are several nuclear power stations in the UK.

  (a) List **two** advantages of nuclear power over renewable energy resources.

    1. Release vast amounts of energy for small amounts of fuel

    2. .... **(2 marks)**

  (b) List **two** disadvantages of nuclear power.

    1. Nuclear waste needs to be stored for a very long time

    2. .... **(2 marks)**

  (c) Giving reasons, discuss if a new nuclear power station should be built in your area.

    ....

    ....

    ....

    .... **(3 marks)**

> Usually, questions like this will accept either a 'yes' or 'no' answer as long as you back up your answer with good arguments.

5 Fossil fuels are the most common source of fuel for transport, for example, petrol and diesel. Suggest why this is.

Fossil fuels are a reliable energy resource. ....

....

.... **(2 marks)**

Patterns of energy use

1 List **two** factors that explain why our energy demand has increased dramatically over the past 200 years.

1. ....

2. .... **(2 marks)**

2 Coal-fired power stations are in use around the world. Describe a drawback of using coal as a fuel.

Coal is a non-renewable energy resource, so it will ....

.... **(2 marks)**

3 The chart shows the efficiencies of various energy resources in the generation of electricity.

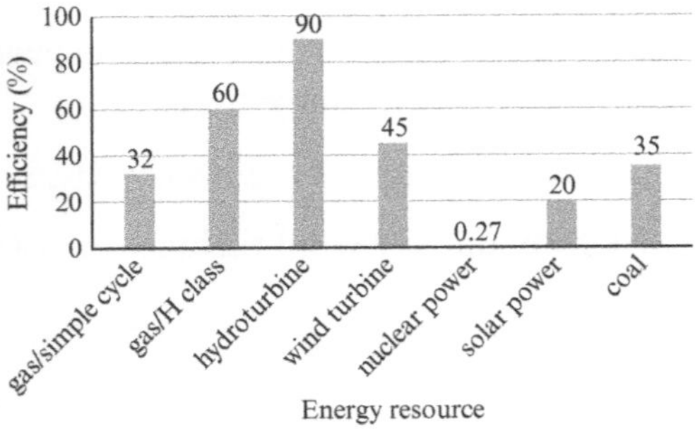

(a) Identify the most and the least efficient methods of generating electricity.

....

....

....

.... **(2 marks)**

(b) In most countries, a mix of energy resources is used to generate electricity. Discuss why this is done.

....

....

....

....

.... **(3 marks)**

4 A region has received a planning application for a hydroelectric power station. Discussing advantages and disadvantages of hydroelectric power, state if planning permission should be granted.

Planning permission should ....

Hydroelectric power relies on a renewable energy resource. However, it takes up a

large amount of land. ....

....

.... **(3 marks)**

5 Discuss how the trend of population growth compares to the use of energy resources and suggest how energy use might change in future.

....

....

....

....

.... **(4 marks)**

Potential and kinetic energy

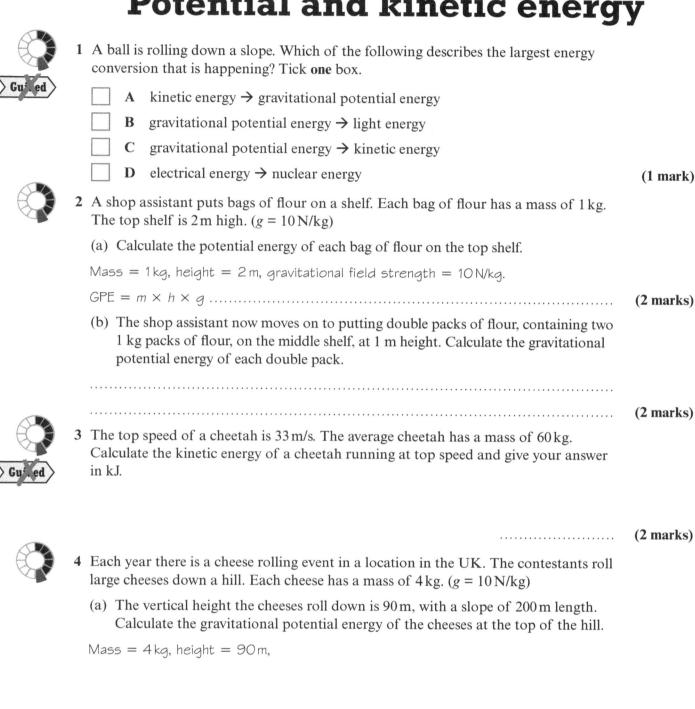

1 A ball is rolling down a slope. Which of the following describes the largest energy conversion that is happening? Tick **one** box.

  ☐   **A**   kinetic energy → gravitational potential energy

  ☐   **B**   gravitational potential energy → light energy

  ☐   **C**   gravitational potential energy → kinetic energy

  ☐   **D**   electrical energy → nuclear energy   **(1 mark)**

2 A shop assistant puts bags of flour on a shelf. Each bag of flour has a mass of 1 kg. The top shelf is 2 m high. (g = 10 N/kg)

(a) Calculate the potential energy of each bag of flour on the top shelf.

Mass = 1 kg, height = 2 m, gravitational field strength = 10 N/kg.

GPE = $m \times h \times g$ .... **(2 marks)**

(b) The shop assistant now moves on to putting double packs of flour, containing two 1 kg packs of flour, on the middle shelf, at 1 m height. Calculate the gravitational potential energy of each double pack.

....

.... **(2 marks)**

3 The top speed of a cheetah is 33 m/s. The average cheetah has a mass of 60 kg. Calculate the kinetic energy of a cheetah running at top speed and give your answer in kJ.

.... **(2 marks)**

4 Each year there is a cheese rolling event in a location in the UK. The contestants roll large cheeses down a hill. Each cheese has a mass of 4 kg. (g = 10 N/kg)

(a) The vertical height the cheeses roll down is 90 m, with a slope of 200 m length. Calculate the gravitational potential energy of the cheeses at the top of the hill.

Mass = 4 kg, height = 90 m,

.... **(2 marks)**

> Remember to use the vertical height for GPE calculations as GPE is about the energy an object stores when raised to a certain height. Sometimes the question will give you some extra information that you don't need to answer it!

(b) Calculate the maximum speed of the cheeses at the bottom of the hill, to two significant figures.

Kinetic energy = ... gravitational potential energy = ..., mass = 4 kg.

KE = $\frac{1}{2} mv^2$, so, $v = \sqrt{\frac{2KE}{m}}$ =

.... **(3 marks)**

Extended response – Conservation of energy

1 A microgeneration water generator consists of a store of water at 10 m height and a micro hydroelectric generator. The user wishes to boil a 1 kW kettle of water for 2 min.

Describe the energy transfers. Name **one** energy loss in the process. Use the data to support your answer.

> You will score more marks in an extended response question if you plan your answer.
>
> Include the following points in your answer:
>
> • Identify the energy types in the water generator and the hydroelectric generator.
> • Name the energy transfer and the stores involved in both generators.
> • How is electricity generated? (use your knowledge of power stations here)
> • What is the electricity then used for?
> • What happens inside the kettle?
> • Name an energy loss.

Water stored in the tank at 10 m has gravitational potential energy. ....

....

....

....

....

....

....

....

....

....

....

....

....

....

....

....

....

....

....

....

....

(6 marks)

Waves

1 Define what a wave is.

A wave transfers energy or information, but does not transfer any matter. **(2 marks)**

2 Label wavelength and amplitude on the diagram.

- The wavelength is the distance between adjacent crests (or troughs) of a wave.
- The amplitude is the greatest height of a wave above its undisturbed level (the line going through the centre of the wave).

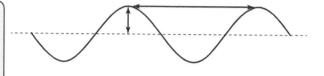

(2 marks)

3 Longitudinal and transverse waves are both types of waves.

(a) Describe **one** difference between longitudinal and transverse waves.

In longitudinal waves the vibration of the particles is parallel to the direction in

which the wave is travelling, whereas in a transverse wave................................ **(2 marks)**

(b) Name **one** similarity between transverse and longitudinal waves.

....

.... **(1 mark)**

4 The diagram shows a water wave in a puddle. The horizontal and vertical scales are in cm.

(a) Calculate the wavelength of the wave.

From crest to crest: 7.9 – 1.8 =

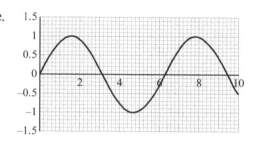

.... **(2 marks)**

Alternatively, you could read from zero to the second intercept with the x-axis. The wavelength is one complete cycle, for example, from crest to crest, or going from the zero line through a crest and a trough back to zero.

(b) Calculate the amplitude of the wave.

....

.... **(2 marks)**

5 Compare light waves to sound waves.

Light waves are transverse waves, whereas sound waves are longitudinal waves.

In transverse waves, the vibrations are ....

In longitudinal waves ....

....

....

.... **(4 marks)**

Wave equations

1 Tick the equation that correctly connects wave speed, frequency and wavelength.

☐ **A** speed = frequency × wavelength

☐ **B** speed = frequency^2 × wavelength

☐ **C** speed = frequency/wavelength

☐ **D** speed = wavelength/frequency

(1 mark)

2 Calculate the speed of a 600 kHz wave which has a wavelength of 500 m.

Frequency = 600 kHz = 600 000 Hz, wavelength = 500 m; speed =

.... **(2 marks)**

3 Orange light has a frequency of 5×10^{14} Hz. The speed of light is 3×10^8 m/s. Calculate the wavelength of orange light.

.... **(2 marks)**

> $v = f\lambda$. You can use the following triangle to help you rearrange the equation for wavelength, λ:

4 An ocean wave is travelling at a speed of 50 m/s. Calculate how long it will take to cover a distance of 0.5 km.

Speed = 50 m/s, distance = 0.5 km = 500 m. $v = d/t$

.... **(2 marks)**

5 A sound wave has a frequency of 3.3 kHz with a corresponding wavelength of 10 cm.

(a) Calculate the speed of this wave.

> Remember to convert the units!

.... **(2 marks)**

(b) Calculate how long would it take this wave to travel a distance of 0.5 km.

.... **(2 marks)**

6 Calculate the frequency, in Hz, of a wave which has a wavelength of 400 mm and is travelling at a speed of 2 km/h.

.... **(3 marks)**

Measuring wave velocity

1 Describe how you would measure the speed of sound using an echo.

Practical skills

You could stand at a measured distance from a wall. You would then make a loud noise.

....

....

.... **(4 marks)**

2 A student is standing 300 m from a high wall and has measured the following times in an experiment to measure the speed of sound.

| 1.81 s |
| 2.15 s |
| 1.79 s |
| 1.82 s |

Practical skills

(a) Explain why the student took four measurements.

.... **(1 mark)**

(b) Identify the outlier.

.... **(1 mark)**

(c) Calculate the mean of the values.

$\frac{1.81 + 1.79 + 1.82}{3}$ = ... **(1 mark)**

> The first thing to do with an outlier is to check it, if possible. If there is an outlier, it is not used in any calculations.

(d) Calculate the speed of sound.

....

.... **(2 marks)**

> The sound wave travels twice the distance as it travels to the wall and back to the student. Hence the distance is double the distance given in the question. Alternatively, you can divide the time by 2.

(e) The sound the student used has a frequency of 500 Hz. Calculate its wavelength.

Frequency = 500 Hz, speed = ...

.... **(2 marks)**

3 The frequency of a wave in a ripple tank is 5 Hz. It is travelling at a speed of 2 cm/s. Calculate the wavelength of the wave. Give your answer in standard notation and metres.

Frequency = 5 Hz, speed = 2 cm/s = 0.02 m/s; wavelength = ...

.... **(4 marks)**

4 A wave has a frequency of 50 kHz and wavelength of 1.25 m. Show if this wave could be an electromagnetic wave.

Frequency = 50 kHz = 50 × .... Hz, wavelength = ... m.

Speed = ...

.... **(4 marks)**

Had a go ☐ Nearly there ☐ Nailed it! ☐

Waves and boundaries

1 Define the term refraction.

Refraction is the change in direction of a wave when it enters a .... **(1 mark)**

Guided

2 Draw in the refracted ray when it enters the glass block and when it exits the glass block.

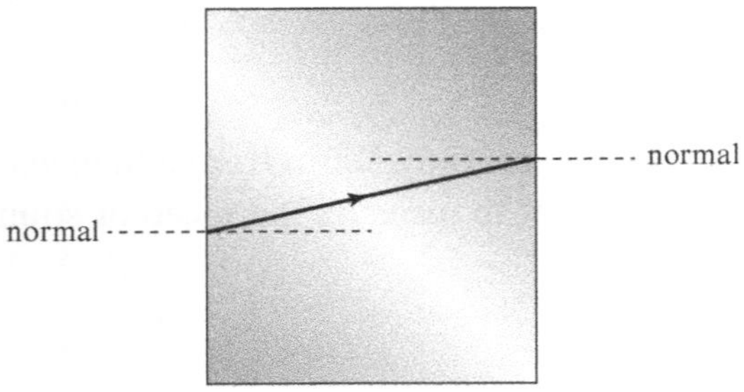

(2 marks)

3 Sound requires particles to transfer the sound.

(a) Explain why sound needs particles for the sound to travel.

Sound is a longitudinal wave. ....

....

.... **(3 marks)**

(b) Explain why sound travels slightly more slowly in cold air than in warm air.

....

.... **(3 marks)**

Air molecules have kinetic energy. How does this change with temperature and how does this affect sound waves?

Guided

4 Explain why a light wave is refracted as it enters water at an angle.

....

....

.... **(2 marks)**

Guided

5 Describe how a light wave is refracted when a wave enters a medium at right angles to the surface.

.... **(1 mark)**

Guided

6 The picture shows a pencil in a transparent glass of water. Explain why the pencil appears kinked.

....

....

....

....

....

....

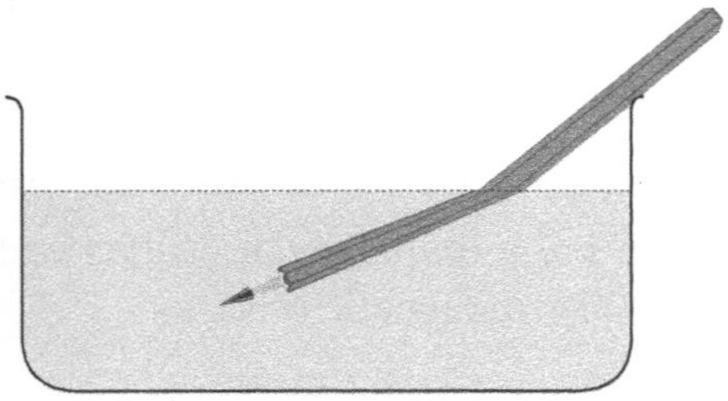

(3 marks)

 **Practical skills**

Waves in fluids

1 Choose suitable equipment that can be used together to measure the speed of a wave.
   You can tick as many options as required.

Guided

   ☐ **A** a ripple tank

   ☐ **B** a stopwatch

   ☐ **C** a strobe light

   ☐ **D** a thermometer   **(1 mark)**

2 Explain how you would use a ripple tank to measure the frequency of a wave.

   Set up the ripple tank and produce waves.. Count the number of waves that pass

   a point ....

   ....

   .... **(4 marks)**

   ┌───┐
   │ Think about how to make your results as accurate as possible. │
   └───┘

3 An experiment is set up to measure the frequency of a wave. The wave is passing a
   point in a ripple tank 150 times in 1 min. Calculate the frequency of the wave.

   1 min = 60 s. frequency = ... **(2 marks)**

4 Explain how the wavelength of a wave in a ripple tank can be measured.

Practical skills

   Set up a ripple tank. Use a stroboscope ....

   ....

   .... **(3 marks)**

5 A student set up an experiment to measure the speed of a wave in a ripple tank. He
   measured the wavelength four times: 1.0 cm, 1.2 cm, 1.1 cm, 1.1 cm. He also measured the
   frequency four times: 5 waves in 1 min, 6 waves in 1 min, 3 waves in 30 s, 4 waves in
   1 min.

   (a) Calculate the mean for both the wavelength and the frequency.

   Mean of wavelength = $\frac{1.0 + 1.2 + 1.1 + 1.1}{4}$ = ...

   ....

   .... **(2 marks)**

   (b) Calculate the speed of the wave.

   ....

   ....

   ┌───┐
   │ The equation to calculate speed from wavelength and frequency is: $v = f \times \lambda$. │
   └───┘

6 A sound wave is produced and the frequency reduced to reduce the pitch of the wave.
   Provided that the speed of the wave remains the same, explain how this will affect the
   wavelength.

   The equation used to calculate speed is $v = f\lambda$. If the frequency is decreased and

   the speed stays the same, ...

   .... **(2 marks)**

Extended response – Waves

1 Your teacher gives you the following equipment. Describe how you would use the
   equipment to measure the speed of sound.

   Equipment given: metre ruler, two microphones, electronic timer with cables to connect
   microphones, two wooden bricks. You can make a sketch to illustrate your answer.

> Make a plan before you start writing, as your answer is also marked for grammar
> and how the text flows. For your answer, you could think about how to:
> - set up the experiment, for example, two microphones set at a certain distance
> - measure the time to pick up the sound
> - use the information to calculate speed
> - make this a fair test.

....

....

....

....

....

....

....

....

....

....

....

....

....

....

....

....

....

....

....

....

....

....

....

....

                                                                                                          (6 marks)

Electromagnetic spectrum

1 State what type of wave electromagnetic waves are.

Electromagnetic waves are transverse waves.   **(1 mark)**

2 List the main groups of electromagnetic waves from lowest to highest frequency.

Radiowaves, microwaves, infrared...

.... **(1 mark)**

3 Gamma rays have a very high frequency, whereas radio waves have a very low frequency. Decide if one of these has a higher speed and explain your answer.

Speed = frequency × wavelength. As the frequency of an electromagnetic wave

increases, the wavelength decreases, so the speed ....

.... **(3 marks)**

4 Explain how light waves travel through a vacuum.

> Longitudinal waves such as sound waves need particles to propagate. Some transverse waves also involve particles, e.g. water waves. However, it is not the particles that move along the wave, but it is energy that is transferred along a wave. If particles are involved, they either move back and forth parallel to the direction the wave is travelling (longitudinal waves), or up and down at right angles to the direction the wave is travelling (transverse waves).

Electromagnetic waves are transverse waves. They transfer energy from one place to another and do not require particles to travel. The vibrations of the wave are

....

.... **(3 marks)**

5 A radiowave has a frequency of 300 GHz. The speed of light is 3×10^8 m/s. Calculate the wavelength of the wave.

300 GHz = 300 × 10^9 Hz ....

.... **(2 marks)**

6 Visible light ranges in frequency from 4.3×10^{14} Hz to 7.7×10^{14} Hz. The speed of light is 3×10^8 m/s. Calculate the range of wavelengths for visible light.

Guided

....

....

....

.... **(4 marks)**

Investigating refraction

1 State what changes when a light ray is refracted.

The speed changes. If the light ray is incident at an angle, then the ray also changes direction.

(1 mark)

2 Describe how the direction of a light ray changes when it enters and exits a glass block.

The light ray bends towards the normal as it enters the glass block and ....

....

(2 marks)

> When the light ray enters a more dense material, like glass, it bends towards the normal. If it enters a less dense material, like air, it bends away from the normal.

3 Using the diagram below, describe how you would measure the angles of refraction with a glass block.

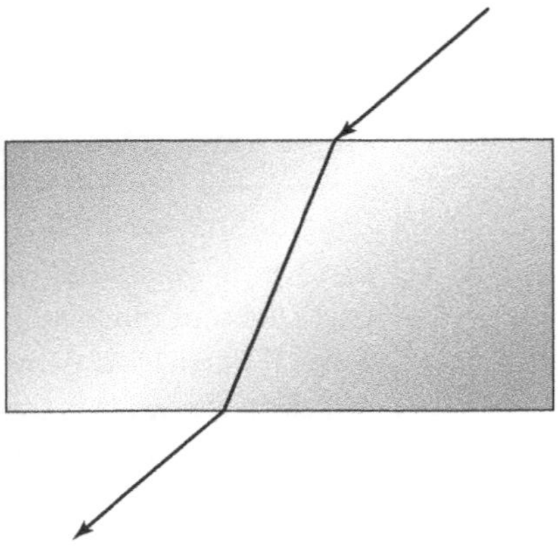

Draw a normal on the surface through which the incident ray enters and a normal on the exit

surface. Then ....

....

....

....

....

(2 marks)

4 Describe a situation where the angle of refraction through a glass block is 0°.

....

....

(1 mark)

> Think about at what angle the incident ray enters the glass block. What does it mean when the angle of refraction is 0°?

5 Describe an experiment to measure the angle of refraction through a rectangular glass block.

Practical skills

For the experiment I will need a rectangular glass block, a sheet of paper, a light source, a ruler, a pencil and a protractor. I will put the glass block on the sheet of

paper and draw the outline using the pencil.......................................

....

....

....

....

(5 marks)

6 Name the organ in the body where refraction happens, and describe the function of this organ.

Guided

....

....

(2 marks)

Dangers and uses

1 State which type of electromagnetic radiation is used in photography.

.... **(1 mark)**

2 Explain how ultraviolet rays can cause damage to the human body.

UV rays cause mutations of the DNA inside living cells. This can lead to ....

.... **(2 marks)**

> • Very often with 2 mark questions you need to give a broader, introductory sentence and then get more specific.
> • Think about the broad concept first (mutations) and then about what damage this can cause.

3 This question is about microwaves.

(a) Describe **two** uses for microwave radiation.

Microwaves are used for cooking because they heat water. They are also used

....

.... **(2 marks)**

(b) Microwaves can have a frequency of 500 MHz. Calculate the wavelength of these waves. (Speed of light = 3×10^8 m/s.)

Frequency = 500 MHz = ... Hz, speed = 3×10^8 m/s, speed = frequency ×

wavelength. Wavelength = ...

.... **(2 marks)**

> Check page 176 for help if you can't remember how to rearrange the equation.

4 Explain how infrared radiation can be both useful and harmful to us.

Infrared radiation is used for many different applications. It is used, for example, to heat up food in grills and toasters. It is also used in communication, for example,

over short distances ....

.... Although it can be very

useful, it can also be dangerous. Too much..

....

.... **(3 marks)**

5 Explain why gamma rays can both cause cancer and treat it.

....

....

....

.... **(4 marks)**

> Think about what gamma rays do to cells. How does this cause cancer and how does this also help to treat cancer?

Changes and radiation

1 Describe when radiation is absorbed or emitted from atoms.

Radiation is absorbed or emitted when electrons ....

.... **(1 mark)**

2 List **three** sub-atomic particles in an atom.

.... **(3 marks)**

3 Describe how the nucleus and electrons are arranged in atoms.

The nucleus is in the centre of an atom. It contains ....

.... Electrons are arranged outside the nucleus.

They are found on ....

.... **(3 marks)**

4 Explain when electrons can jump to a higher energy level.

....

.... **(1 mark)**

> The energy shells on which electrons are located have certain energy levels. To jump between levels, a particular amount of energy is absorbed or emitted. The exact amount of energy involved depends on the atom and the shell involved.

5 Describe what nuclear radiation is.

....

.... **(1 mark)**

6 Compare energy emission from nuclei of atoms to that of electrons.

....

....

.... **(3 marks)**

> 'Compare' means you have to describe both nuclear energy emission and electron energy emission. Do they have anything in common? What are the differences?

7 Gamma radiation can be used, among other applications, to sterilise medical equipment and to treat cancer.

(a) Describe how gamma radiation is emitted from atoms and what makes it useful for these applications.

....

....

.... **(4 marks)**

(b) Describe a disadvantage of using gamma radiation in medicine.

Gamma radiation can kill cells, ...

....

.... **(2 marks)**

Extended response – Light and the electromagnetic spectrum

1 Describe the seven groups of electromagnetic waves from lowest to highest energy. In your response you should also give **one** use for each group.

> The student started writing the answer – can you complete it?
> The question asks you to 'describe' the wave groups. This means you have to give a bit more detail than just listing them, for example, which group has the highest or lowest frequency, or the colours we see in the visual range.

The lowest energy group is radiowaves. They have the highest frequency. They are used in communication. The next lowest energy group is microwaves, which are used for cooking. Infrared radiation is used in remote controls. Visible light can be divided into different colours: red, orange, yellow, green, blue, indigo, violet

....

....

....

....

....

....

....

....

....

....

....

....

....

....

....

....

....

....

....

....

....

....

.... **(6 marks)**

Structure of the atom

1 Name the particles that make up an atom.

....

.... **(3 marks)**

2 Describe the structure of the atom.

There is a nucleus at the centre. Neutrons and protons are in the nucleus. The

electrons...

.... **(4 marks)**

3 Compare the size of an atom to that of a nucleus.

A typical atom has a diameter of about 10^{-10} m, and the diameter of a typical

nucleus is about 10^{-14} m. This means that the atom is bigger by a factor of ....

.... **(2 marks)**

> A good way to compare two values is by calculating how
> much bigger one of the numbers is compared to the other.

4 Explain why the overall charge on an atom is always zero.

....

....

.... **(3 marks)**

> Which factors have an effect on the charge of the atom? Why is the overall charge
> zero when some of the subatomic particles making up the atom are charged?

5 This question is about subatomic particles and atoms.

(a) Make a labelled diagram of an atom showing the subatomic particles.

.... nucleus

(4 marks)

(b) Describe how mass is distributed within an atom.

Electrons don't have much mass. The protons and neutrons inside the nucleus.........

....

....

.... **(2 marks)**

(c) Explain how different elements can exist although all atoms have the same types of
subatomic particles.

....

....

....

.... **(2 marks)**

Atoms and isotopes

1 State what is meant by an isotope.

An isotope of an element has the same number of protons, but ....

.... **(2 marks)**

2 Chlorine has two main isotopes, one of mass 35 and one of mass 37. The atomic number of chlorine is 17. Write down the **two** main isotopes in the format $^A_Z X$.

Mass number = 35 and 37, atomic number = 17 ....

.... **(2 marks)**

> In the format $^A_Z X$, the mass number is at the top (A) and the atomic number at the bottom (Z). X is just the chemical symbol for the element.

3 The table shows the number of protons and neutrons in different atoms. Explain which **two** are isotopes of the same element.

Atom	Number of protons	Number of neutrons
A	11	12
B	12	12
C	12	11

....

.... **(3 marks)**

> Check which atoms have the same number of protons, but a different number of neutrons. Don't forget to explain why you chose the atoms.

4 Complete the table. One example has been done for you.

	Number of protons	Number of neutrons	Number of electrons
$^7_3 Li$	3	4	3
$^{32}_{16} S$			
$^{40}_{20} Ca^{2+}$			
$^{19}_9 F^-$			
$^{200}_{80} Hg$			

> A charged atom is an ion. A positive charge means that there are fewer electrons and a negative charge means that there are more electrons.

(5 marks)

5 Draw and label an atom of $^{23}_{11} Na$. You should show the nucleus and the electrons on their energy shells.

(4 marks)

Atoms, electrons and ions

1 State what an ion is.

....

....   **(1 mark)**

2 Describe what happens when an atom absorbs energy.

When atoms absorb energy, electrons can jump from...

Because the energy levels are a certain amount of energy apart, the atom would

have to absorb exactly the required energy for this to happen. ....   **(2 marks)**

3 Describe **one** way in which ions can be formed.

Ions can be formed if they are hit by ....

....   **(1 mark)**

> There are several ways in which ions can be formed. The student who started to write
> the answer above only listed one of them, as that was what the question asked.

4 Potassium (K) is an element in group 1 of the periodic table.
   (a) State the charge on an atom of potassium.

....   **(1 mark)**

> Atoms have the same number of protons and electrons.
> What does this mean for the overall charge?

   (b) State the charge on an atom of potassium which has lost one electron.

....   **(1 mark)**

   (c) Potassium has an atomic number of 19 and a mass number of 39. Calculate how
       many protons, neutrons and electrons one atom of potassium has.

Protons: 19, neutrons: 39 − 19 = ...

....   **(3 marks)**

> The number of neutrons is equal to: mass number − atomic number.

5 Describe how you would expect an ion in solution to behave when a potential
   difference is applied to the solution.

Ions are charged species ....

....   **(3 marks)**

6 Describe the subatomic particles in atoms.

Protons and neutrons are found in the nucleus of atoms. Protons are positively

charged, neutrons ....

....

....   **(5 marks)**

Ionising radiation

1 Describe what alpha radiation is.

Alpha radiation is a type of ionising radiation. It consists of ....

.... **(2 marks)**

2 An unknown radioactive material was found in a school science room. Describe how it could be determined whether this is an alpha source.

Set up a Geiger counter. Check if radiation can be detected at about 5 cm from the radioactive material or put a sheet of paper between the Geiger counter and

the material .... **(3 marks)**

3 Describe the differences between β^+-particles and β^--particles.

....

.... **(2 marks)**

> β^+-particles and β^--particles are very similar, but have opposite charges. How does this affect some of the properties?

4 Explain why gamma radiation is only weakly ionising.

Gamma radiation is stopped by thick lead or concrete only, which means that ......

....

....

.... **(2 marks)**

5 Fill in the table to compare different types of radiation. The first one has been done for you.

Type of radiation	Relative mass	Charge	Penetrating power
Alpha	4	+2	Very low
Beta$^+$			
Beta$^-$			
Gamma			
Neutron			

(5 marks)

6 Compare neutron radiation to alpha radiation in terms of penetrating power.

....

....

....

....

....

.... **(4 marks)**

> This is a 4 mark question, so you will have to give some more detail than simply stating by which materials alpha and neutron radiation are stopped.

Had a go ☐ Nearly there ☐ Nailed it! ☐

Background radiation

1 Describe what background radiation is.

Guided

....

.... **(1 mark)**

2 Name the **two** most important forms of background radiation.

Guided

....

.... **(2 marks)**

3 Describe how radon gas, emitted from certain rocks, is produced.

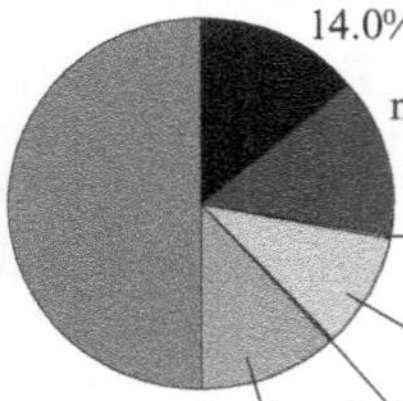
ground and buildings 14.0%
medical 14.0%
nuclear power 0.3%
cosmic rays (from space) 10.0%
other 0.2%
food and drink 11.5%
radon gas 50.0%

....

.... **(2 marks)**

The source of radon gas is radioactive decay of uranium in certain types of rocks.

4 List **three** artificial sources of background radiation.

Guided

....

....

.... **(3 marks)**

5 Radon gas is emitted from certain types of rock. Explain why radon gas (an alpha emitter) is a health risk.

Radon gas is an alpha emitter. Think about what happens when radon gas gets inside someone's body. How damaging is alpha radiation in the body?

Radon gas is emitted by certain rocks and gets into people's houses. If it is breathed in ....

.... **(4 marks)**

6 Explain why the composition of the background radiation changes depending on where you live.

Guided

....

....

.... **(2 marks)**

7 Suggest a method to reduce the exposure to radon gas in your home.

....

....

.... **(2 marks)**

You could think of ways to keep the radon gas and the radiation out, or how to remove it from the house once it's there. The question asks you to 'suggest' a method; often these types of questions do not have a 'correct' answer but are open for you to apply your knowledge in a novel situation.

Measuring radioactivity

1 State **one** method by which radioactivity can be detected.

.... **(1 mark)**

2 Define what the count rate is.

It is the number of .... detected by
a GM tube in a certain time. **(1 mark)**

> It is a good idea to learn definitions by heart. This means that you don't have to try to word a definition from scratch in the exam and so saves time. They will give you easy marks in your exam.

3 Explain why people working in nuclear power stations need to wear a dosimeter.

A dosimeter is a badge or device that will show exposure to radiation. People

working in nuclear power stations ....

.... **(3 marks)**

> Start off with a general introductory sentence, a definition or description in this case. Then apply this to the question.

4 A dosimeter contains a photographic film which darkens when the meter is exposed to radiation. Explain how different types of radiation can be distinguished.

....

....

....

.... **(3 marks)**

> Think about differences between beta and gamma radiation. How could one be blocked and the other let through?

5 Describe how a Geiger-Müller counter works.

In a GM counter the radiation goes through a tube where it ionises a gas. ....

....

....

.... **(4 marks)**

> You need to be able to describe the basics of how a GM counter works.

6 Describe how you would measure the amount of radioactivity emitted from rocks in your area.

....

....

....

.... **(4 marks)**

Models of the atom

1 Describe J.J. Thomsom's model of the atom. You may make a drawing to illustrate your answer.

The plum pudding model says that the atom is made of a uniform positive mass, and

....

....

(2 marks)

2 Make a flow diagram to describe the process through which new data becomes available, which can then lead to new models being proposed.

Practical skills

Observation → ask a scientific question → hypothesis → ....

....

(2 marks)

3 Describe Rutherford's conclusion from his gold foil experiment.

There is a central positive nucleus ....

....

(2 marks)

> The question asks you to **describe** the conclusions, so you don't need to explain how they came to the conclusion.

4 Describe how Bohr's model of the atom is different from Rutherford's model.

In both models there is a central positive nucleus. In Rutherford's model, the

electrons ....

....

(4 marks)

5 Explain why the model of the atom has changed over time.

Guided

....

....

....

(3 marks)

> There were lots of different models of atoms over time. You will only have encountered a few at school.

6 Geiger and Marsden, working in Rutherford's lab, carried out the gold foil experiment that led to Rutherford's model of the atom. Explain why the observation, that most of the radiation that the gold foil was bombarded with went straight through but a small amount was deflected backwards, suggested that the plum pudding model was not correct.

The plum pudding model says that ....

....

If the plum pudding model was correct, most of the radiation would have ....

....

(2 marks)

Beta decay

1 State what is emitted from the nucleus in β^+ and β^- decay.

....

.... **(2 marks)**

2 Describe the process of β^- decay.

An unstable neutron is converted to ....

.... **(3 marks)**

3 Name **one** use of beta decay.

.... **(1 mark)**

4 Radium-228 decays via β^- decay. Complete the equation below.

$^{228}_{88}\text{Ra} \rightarrow ^{228}_{......}\text{Ac} +$ .... **(2 marks)**

> Usually in exam questions you will be given the product of decay. However, if you need to figure out the element the radioactive element decays to yourself, you can do this by looking at the periodic table:
> • look one element to the right if an element has undergone β^- decay (neutron → proton + electron)
> • look one element to the left if an element has undergone β^+ decay (proton → neutron + positron).

5 Carbon-10 decays via β^+ decay. Complete the equation below.

$^{10}_{6}\text{C} \rightarrow ^{10}_{...}\text{B} +$ .... **(2 marks)**

6 Beta radiation can be used to measure the thickness of materials such as paper, plastic or aluminium, as shown in the diagram. Describe how this process works.

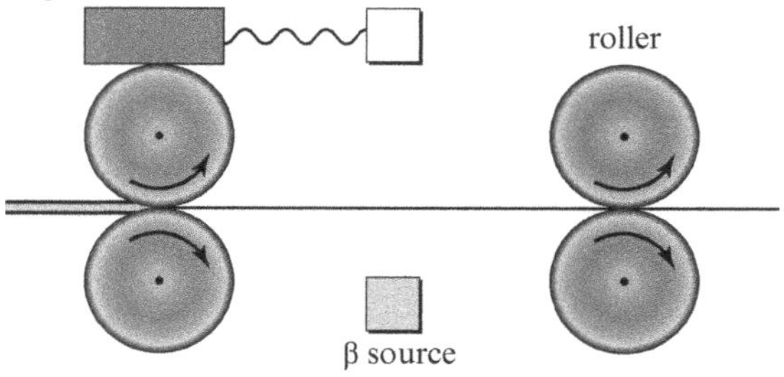

pressure control   detector   roller

β source

The beta source sends out beta radiation and the detector on the other side of the material picks up

how much radiation can travel through the material. ....

....

.... **(5 marks)**

7 Name the process involved in this decay and complete the equation:

$^{28}_{15}\text{P} \rightarrow ^{28}_{14}\text{Si} +$ .... **(2 marks)**

8 Describe a difference between a β^+ and a β^- particle. Name the location of a particle similar to the β^- particle in an atom and state the difference between this particle and a β^- particle.

In a β^- decay an electron is emitted from the nucleus which is negatively charged.

In an atom, electrons are found ....

....

.... **(5 marks)**

Radioactive decay

1 Complete the table below, describing the effect of changes to the nucleus of atoms.

Radiation	Effect on the mass number of the nucleus	Effect on the number of protons in the nucleus
α	−4	−2
β⁺		
β⁻		
Gamma		
Neutron		

(5 marks)

> • When a particle of mass (proton, neutron, alpha particle) is emitted, the mass goes down.
> • The number of protons in the nucleus will depend on the process: beta decays affect the number of protons as a neutron is converted to a proton (β⁻), or a proton to a neutron (β⁺).

2 Zinc decays by β⁻ decay.

(a) Describe what happens in a β⁻ decay.

A neutron is changed to .... **(3 marks)**

(b) Complete the equation below:

$${}^{73}_{30}\text{Zn} \rightarrow {}^{73}_{...}\text{Ga} + ...$$ **(2 marks)**

3 Radium decays by alpha decay.

(a) Describe how the nuclear charge changes during an alpha decay.

The nuclear charge decreases by .... **(2 marks)**

(b) Complete the equation below:

$${}^{226}_{88}\text{Ra} \rightarrow {}^{222}_{...}\text{Rn} + ...$$ **(2 marks)**

4 Describe what happens in a gamma decay.

....

> Gamma radiation does not have mass or charge.

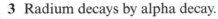Guided

.... **(3 marks)**

5 Balance these equations:

(a) $${}^{...}_{53}\text{I} \rightarrow {}^{125}_{...}\text{I} + \gamma$$

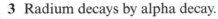Guided

(b) $${}^{90}_{...}\text{Sr} \rightarrow {}^{...}_{39}\text{Y} + {}^{...}_{-1}\beta$$

(c) $${}^{238}_{...}\text{U} \rightarrow {}^{...}_{90}\text{Th} + {}^{...}_{...}\alpha$$ **(3 marks)**

6 Uranium-238 decays via a chain of radioactive decays to lead-206. Write the equations to show the following decay reactions.

(a) $${}^{218}_{84}\text{Po}$$ decays by alpha decay to Pb-214.

$${}^{218}_{84}\text{Po} \rightarrow {}^{214}_{82}\text{Pb} + {}^{4}_{2}\alpha$$

(2 marks)

(b) $${}^{214}_{83}\text{Bi}$$ decays by β⁻ decay to Po-214.

.... **(2 marks)**

Half-life

1 Describe what half-life means.

It's the average time it takes for ....

.... **(1 mark)**

2 Explain why it is impossible to predict which nucleus will decay next.

> What does random mean?

Radioactive decay is a random process ....

.... **(2 marks)**

3 A radioactive sample has an activity of 5000 Bq. The half-life of these nuclei is 10 days. What will the activity be after 30 days?

> After every half-life the amount halves.

After 10 days = 2500 Bq, after 20 days = 1250 Bq, after 30 days = ...

.... **(2 marks)**

4 The graph shows the activity of a radioactive substance. State what the half-life of the substance is. Show your working.

....

....

....

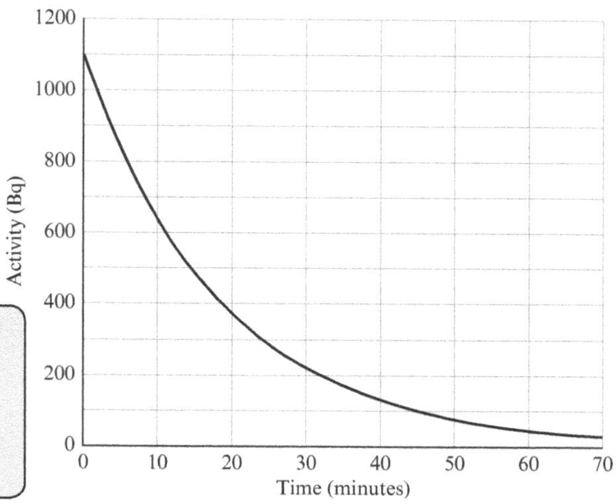

> To find the half-life from a graph, you need to read off the activity at the start. Then divide this number by 2. At this new value for activity, go along the time-axis to read off the value for time.

(2 marks)

5 A radioactive substance has a half-life of 2 days. Calculate the fraction of radioactive nuclei left after 6 days.

....

.... **(2 marks)**

> Six days are 3 half-lives. After one half-life, the fraction will be ½. After the second half-life, the fraction will be ½ × ½ = ¼. What will it be after 3 half-lives?

6 Radioactive waste has to be stored in a safe place for many years. Some types of waste have very short half-lives whereas some have very long half-lives, in the region of many hundreds of thousands of years. Explain why the waste will remain radioactive for many years.

....

....

....

.... **(3 marks)**

Dangers of radiation

1 Describe **one** way in which ionising radiation can be dangerous to human tissue.

Ionising radiation can cause radiation burns by ....

....
(2 marks)

2 Suggest **two** ways in which a person handling radioactive materials can protect themselves.

....

....
(2 marks)

> Remember that film badges will not protect the person, but can be used to monitor the exposure to radiation.

3 Describe the difference between ionising radiation and non-ionising radiation.

Ionising radiation can convert atoms into ions by removing electrons. Non-ionising

radiation ....
(2 marks)

4 A patient is having an X-ray taken.

(a) Explain how wearing a lead apron reduces the exposure to the X-rays.

....

....

....
(2 marks)

> Think about how much of the X-rays can be stopped.

(b) Suggest a way in which the X-ray nurse can reduce their exposure to the X-rays.

....

....
(1 mark)

5 Patients are sometimes exposed to radioactive materials.

(a) Describe circumstances in which a patient in a hospital would be exposed to a high dose of radiation.

The risk and benefit would be carefully weighed up, and a patient would only be

exposed to radiation if the benefit outweighs the risk. ....

....
(2 marks)

(b) Describe how the hospital staff can make sure they stay safe when using radioactive materials with patients.

....

....

....
(3 marks)

Contamination and irradiation

1 Radioactive dust can come into contact with people many miles away from the original source. Which of the following describes this process? Tick **one** box.

☐ **A** radiation

☐ **B** contamination

☐ **C** irradiation

☐ **D** electromagnetic radiation **(1 mark)**

2 Describe what irradiation is and give an example.

When something is irradiated, it is in contact with ionising radiation. An example is

.... **(2 marks)**

3 Explain the difference between irradiation and contamination.

....

.... **(2 marks)**

> Irradiation is when something is in contact with ionising radiation, but not in contact with the source of the radiation; contamination is when something is in contact with the radiation source.

4 Explain the difference between external and internal contamination. Give an example for each.

In external contamination the radioactive material is on the outside of someone's

body. In internal contamination ....

.... **(3 marks)**

5 State whether exposure to cosmic radiation from the Sun comes under irradiation, external or internal contamination. Explain why.

....

....

.... **(2 marks)**

6 Suggest how a person living in a low-radiation region and eating healthily could be internally contaminated with radioactive material.

....

....

....

.... **(2 marks)**

> Think about sources of internal contamination. How could they get into a person's body?

7 State which type of radiation would cause the most damage by internal contamination and explain why.

Alpha particles would cause the most damage because ....

.... **(3 marks)**

197

Extended response – Radioactivity

1 In March 2011 a tsunami caused the release of radioactive material from the nuclear power station in Fukushima, Japan. Among other radioisotopes, iodine-131 and caesium-137 were released. The table below gives some information about these two isotopes. Compare the two isotopes.

	Iodine-131	Caesium-137
Half-life	8 days	30 years
Where it goes in the human body	Thyroid gland	Soft tissue

Your response you should include:

- An estimate of exposure to these isotopes in 2017
- How exposure will affect people.

Exposure to iodine-131 is highest during the first few weeks after the accident,

....

....

....

....

....

....

....

....

....

....

....

....

....

....

....

....

....

....

....

....

....

(6 marks)

Work, energy and power

1 Which one of the following is the same as 'work done'? Tick **one** box.

☐ **A** energy transferred

☐ **B** time

☐ **C** power

☐ **D** voltage **(1 mark)**

2 A force of 50 N is applied to move a box by 10 cm. Calculate the energy transferred.

Force = 50 N, distance = 10 cm = ...

.... **(2 marks)**

$E = F \times d$. You need to learn this equation as it is not on the equation sheet.

3 A 1.5 kW kettle takes 2 min to boil some water. Calculate the energy transferred by the kettle.

Power = 1.5 kW = 1500 W, time = 2 min = 120 s. ....

.... **(2 marks)**

$E = P \times t$. You need to learn this equation as it is not on the equation sheet.

4 A 2000 W electric motor takes 60 s to move an object by 50 cm. Calculate the force the electric motor exerts on the object.

Distance = 50 cm = 0.5 m, power = 2000 W, time = 60 s. energy = power ×

time = energy transferred = work done = force × distance ....

.... **(3 marks)**

Calculate the energy transferred via $E = P \times t$ first. Then rearrange the equation $E = F \times d$ to calculate force. To do this, divide both sides by distance, or use the triangle: $\frac{E}{F \times D}$

5 An electric water heater transfers 14.4 MJ in 2 hours. Calculate its power rating.

Energy = 14.4 MJ = 14 400 000 J, time = 2 hours = ...

.... **(2 marks)**

6 A site crane lifts a 125 kg cement bucket at 4 m/s. Calculate the power of the motor.

....

....

....

.... **(3 marks)**

7 Dominic is driving a van the engine of which needs 60 kW of power. He takes 2 hours to drive 200 km. The very efficient engine is able to extract 36 000 000 J per litre from the fuel. Calculate how many litres of fuel are needed for this journey.

Power = 60 kW = 60000 W. Time = 2h = 7200 s. ....

.... **(4 marks)**

Extended response – Energy and forces

A company is designing a new houseboat made from steel which will be used for cruising. They want to make it as energy-efficient as possible, so that heat loss is minimal. Discuss ways by which heat loss could be reduced and by which the boat owner can stay warm in winter.

> Start by making a list of possible points. Sort them into a logical order before you start writing. You need to make at least 6 points to cover the 6 marks. You could apply your knowledge from insulation in a house to this problem, for example, insulation of walls, windows, the floor and roof, and apply this to a boat. Also, bear in mind that a boat will sometimes be out of port and be independent of the grid.

> You could add to this answer by adding how to heat the boat in the first place. Just like in a house, a boat will have to have ventilation – how will this affect the temperature inside the boat? How could heat loss be improved and are there any risks involved, for example, if you were to close up the vents?

The sides of the boat should be insulated well, maybe by using sheets of insulation material or sprayfoam. The company could also insulate the bottom of the boat to stop heat loss through the floor. They could also make the windows very small or use double-glazing

....

....

....

....

....

....

....

....

....

....

....

....

....

....

....

....

....

.... **(6 marks)**

Interacting forces

1 Describe what non-contact force means.

A non-contact force acts when two forces act between objects that don't

directly touch. **(1 mark)**

2 Name **one** contact force and **one** non-contact force.

.... **(2 marks)**

> Contact forces are forces where the objects are in direct contact,
> whereas non-contact forces are forces that act over a distance.

3 Explain why gravity is a non-contact force.

Gravity is a force between two masses. ....

.... **(2 marks)**

4 Describe the forces acting between two magnets.

Magnetism is a non-contact force. The two magnets will ....

....

.... **(3 marks)**

> It is often a good idea to start off with a general introductory sentence, as the first
> mark is often allocated for a description or a definition, and then to go into more detail.

5 Show and label the contact and non-contact forces acting on a moving bicycle at constant speed.

> The length of the arrow shows
> the size of the force, the direction
> of the force is given by the
> direction the arrow is pointing.

(2 marks)

6 Describe the forces acting on a book lying on a desk.

> Guided

....

....

....

.... **(4 marks)**

7 Describe the forces acting on a motorbike that is accelerating along a flat road.

....

....

....

.... **(3 marks)**

> How do the forces compare when an object is accelerating?
> Think of Newton's second law to answer this question.

Circuit symbols

1 Match the circuit symbol with the name for the component.

Voltmeter	▭
Fixed resistor	(LDR symbol)
Filament lamp	Ⓥ
Diode	⊗
LDR	▷ᴉ

(5 marks)

2 Explain how a voltmeter should be inserted into a circuit.

A voltmeter should be inserted in parallel with a component because it ....

.... **(2 marks)**

3 Draw the circuit symbols and explain the difference between a fixed resistor and a variable resistor.

fixed resistor   variable resistor

A fixed resistor gives a fixed resistance, which means the resistance cannot be

changed. A variable resistor ....

.... **(4 marks)**

4 Describe what an LDR is and give an example of a use.

LDR stands for light-dependent resistor. ....

....

.... **(3 marks)**

> Light-dependent resistors can be used in control circuits where the output changes when the light level changes, for example, street lights being turned on or off when it gets dark or light.

5 Describe the energy conversions in an electric motor.

....

.... **(2 marks)**

Series and parallel circuits

1 Describe the difference in wiring between parallel and series circuits.

In a series circuit, all the components are arranged in a loop. In a parallel circuit

....

.... **(2 marks)**

2 This question is about series circuits.

(a) Draw a series circuit containing a cell, two light bulbs and three ammeters. How do the ammeter readings compare in this circuit?

The current in a series circuit .... **(2 marks)**

(b) Describe how you would measure the voltage across the light bulbs.

You could connect a voltmeter ....

.... **(1 mark)**

(c) The cell is providing 3 V. Provided the light bulbs are identical, calculate the potential difference across each lightbulb.

....

.... **(1 mark)**

> The voltages in a series circuit add up: $V_{total} = V_1 + V_2 +$

3 This question is about parallel circuits.

(a) Draw a circuit diagram in which two identical light bulbs are connected in parallel. Add three ammeters to measure the total current in the circuit and the current in each of the branches.

> The first ammeter needs to go close to the cell, before the circuit branches. The other two ammeters need to go in the branches. Ammeters are connected in series.

(2 marks)

(b) The cell is providing 6 V. Calculate the voltage you would measure across each of the identical light bulbs.

....

.... **(1 mark)**

(c) The current near the cell measures 3 A. Calculate the current measured in each branch.

....

.... **(1 mark)**

> In a parallel circuit, the currents in the branches add up to give the total current of the circuit.

Current and charge

1 Give a definition for 'electric current'.

The electric current is the rate of flow of charge.
(1 mark)

2 Which of these equations correctly connects current, charge and time? Tick **one** box.

☐ **A** $Q = \frac{I}{t^4}$

☐ **B** $Q = \frac{t}{I}$

☐ **C** $Q = \frac{I}{t}$

☐ **D** $Q = I \times t$

> You need to learn this equation. It's not on the equation sheet. Current is the amount of charge flowing past a point in a certain time.

(1 mark)

3 A charge of 60 C is flowing through a light bulb for 1 min. Calculate the current.

Charge = 60 C, time = 1 min = ...

.... **(2 marks)**

4 A 2 kW electric kettle transfers 120 kJ with a charge of 600 C flowing. Calculate the current the kettle is drawing.

Power = 2 kW = 2000 W, energy transferred = 120 kJ = ... J, charge = 600 C.

energy = power × time ....

....

.... **(3 marks)**

> You will need two equations here: *energy = power × time* and *charge = current × time*. Work out time using the first equation first, then insert this into the second equation. These triangles may help you rearrange the equations: $\frac{energy}{power \times time}$ and $\frac{charge}{current \times time}$.

5 Calculate the time 100 C of charge was passing through a 15 A motor.

Charge = 100 C, current = 15 A. charge = current × time ....

.... **(2 marks)**

6 Describe the difference between conventional current and the current in terms of electrons.

> Guided

....

....

.... **(2 marks)**

7 An LED desklight has a power rating of 5 W. Explain, using the equation for power, how the power consumption remains constant despite the LED being on for a long period of time.

The equation for power is Power = $\frac{Energy}{Time}$ ....

.... **(3 marks)**

Energy and charge

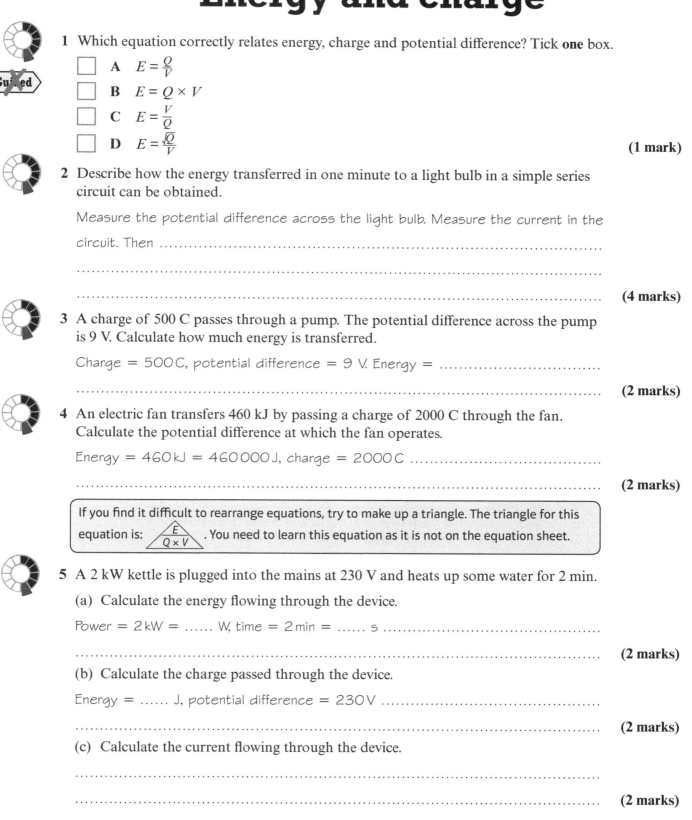

1 Which equation correctly relates energy, charge and potential difference? Tick **one** box.

☐ **A** $E = \frac{Q}{V}$

☐ **B** $E = Q \times V$

☐ **C** $E = \frac{V}{Q}$

☐ **D** $E = \frac{\sqrt{Q}}{V}$ **(1 mark)**

2 Describe how the energy transferred in one minute to a light bulb in a simple series circuit can be obtained.

Measure the potential difference across the light bulb. Measure the current in the

circuit. Then ....

....

....   **(4 marks)**

3 A charge of 500 C passes through a pump. The potential difference across the pump is 9 V. Calculate how much energy is transferred.

Charge = 500 C, potential difference = 9 V. Energy = ...

....   **(2 marks)**

4 An electric fan transfers 460 kJ by passing a charge of 2000 C through the fan. Calculate the potential difference at which the fan operates.

Energy = 460 kJ = 460 000 J, charge = 2000 C ....

....   **(2 marks)**

> If you find it difficult to rearrange equations, try to make up a triangle. The triangle for this
> equation is: $\frac{E}{Q \times V}$. You need to learn this equation as it is not on the equation sheet.

5 A 2 kW kettle is plugged into the mains at 230 V and heats up some water for 2 min.

(a) Calculate the energy flowing through the device.

Power = 2 kW = ... W, time = 2 min = ... s ....

....   **(2 marks)**

(b) Calculate the charge passed through the device.

Energy = ... J, potential difference = 230 V ....

....   **(2 marks)**

(c) Calculate the current flowing through the device.

....

....   **(2 marks)**

Ohm's law

1 State Ohm's law.

....

Guided .... **(2 marks)**

2 A resistor is connected to a 3 V battery. A current of 6 A is flowing through the resistor. Calculate the resistance of the resistor.

Potential difference = 3 V, current = 6 A ....

.... **(2 marks)**

3 Describe how the resistance for a component such as a light bulb could be measured.

....

.... **(3 marks)**

> Resistance can't be measured directly, but it is related, by Ohm's law, to current and voltage. How can you measure current and voltage?

4 The graph shows current plotted against potential difference for two components. Explain which component has the higher resistance.

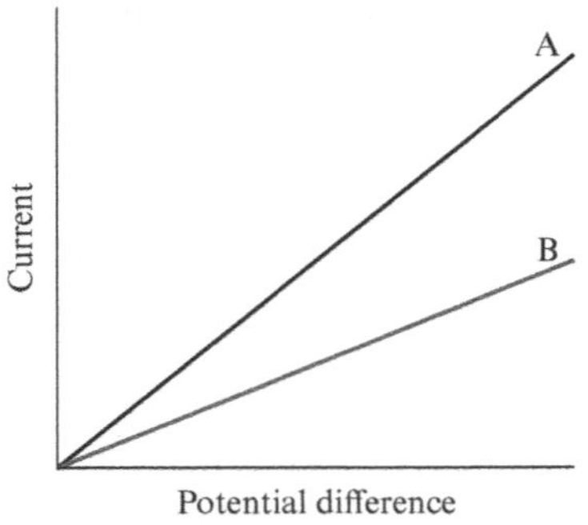

....

....

....

.... **(2 marks)**

> When the resistance is higher, this means that a lower current is flowing. Looking at the graph, compare the two devices and decide which one has less current flowing for the same potential difference.

5 (a) Calculate the resistance of light bulb 1.

Potential difference = 1.5 V, current = 4 A.

Resistance = ...

.... **(2 marks)**

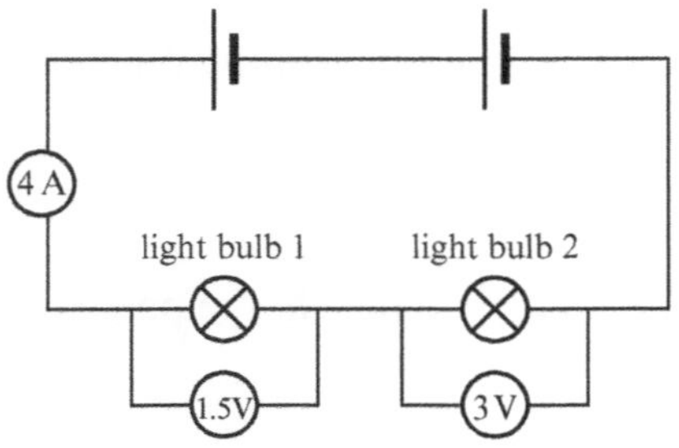

> If you find rearranging equations difficult, try using a triangle:
> $$\frac{voltage}{current \times resistance}$$

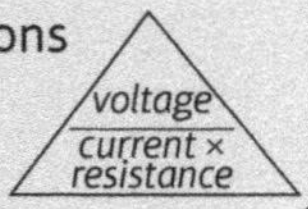

(b) (i) Calculate the potential difference across the battery.

.... **(2 marks)**

(ii) Calculate the total resistance in the circuit.

.... **(2 marks)**

> The potential difference across the battery is the sum of all the potential differences in the circuit. Use this knowledge to calculate the total resistance in the circuit.

Resistors

1 State how you can calculate the total resistance of resistors in a series circuit.

Guided

....

.... **(1 mark)**

2 The diagram shows a parallel circuit with two resistors.

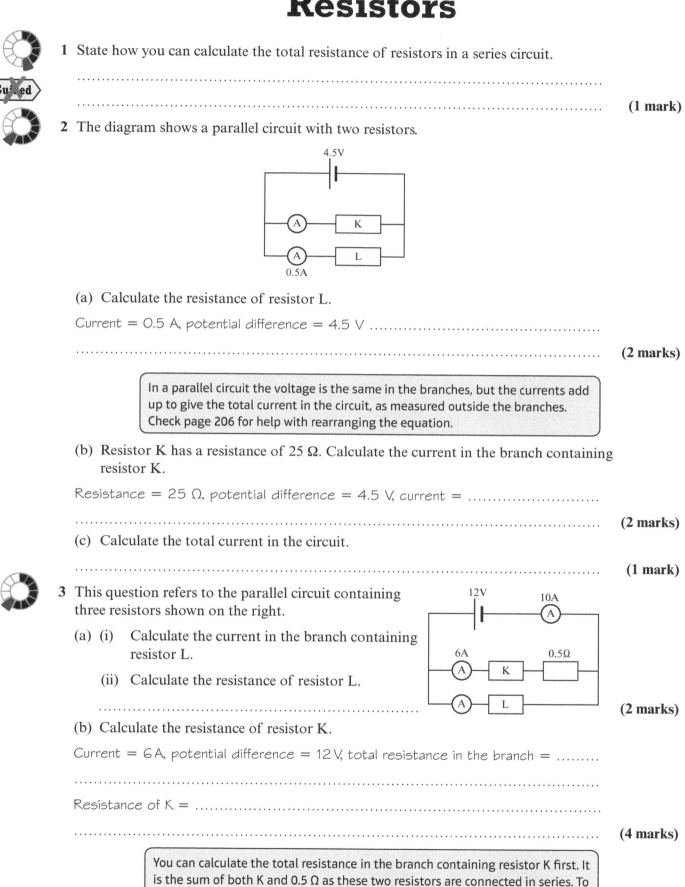

(a) Calculate the resistance of resistor L.

Current = 0.5 A, potential difference = 4.5 V ....

.... **(2 marks)**

> In a parallel circuit the voltage is the same in the branches, but the currents add
> up to give the total current in the circuit, as measured outside the branches.
> Check page 206 for help with rearranging the equation.

(b) Resistor K has a resistance of 25 Ω. Calculate the current in the branch containing
     resistor K.

Resistance = 25 Ω, potential difference = 4.5 V, current = ...

.... **(2 marks)**

(c) Calculate the total current in the circuit.

.... **(1 mark)**

3 This question refers to the parallel circuit containing
   three resistors shown on the right.

   (a) (i)   Calculate the current in the branch containing
              resistor L.

        (ii) Calculate the resistance of resistor L.

        .... **(2 marks)**

   (b) Calculate the resistance of resistor K.

Current = 6 A, potential difference = 12 V, total resistance in the branch = ...

....

Resistance of K = ...

.... **(4 marks)**

> You can calculate the total resistance in the branch containing resistor K first. It
> is the sum of both K and 0.5 Ω as these two resistors are connected in series. To
> calculate the resistance of resistor K, take 0.5 Ω away from the total resistance.

I–V graphs

1 State for which type of component the I–V graph would be a straight line through the origin.

.... **(1 mark)**

2 Sketch an I–V graph for a filament lamp. Explain why the graph has the shape drawn.

The filament gets hotter as the current increases, leading to ....

.... **(4 marks)**

3 The I–V graph shows an ohmic resistor.

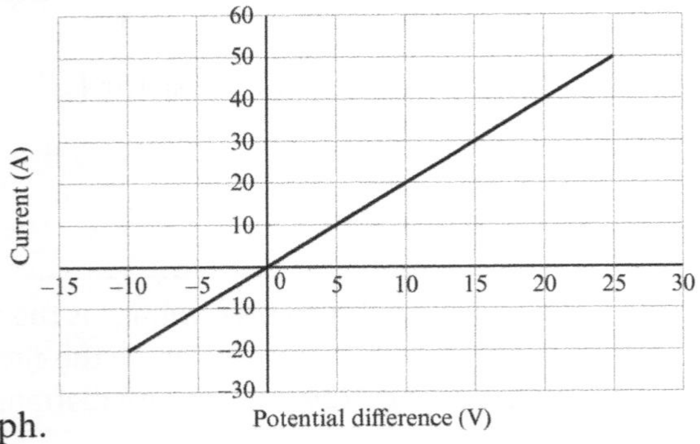

(a) Give an example of a component that would give the I–V graph.

....

....

....

Current (A) on vertical axis with values 60, 50, 40, 30, 20, 10, −10, −20, −30. Horizontal axis *Potential difference (V)* with values −15, −10, −5, 0, 5, 10, 15, 20, 25, 30.

(1 mark)

(b) Explain how you would set up a circuit to obtain the data for this graph.

Connect a ...., an ammeter, a variable resistor in series and a

voltmeter across the ....

....

....

.... **(5 marks)**

(c) Calculate the resistance of the component shown in the I–V graph.

....

....

....

> $R = \frac{V}{I}$. Read off a value for V and a value for I and insert them into the equation. Note that you can only do this for a straight line.

(2 marks)

4 Describe the shape of the I–V graph you would get for a diode.

The resistance is very high in one direction, so the graph ....

In the other direction ....

....

....

.... **(4 marks)**

> • In a diode, current only flows in one direction because the resistance is very high in this direction. What does this mean for the graph?
> • In the other direction current does flow. What is the shape of the graph then?

Electrical circuits

1 A student sets up an experiment to measure the resistance of a light bulb. Name a hazard the student would have to think of before starting the experiment.

....

.... **(1 mark)**

Guided

Practical skills

2 Describe what the difference between accurate data and reliable data is.

....

....

.... **(2 marks)**

> Accurate means close to the true value. How does this compare to 'reliable'?

3 Explain how the shape of the I–V graph of an ohmic and a non-ohmic resistor are different and why.

The I–V graph of an ohmic resistor is a straight line through the origin, whereas the

I–V graph of a non-ohmic resistor ....

....

The resistance of an ohmic resistor doesn't change, but for a non-ohmic resistor ...

....

.... **(4 marks)**

4 A student sets up a parallel circuit with two identical light bulbs connected in parallel and a 3 V battery. She then measures the potential difference across the light bulbs and the current in the branches. Describe what she will see.

The potential difference in the branches will be ....

.... The current ....

.... **(2 marks)**

> In a parallel circuit the potential difference is the same in all the branches, but the current in the branches adds up to the total current of the circuit, as measured outside the branches.

5 A student wants to measure the resistance of two light bulbs connected in series and the total resistance in the circuit. Describe how he could do this.

Guided

....

....

....

....

....

....

....

.... **(4 marks)**

The LDR and the thermistor

1 Describe how the resistances of an LDR change with light intensity.

The resistance is higher .... **(2 marks)**

> LDR stands for light-dependent resistor.

2 A component was found to change resistance with temperature. The resistance was lower at higher temperatures. Name the device.

> Guided

.... **(1 mark)**

3 Explain what a thermistor does.

A thermistor is a component which transfers electrical energy into heat energy.

This decreases ....

.... **(2 marks)**

> When a current flows through a wire or component, the electrons (charge) constantly collide with the metal ions making up the wire or component. This causes friction, which releases heat, and slows down the electrons on their path. In a thermistor, the wire would be of a material that causes the electrons to be slowed down more than in the copper wire connecting the circuit.

4 A student wants to design a circuit that could be used in a fire alarm.

(a) Name and draw the circuit symbol for the temperature-sensitive component the student should use.

.... **(2 marks)**

(b) Explain why this component is ideal for this circuit.

This component is ideal because its resistance is lower as the temperature increases,

....

.... **(2 marks)**

(c) Draw a circuit that could be used in a fire alarm.

> Think about how you would convert the temperature signal picked up by the thermistor into a signal that would alert you of a fire. Which component could you add?

3.0V

5 LDRs are used in street lights. Explain how they can control whether the street light is on or off.

....

....

.... **(2 marks)**

> An LDR is light-sensitive. How does the resistance change?

Current heating effect

1 Describe how the resistance of a wire or component affects the heating effect, when a constant current is flowing through the wire.

The higher the resistance, the higher the heating effect.　**(1 mark)**

2 Give **one** device where the heating effect is useful and **one** where the heating effect is not useful.

....

....　**(2 marks)**

3 Describe what happens to the heat released by the heating effect of a wire.

It is given off to the ....　**(1 mark)**

> Giving off heat to the environment is called 'dissipation'.

4 Explain how the heating effect is created.

When electrons flow through a wire, they will collide with ....

....

....　**(4 marks)**

> A wire is made of metal, which is made of a regular arrangement (lattice) of metal ions surrounded by a sea of electrons. What will happen when electrons flow through this lattice when a potential difference is applied? What will happen if the current is increased?

5 Describe how a fuse makes use of the heating effect.

A fuse is a component that cuts the circuit if the current gets too high. ....

....

....

....　**(3 marks)**

> A fuse is a component that protects the circuit and any devices in the circuit from damage caused by too much current. It does this by breaking the circuit if too much current flows.

6 Explain how a kettle makes use of the current heating effect.

....

....

....　**(4 marks)**

7 The wires and circuits in a computer are subject to the current heating effect. Suggest what effect this might have on the computer and ways to reduce these.

The heating effect is when wires or components get hot when current flows through

them. This could damage the circuits in a computer. A way to reduce this ....

....　**(3 marks)**

Energy and power

1 Describe what electrical power is.

Guided

....

.... **(1 mark)**

2 A kettle is plugged into a 230 V supply and has a current of 10 A flowing through it. It is on for 50 s to heat up some water. Calculate the amount of energy transferred to the water.

Potential difference = 230 V, current = 10 A, time = 50 s ....

.... **(3 marks)**

> Energy = current × potential difference × time. You need to learn this equation as it is not on the equation sheet.

3 A radio is supplied by a 9 V battery and has a current of 6.7 A flowing through it. Calculate the power of the radio. State the unit of power in your answer.

Potential difference = 9 V, current = 6.7 A ....

....

.... **(3 marks)**

> Power = current × potential difference. You need to remember this equation as it is not on the equation sheet.

4 288 420 J of energy was transferred to a room by a fan heater in 2 min. It is plugged into the mains (230 V) with a current of 10.45 A flowing through it.

(a) Calculate the power of the heater.

Energy = 288 420 J, time = 2 min = 120 s ....

.... **(2 marks)**

> Energy = power × time. You need to learn this equation as it is not on the equation sheet.

(b) Calculate the resistance in the heating wires of the heater.

Current = 10 A, power = ...

....

.... **(2 marks)**

> • You can use the power you calculated to work out the resistance from the equation: power = current² × resistance. Remember that current is squared in this equation. Learn this equation as it is not on the equation sheet!
> • Alternatively you can use $V = IR$.

5 A 2 kW water heater is connected to a 230 V supply. Which fuse should be used to protect the heater? Tick **one** box.

☐ **A** 1 A
☐ **B** 3 A
☐ **C** 5 A
☐ **D** 13 A

> The fuse needs to protect the heater so it shouldn't be too high. At the same time it needs to allow a high enough current through the circuit to supply the heater, before it breaks.

(1 mark)

a.c. and d.c. circuits

1 Describe what the oscilloscope trace of a d.c. current looks like.

.... **(1 mark)**

2 In terms of flow of current, describe a difference between a.c. and d.c. supply.

For direct current, the direction of the flow of current does not change.

.... **(2 marks)**

3 Give **two** examples each of devices that use (a) a.c. and (b) d.c.

....

....

....

.... **(4 marks)**

4 A hairdryer has a power rating of 1700 W. Explain how much energy it transfers.

Power $= \frac{energy}{time}$ ....

.... **(2 marks)**

5 Describe what an electric current is.

An electric current is the flow of electrons through an electric circuit. It is supplied

.... **(2 marks)**

> A cell supplies a potential difference for the electrons in a circuit, similar to a
> waterfall where water runs down from a height to a lower area. The battery has
> a positive terminal and a negative terminal. Electrons are negatively charged
> and are attracted to the positive terminal of the battery as well as repelled by
> the negative terminal. This is the driving force for the current to flow in a circuit.

6 Sketch an oscilloscope trace for an a.c. supply.

(1 mark)

7 A laptop battery gives a potential difference of 19.5 V and supplies a current of 2.31 A.

(a) Calculate the power rating of the battery.

Potential difference = 19.5 A, current = 2.31 A. Power = ...

.... **(2 marks)**

(b) Calculate how much energy the battery supplies in 10 min.

....

.... **(2 marks)**

Mains electricity and the plug

1 Describe the colour-coding of wires used in a plug.

The live wire is brown, the neutral wire is ....

.... **(3 marks)**

2 Explain why it is important to use a fuse in domestic and industrial applications.

....

....

....

.... **(4 marks)**

> A fuse breaks the circuit if there is a current higher than the specifications of the fuse going through the circuit. A high current might be a result of a fault.

3 Describe the potential difference found in the three cables wired into a plug.

The earth wire is not part of the circuit, but is a safety feature. The live wire has a

potential difference of ....

....

.... **(3 marks)**

4 Explain why a circuit breaker is sometimes used instead of a fuse.

....

....

.... **(2 marks)**

> A circuit breaker is similar to a fuse in that it breaks the circuit when it detects a high current. However, it has a switch which can be reset.

5 Describe the use of the earth wire.

The earth wire is a safety feature. ....

....

....

.... **(4 marks)**

6 Most appliances are fitted with an earth wire.

(a) Explain the need for an earth wire in an appliance with a metal casing.

If any of the cables inside the appliance come loose, they might come into contact

with the metal casing. ....

.... **(2 marks)**

(b) Some appliances are double-insulated. This means that they have another casing, usually plastic, around their metal case. Explain why they do not need an earth cable.

....

....

.... **(3 marks)**

Extended response – Electricity and circuits

 Explain the role of transformers in the distribution of mains electricity in the UK.

> Make a short plan before starting to write to make sure that your answer is easy to read and is in a logical order. You should include in your answer:
> - what the advantage of transferring mains electricity at high voltage over great distances is
> - step-up and step-down transformers (including primary and secondary coils)
> - safety
> - energy loss (reduction of).

....
....
....
....
....
....
....
....
....
....
....
....
....
....
....
....
....
....
....
....
....
....
....
....
....
....
....

(6 marks)

Magnets and magnetic fields

1 Which material is **not** magnetic? Tick **one** box.

☐ **A** steel   ☐ **C** nickel

☐ **B** iron   ☐ **D** sulfur   **(1 mark)**

2 Sketch the field lines around the bar magnet shown.

> Magnetic field lines go from north to south.

bar magnet

N   S

(2 marks)

3 A student is given an iron nail and a bar magnet. Describe how he could magnetise the nail.

He could move one pole of the bar magnet along the nail ....

....

.... **(2 marks)**

4 A permanent magnet and an unmagnetised piece of iron are placed next to a permanent magnet, one at a time. Describe what you would see.

The permanent magnet would be repelled by the other permanent magnet if both like poles point towards each other, or attracted to the other permanent magnet if the poles facing each other are unlike poles. The unmagnetised iron

....

.... **(3 marks)**

5 This question is about compasses.

(a) State the use of plotting compasses.

Tracing the direction and shape of magnetic field lines.   **(1 mark)**

> You will have used a plotting compass at school to trace magnetic field lines.

(b) Explain why a compass can be used for directions.

....

....

....

.... **(3 marks)**

6 Describe how you would use a plotting compass to trace the magnetic field around a bar magnet.

Practical skills

Guided

....

....

....

.... **(4 marks)**

Current and magnetism

1 State **two** variables the strength of the magnetic field around a long straight conductor will depend on and how these will affect the magnetic field.

The larger the size of the current in the wire, the stronger the magnetic field.

....

.... **(2 marks)**

2 Describe the shape of the magnetic field around a long, straight conductor.

....

.... **(1 mark)**

3 Describe how you can work out the direction of the magnetic field around a long, straight conductor.

....

....

.... **(3 marks)**

4 A current runs through a long, straight wire. Explain how the magnetic field strength changes when the current decreases.

....

.... **(2 marks)**

> Magnetic field strength is directly proportional to the size of the current. Directly proportional means that increasing one variable will lead to an increase of the other variable by the same rate.

5 Describe the magnetic field of a solenoid.

There is a strong uniform field in the centre of the solenoid. On the outside, ...

....

.... **(3 marks)**

6 (a) Define the term 'inversely proportional'.

As one variable increases ....

.... **(1 mark)**

(b) Describe what happens to the strength of the magnetic field as the distance from the conductor increases and decreases.

....

....

.... **(2 marks)**

7 Describe how you would make an electromagnet.

....

....

.... **(3 marks)**

Extended response – Magnetism and the motor effect

 Discuss, using **three** examples, how the properties of permanent magnets, unmagnetised magnetic materials and temporary magnets are used in various applications or procedures.

> After making a short list of points to include, start off with a description of permanent magnets, unmagnetised magnetic materials and temporary magnets. You could add an example to each description. Then think about how this is used in processes or applications such as sorting metals in a scrap yard, in recycling and magnetic door catches.

....
....
....
....
....
....
....
....
....
....
....
....
....
....
....
....
....
....
....
....
....
....
....
....
....
....

.... **(6 marks)**

Transformers

1 State by which process the size of the potential difference is changed in a transformer.

.... **(1 mark)**

2 Describe the set-up of a step-up transformer.

There are two coils wound around an iron core. The primary coil has a certain number

of turns and is connected to a power supply. The secondary coil ....

....

....

.... **(4 marks)**

> In a step-up transformer there are more coils on the secondary coil than the primary coil.
> In a step-down transformer there are fewer coils on the secondary coil than the primary coil.

3 Explain why a step-up transformer produces a low current.

....

....

.... **(2 marks)**

> $P = IV$. Hence if the potential difference increases, assuming
> there are no power losses, the current must decrease.

4 The potential difference entering the transformer supplying current to a laptop battery is 230 V with a current of 1 A. The laptop battery states that the output potential difference is 19 V. Calculate the output current and state whether this is a step-up or step-down transformer.

V_p = 230 V, I_p = 1 A, V_s = 19 V. $V_p \times I_p = V_s \times I_s$ ....

....

....

.... **(2 marks)**

> In order to rearrange the equation, just divide both sides by V_s.

5 Explain why step-down transformers are necessary before electricity from the national grid can be used in your home.

Electricity is transported through the national grid at very high potential difference.

....

.... **(2 marks)**

6 A transformer has an output potential difference of 575 V and an output current of 2 A. It is connected to mains electricity of 230 V. Calculate the input current.

....

....

.... **(2 marks)**

Extended response – Electromagnetic induction

Discuss how electromagnetic induction is used in a dynamo.

In your answer you should:

- Describe how a dynamo works
- Compare the dynamo to an a.c. generator
- Discuss advantages and disadvantages of using a dynamo on your bicycle to power the lights.

You can use a diagram to illustrate your answer.

> You can gain marks for good layout, grammar and spelling. Take a moment to make sure you have a good plan and that you know how to spell all of the keywords.
>
> In your answer, you could think about the following:
>
> - What is the purpose of a dynamo on a bicycle? Describe how it works. You will need to describe the process of electromagnetic induction in a dynamo.
>
> - The question gives you a clue in that you need to give differences between a dynamo and a simple a.c. generator.
>
> - For the last part of the question, think about a bicycle moving and stopping – what effect will this have on the lights?

....

....

....

....

....

....

....

....

....

....

....

....

....

....

....

....

....

....

.... **(6 marks)**

Changes of state

1 A sample of krypton takes up the volume of its container. The particles are moving around randomly and do not touch. Which physical state is the sample in?

.... **(1 mark)**

2 Describe the arrangement of particles in solids.

In a solid the particles are arranged in fixed positions in an ordered lattice. They

vibrate ....

.... **(3 marks)**

3 Describe the properties of liquids and explain these using the particle model.

....

....

....

.... **(3 marks)**

> In a liquid the particles can slide past each other and are not in fixed positions. What properties does this result in?

4 Name and explain the state change from a solid to a liquid.

Melting is caused by heating the solid. ....

.... **(3 marks)**

5 Explain why condensation is an exothermic process.

....

....

.... **(2 marks)**

> Exothermic means that the process gives energy to the environment.

6 The boiling point of oxygen is –218 °C. Describe the movement and arrangement of particles in oxygen at room temperature (25 °C).

....

....

....

.... **(3 marks)**

> The boiling point is the temperature at which a substance turns into a gas. Since this is well below room temperature for oxygen, it will be a gas.

7 Explain why particles in a liquid can move around, but those in a solid cannot.

....

....

....

.... **(3 marks)**

Density

1 Define the term density.

....

.... **(1 mark)**

2 A 70 000 cm³ sample of oxygen contained a mass of 98 g of oxygen. Calculate the density of oxygen. State the unit.

Mass = 98 g, volume = 70 000 cm³ ....

.... **(3 marks)**

> The equation for density is: $density = \frac{mass}{volume}$. You need to learn this equation as it is not on the equation sheet.

3 An old iron tool was found to have a volume of 6.35 cm³. The density of iron is 7.87 g/cm³. Calculate the mass of this tool.

Density = 7.87 g/cm³, volume = 6.35 cm³ ....

....

.... **(2 marks)**

> You can easily rearrange the equation using this triangle: $\frac{mass}{density \times volume}$.

4 Density changes when a material changes state.

(a) Explain why a liquid is usually denser than the gas of the same material.

When the liquid is warmed, it expands. ....

....

.... **(3 marks)**

(b) Ice is special in that it is less dense than liquid water. Explain why this is unexpected.

Usually a solid is denser than the liquid. This is because ....

....

.... **(3 marks)**

> Ice actually has a larger volume than water. You can try this out – put a container filled with water into the freezer and mark the water level. Check the level when the water is frozen.

5 An artist wants to obtain the volume of a piece of oak, but does not have any equipment to hand to measure the volume. She knows that oak has a density of 0.8 g/cm³. She weighs the piece of wood and finds it has a mass of 20 g. Calculate the volume of the piece of wood.

....

....

....

.... **(2 marks)**

Investigating density

1 A London brick has the following dimensions: length 21.5 cm, height 10.25 cm and depth 6.5 cm. It has a mass of 2800 g. Calculate the density of the brick.

Volume = 21.5 cm × 10.25 cm × 6.5 cm = ...

.... **(3 marks)**

> • The equation for density is: $density = \frac{mass}{volume}$. You need to learn this equation as it is not on the equation sheet.
> • Volume is calculated using: $volume = length \times height \times depth$.

2 A student wants to identify a stone he found in his father's stone collection. He found a list of densities for various materials, as shown in the table.

(a) Describe how he should measure the mass of the stone.

....

....

....

....

Material	Density (g/cm³)
Apatite	3.1
Feldspar	2.55
Gypsum	2.3
Halite	2.16
Hematite	5.26
Olivine	3.27
Pyrite	5.02
Quartz	2.65
Sphalerite	3.9

(1 mark)

(b) Describe a method by which he could measure the volume.

Fill a measuring cylinder to a certain volume with water. Carefully drop the stone into

the water. ....

....

.... **(3 marks)**

(c) The mass was found to be 50 g and the volume was 19 cm³. Calculate the density and identify the stone.

....

....

.... **(3 marks)**

3 Describe how the volume of a liquid can be measured.

Use a measuring cylinder and read off the level from the bottom of the .... **(2 marks)**

4 The diagram shows a brick of a material.

The brick has been subdivided into cubes with sides of 1 cm each. Each cube has a density of 3 g/cm³. Calculate the mass of the whole brick.

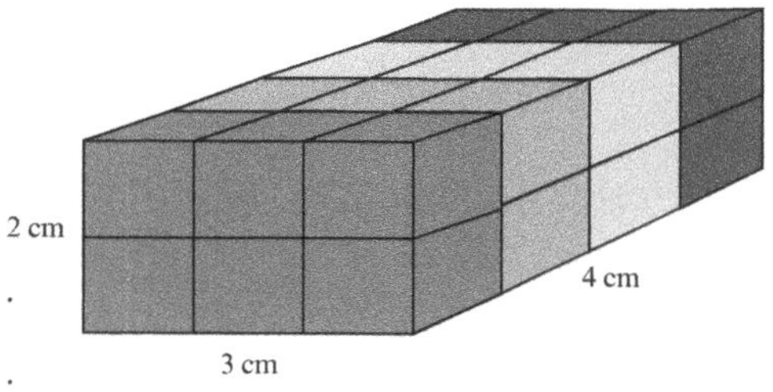

2 cm　3 cm　4 cm

....

....

.... **(2 marks)**

> You should be able to realise that the whole brick will have the same density as density is a property of a material. This does not change when you have a bigger or smaller shape of the same material.

Energy and changes of state

1 Water has a specific heat capacity of 4200 J/kg °C. State what specific heat capacity means.

It is the thermal energy that is required to raise the temperature of 1 kg of a material

by .... **(1 mark)**

2 Describe the difference between the specific latent heat of fusion and the specific latent heat of vaporisation.

Latent heat of fusion is the energy needed to convert 1 kg of ....

....

.... **(2 marks)**

3 Calculate the energy required to raise the temperature of 2 kg of water from 25 °C to 95 °C. Water has a specific heat capacity of 4200 J/kg °C.

Mass = 2 kg, specific heat capacity = 4200 J/kg °C, change in temperature =

95 − 25 = ...

.... **(2 marks)**

> The equation to use is $\Delta Q = mc\Delta\theta$. Δ means 'change in'.

4 Explain why calculations of specific latent heat never involve a temperature change.

....

....

....

.... **(2 marks)**

> Think about what specific latent heat describes. Does the temperature change?

5 The specific latent heat of fusion of water is 334 000 J/kg. 16 700 J of energy were used to melt some ice. Calculate the mass of the water produced and convert this to the volume in cm³ (1 g = 1 cm³).

Q = 16 700 J, L = 334 000 J/kg, mass = ...

....

.... **(3 marks)**

> The equation to use is: $Q = mL$. Divide both sides by L to calculate the mass.

6 The specific heat capacity of lead is 128 J/kg °C. 10 g of lead at 25 °C is supplied with 32 kJ of energy. Calculate the new temperature of the sample of lead.

> Guided

....

....

....

.... **(3 marks)**

Thermal properties of water

1 A student sets up an experiment to measure the specific heat capacity of water as shown.

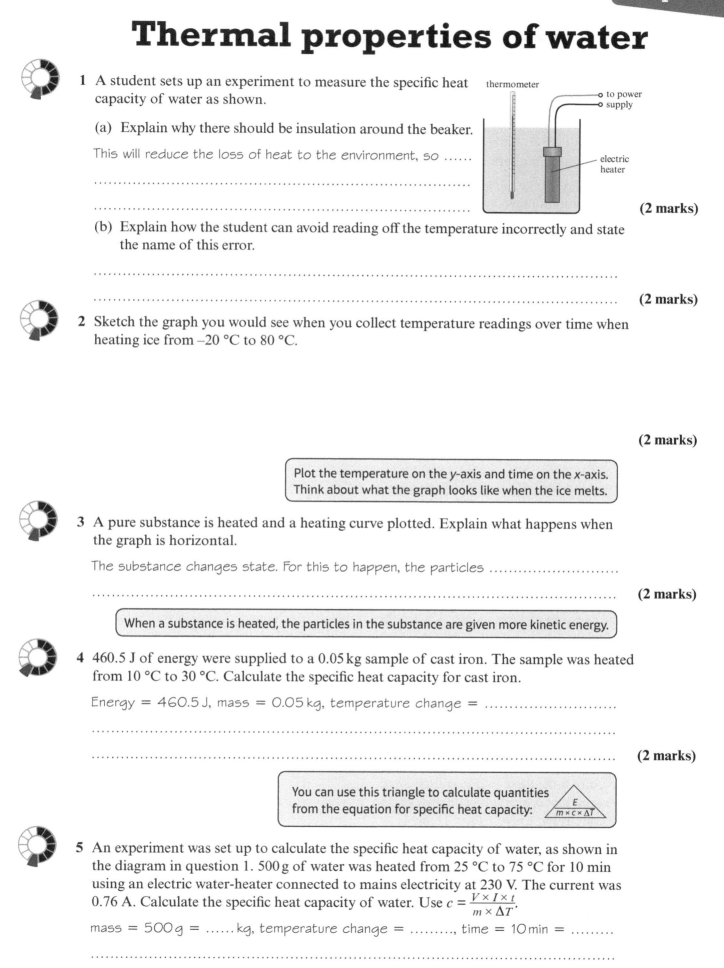

thermometer

to power supply

electric heater

(a) Explain why there should be insulation around the beaker.

This will reduce the loss of heat to the environment, so ......

....

.... **(2 marks)**

(b) Explain how the student can avoid reading off the temperature incorrectly and state the name of this error.

....

.... **(2 marks)**

2 Sketch the graph you would see when you collect temperature readings over time when heating ice from –20 °C to 80 °C.

(2 marks)

> Plot the temperature on the *y*-axis and time on the *x*-axis.
> Think about what the graph looks like when the ice melts.

3 A pure substance is heated and a heating curve plotted. Explain what happens when the graph is horizontal.

The substance changes state. For this to happen, the particles ....

.... **(2 marks)**

> When a substance is heated, the particles in the substance are given more kinetic energy.

4 460.5 J of energy were supplied to a 0.05 kg sample of cast iron. The sample was heated from 10 °C to 30 °C. Calculate the specific heat capacity for cast iron.

Energy = 460.5 J, mass = 0.05 kg, temperature change = ...

....

.... **(2 marks)**

> You can use this triangle to calculate quantities from the equation for specific heat capacity:
> $\frac{E}{m \times c \times \Delta T}$

5 An experiment was set up to calculate the specific heat capacity of water, as shown in the diagram in question 1. 500 g of water was heated from 25 °C to 75 °C for 10 min using an electric water-heater connected to mains electricity at 230 V. The current was 0.76 A. Calculate the specific heat capacity of water. Use $c = \frac{V \times I \times t}{m \times \Delta T}$.

mass = 500 g = ... kg, temperature change = ..., time = 10 min = ...

....

.... **(3 marks)**

Had a go ☐   Nearly there ☐   Nailed it! ☐

Pressure and temperature

1 A balloon is filled with gas. Describe how gas pressure is created.

The particles inside the balloon move around randomly and ....

.... **(2 marks)**

2 This question is about the effect of temperature on gas pressure.

(a) Describe how the gas pressure changes with increasing temperature and state the assumption made.

Provided that the volume stays constant, when the temperature increases, ...

.... **(2 marks)**

(b) Explain why you expect to see the effect of temperature on gas pressure that you described in (a).

As temperature increases, the gas particles move faster, so ....

.... **(3 marks)**

3 Describe the movement of the particles in a gas at absolute zero.

Absolute zero is the temperature of −273 °C ....

.... **(2 marks)**

> A substance will be a solid at absolute zero.

4 Carry out the following conversions:

> From Celsius to Kelvin: add 273 to the temperature in °C. From Kelvin to Celsius: take away 273 from the temperature in K.

(a) 15 °C = ... K

(b) 100 °C = ... K

(c) 450 K = ... °C

(d) 273 K = ... °C **(4 marks)**

5 The pressure of a gas increases when the temperature is increased, provided that the volume is kept constant. Using the kinetic particle model, describe how the pressure would be affected if the temperature was kept the same, but the volume was decreased.

The particles would have less space to move around and would collide with the

surface of the container ....

....

.... **(3 marks)**

6 Pressure is the force that is exerted on an area. Use this information to calculate the pressure that is exerted on an area of 5 m^2 by a gas with a force of 25 N (the unit for pressure is Pa, where 1 Pa = 1 N/m^2).

Area = 5 m^2, force = 25 N ....

.... **(3 marks)**

> You can work out the equation to calculate this from the information given in the question. Units are very helpful to help you work out what you have to do. 1 Pa = 1 N/m^2, so $pressure = \frac{force}{area}$.

Extended response – Particle model

1   Water has a specific heat capacity of 4200 J/kg °C. Describe how the specific heat capacity could have been obtained.

> You will have done this experiment in class. When describing a process or experiment, but also for other long answers, it is important to lay out your answer in a logical way. Make a short plan before starting to write to make sure all the steps are in a logical order.

Put an electric heater in an insulated beaker, attach a power source and connect a

voltmeter and an ammeter. ....

....

....

....

....

....

....

....

....

....

....

....

....

....

....

....

....

....

....

....

....

....

....

....

.... **(6 marks)**

Elastic and inelastic distortion

1 Describe how two forces can stretch an object.

Two forces must act in opposite directions to each other.   **(1 mark)**

2 Explain why an elastic band is elastically distorted up to a certain limit. Describe what happens past this limit.

If you pull the elastic band and stretch it, it becomes longer. Then when you let go,

....

....

....   **(3 marks)**

3 State the name for the type of distortion when the object is deformed, but does not return to its original shape.

Guided

....   **(1 mark)**

4 Describe when an object is inelastically distorted.

An object is inelastically distorted when ....

....   **(2 marks)**

> Inelastic distortion is when an object is distorted past a certain point (the elastic limit) and does not return to its original shape when the forces acting on it are removed.

5 Describe the relationship between the force and the extension of a spring while it is elastically distorted.

....   **(1 mark)**

> Up to the elastic limit, the graph plotting force against extension of the spring is linear through the origin. What is this relationship called?

6 Draw a diagram to show the forces required to compress an object.

The student has starting drawing the diagram. Can you complete it?   **(2 marks)**

7 List **one** example of a material that is elastically distorted and one example of a material that is inelastically distorted. Explain the difference between elastic and inelastic distortion.

Elastic bands can be elastically deformed. They return to their original shape when

the deforming forces are removed. ....

....   **(4 marks)**

8 Cars contain materials that can deform either elastically or inelastically. Give **two** examples of materials in a car that improve the safety in case of an accident, and describe how they are designed to reduce the impact of an accident.

Guided

....

....   **(2 marks)**

228

Springs

1 Which is the correct relationship between force, spring constant and extension? Tick **one** box.

> **Guided**

☐ **A** $F = k \times x^2$

☐ **B** $F = k \times x$

☐ **C** $F = \dfrac{k}{x}$

☐ **D** $F = \dfrac{x}{k}$

(1 mark)

2 A spring is extended by 5 cm. The spring constant of the spring is 25 N/m. Calculate the force that distorted the spring.

Extension = 5 cm = ..., spring constant = 25 N/m ....

....

(2 marks)

> You need to learn the equation: force = spring constant × extension. It is not on the equation sheet. Remember that the extension is in metres.

3 A spring was extended by a force of 50 N past the elastic limit. The spring constant of the spring was 2 N/m. Comment on the extension of the spring.

You cannot calculate the extension of the spring as it has gone past the ....

....

....

(3 marks)

4 Sketch the force–extension graph for a spring.

> **Guided**

(3 marks)

5 A student is given a force–extension graph. Describe how they can calculate the elastic potential energy stored in the spring.

The energy stored in the spring is the area ....

....

(2 marks)

6 Calculate the work done when a spring with a spring constant of 0.5 N/m is extended by 30 cm.

Spring constant = 0.5 N/m, extension = 30 cm = ...m ....

....

....

(2 marks)

> The equation is: work done = ½ × spring constant × extension². Remember to square the extension!

Forces and springs

1 An experiment was set up to calculate the work done on a spring by a force. A spring was attached to a retort stand via a boss clamp. Name a safety hazard and a precaution you need to take before starting the experiment.

The spring could snap and hurt someone ....

.... **(2 marks)**

2 Describe **one** difference between weight and mass.

Weight is a force, ...

.... **(1 mark)**

3 The table shows the lengths of a spring and the mass of the weights that were attached to the spring.

(a) Complete the table.

Length of spring (mm)	Extension of spring (mm)	Mass (g)	Weight (N)
50	0	0	0
60		100	1
70		200	
80		300	

(5 marks)

> • Weight = mass × gravitational field strength. Remember that mass has to be converted to kg for the calculation and that the gravitational field strength on Earth is 10 N/kg.
> • Extension = length of spring – original length at zero extension.

(b) Evaluate if this spring has gone past the elastic limit or not.

No, because ....

.... **(2 marks)**

4 A spring has a spring constant of 5 N/m. The energy transferred to extend the spring was 5 J. Calculate the extension of the spring.

Spring constant = 5 N/m, energy = 5 J ....

.... **(2 marks)**

> Work done = ½ × k × e². To calculate e, divide both sides by ½ × k and take the square root of the whole expression: $e = \sqrt{\frac{2 \times E}{k}}$

5 Calculate the spring constant of a spring that was extended by 5 cm by an energy transfer of 0.5 J.

....

....

.... **(2 marks)**

Extended response – Forces and matter

Newton meters use springs to measure a force. Using your knowledge of springs, explain how a newton meter measures a force and explain why each type of newton meter can only measure a certain range of forces up to a certain limit.

> You should think about how newton meters work in your answer. The extension of the spring inside is converted to the force – so which property of the spring determines the range of forces the newton meter can measure and why?

....

....

....

....

....

....

....

....

....

....

....

....

....

....

....

....

....

....

....

....

....

....

....

.... **(6 marks)**

Answers

Biology

1. Plant and animal cells

1 C **(1)**

2 D **(1)**

3 (a) 1 Cell membrane **(1)**, 2 Ribosome **(1)**
3 Nucleus **(1)**, 4 Mitochondria **(1)**

(b) 1 The cell membrane controls the movements of substances into and out of the cell. **(1)**
2 The ribosomes are where proteins are made (protein synthesis takes place). **(1)**
3 The nucleus controls all the activities of the cell and contains the genetic material/DNA. **(1)**
4 The mitochondria are where cellular respiration takes place, releasing energy for the cell. **(1)**

4 (a) A chloroplast is an organelle in a plant cell which absorbs light for photosynthesis. **(1)**

(b) Root cell **(1)**. It does not have chloroplasts because the roots are underground so there is no light **(1)** and they don't photosynthesise. **(1)**

2. Different kinds of cell

1 Bacterial cell: cell membrane, plasmid DNA, ribosomes, cell wall **(1)** Plant cell: cell membrane, nucleus, mitochondria, ribosomes, cell wall **(1)**

2 (a) A Cytoplasm **(1)**   B Mitochondria **(1)**

(b) A The nutrients in the cytoplasm provide the egg with the nutrients it needs to start dividing if it is fertilised. **(1)**
B The mitochondria provide the energy needed for the sperm to swim towards the egg. **(1)**

(c) The egg cell **(1)**

(d) The egg needs to be big to contain the nutrients and all the structures needed to grow and divide after fertilisation. **(1)**
The sperm are small because they need to be able to swim through the female reproductive system. **(1)**

3 In non-smokers the ciliated epithelial cells move mucus containing trapped bacteria, viruses, dust and dirt away from the lungs to be removed from the body **(1)**. This prevents many pathogens getting into the body **(1)**. If the ciliated epithelial cells are not working, pathogens get into the lungs where they can cause infectious diseases. **(1)**

3. Microscopes and magnification

1 D **(1)**

2 (a) Image X **(1)**

(b) This cell does not have a nucleus, it has a single chromosome, but cell Y has a nucleus **(1)**. Eukaryotic cells have a nucleus and prokaryotic cells do not **(1)**. This cell is an order of magnitude smaller than cell Y **(1)**. Prokaryotic cells are much smaller than eukaryotic cells. **(1)**

(c) $2.5 \, cm = 25 \, mm = 25\,000 \, \mu m$ **(1)**
Magnification $= \frac{\text{image size}}{\text{real size}} = \frac{25\,000}{10}$ **(1)** $= \times 2500$ **(1)**

3 (a) Resolution is the smallest distance between two points that can still be seen as two separate points. **(1)**

(b) They have a much higher magnification **(1)** and much higher resolution. **(1)**

4 (a) $5 \times 40 = \times 200$ magnification **(1)**

(b) Any three from: one uses light to form the image, the other uses a beam of electrons **(1)** electron microscope has greater magnification than light microscope **(1)** electron microscope has greater resolution than light microscope **(1)** can only view living specimens under light microscope **(1)** any other valid observation

4. Dealing with numbers

1 D **(1)**

2 (a) 1000 nanometres = 1 micrometre **(1)**

(b) 1000 micrograms = 1 milligram **(1)**

(c) 0.000000000001 metres = 1 picometre **(1)**

3 (a) $10\times$

(b) $0.1 \, mm$

(c) (i) $1500 \, g$
(ii) $1500/0.5 = 3000\times$

4 (a) It allows us to work out the approximate size of the real object **(1)**

(b) Approximately 15 chloroplasts across the cell **(1)**. Cell is $100 \, \mu m$ long **(1)**, so chloroplasts are approximately $100/15 = 7 \, \mu m$ **(1)**

5. Using a light microscope

1 (a) A the eyepiece lens **(1)**   B the objective lens **(1)** C the stage for the specimens **(1)**

(b) You multiply the magnification of the eyepiece lens by the magnification of the objective lens to give the overall magnification (eyepiece lens × objective lens). **(1)**

(c) Never point the mirror directly at the Sun **(1)** because it could burn or damage your eyes. **(1)**

(d) Never use the coarse focusing wheel with a high power lens **(1)** as it moves the lens too much and may break the slide or damage the lens. **(1)**

2 (a) Add a drop of named stain to the drop of water so the cells show up more clearly. **(1)**
Lower the coverslip slowly and carefully to avoid trapping air bubbles which form black circles on the slide, making it harder to see the cells. **(1)**

(b) Put the low power lens in place. **(1)**
Clip the slide securely to the stage of the microscope using the clips provided. **(1)**
Adjust the light source so light goes up through the slide (NEVER point the mirror directly at the Sun). **(1)**
Look down the microscope, using the coarse focusing wheel and then the fine focusing wheel to focus on the slide. **(1)**

6. Drawing labelled diagrams

1 So that if you make a mistake you can rub it out carefully and redraw it **(1)**

2 (a) Two from: It is drawn in pencil **(1)**; it is clearly labelled **(1)**; it has a title **(1)**

(b) It does not focus on just one cell from the centre of the image (all the cells are drawn in detail) **(1)**; it does not have a scale bar **(1)**

(c) Single cell drawn in detail **(1)**
Clean, sharp pencil lines **(1)**
Clear labels **(1)**
Scale bar **(1)**

3 Single cell drawn in detail **(1)**
Clean, sharp pencil lines **(1)**
Clear labels **(1)**
Scale bar **(1)**

7. Enzymes

1 (a) An enzyme is a biological catalyst which increases the rate of chemical reactions in the body. **(1)**
   (b) Proteins **(1)**
   (c) A active site **(1)**; B substrate **(1)**; C product **(1)**
   (d) The shape of the active site matches the shape of the substrate molecules and holds them close together so they react more easily **(1)**. Once the product is formed it no longer fits the active site and so it moves away **(1)**. The shape of the active site of an enzyme only fits the shape of specific substrates so the enzyme will only catalyse specific reactions. **(1)**

2 A At lower temperatures molecules move relatively slowly so substrate molecules take more time to fit into the active site of the enzyme and the reaction rate is relatively slow. **(1)**
   B At the optimum temperature substrate molecules are binding to the active site as fast as the enzymes can process them so they are working as fast as they can. **(1)**
   C At higher temperatures the protein structure of the enzyme is affected and the active site starts to change shape. It can't bind to the substrate as well so the rate of reaction starts to decline. **(1)**
   D At very high temperatures the shape of the active site is destroyed, the enzyme is denatured and can no longer catalyse the reaction. **(1)**

8. pH and enzyme activity

1 (a)

pH	Volume of gas produced in 5 mins (cm³)	Rate of catalase reaction (cm³ oxygen/minute)
4	0	0
5	5	1
6	20	**4**
7	**15**	3
8	2	**0.4**

(3)

(b)

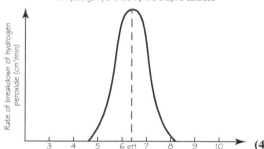

Graph to show the effect of pH on the breakdown of hydrogen peroxide by the enzyme catalase

(4)

(c) Keep the temperature of the reacting mixture constant as temperature also affects the rate of enzyme reactions. **(1)**

9. The importance of enzymes

1 (a) Break down large, complex molecules into small molecules **(1)** which can be absorbed into the blood **(1)**
   (b)

Enzyme	Where it is found in humans	Reaction catalysed
amylase	Saliva and the small intestine	Breaking down starch into small sugars
catalase	Most cells especially liver	Breaking down hydrogen peroxide into water and oxygen
protease	Stomach, small intestine	Breaking down proteins to amino acids
lipase	Small intestine	Breaking down lipids into fatty acids and glycerol

(4)

2 The enzyme catalyses (speeds up) **(1)** the synthesis (building up) of large DNA molecules from smaller subunits **(1)**

3 Food contains proteins (in egg, meat, etc.), lipids in fatty foods and carbohydrates (starches) **(1)**. If these food molecules get stuck on plates, the enzymes will break them down into small, soluble molecules which will be washed off in the water. **(1)**

4 (a) Digesting food molecules in the digestive system **(1)**;
       building up and breaking down molecules in the cells **(1)**
   (b) All reactions in the body controlled by enzymes **(1)**
       Enzymes are proteins and are affected by temperature **(1)**
       Body temperature low – substrate molecules moving more slowly, bind to active sites more slowly – reactions of body become too slow **(1)**
       High temperatures – the active site changes shape so substrate molecules either bind less well or won't bind at all – reactions slow down or stop **(1)**

10. Getting in and out of cells

1 C **(1)**
2 (a) The net movement of molecules from an area of high concentration to an area of low concentration **(1)** down a concentration gradient **(1)**
   (b) Osmosis is a type of diffusion **(1)**. It involves the net movement of water molecules across a partially permeable membrane/It is the diffusion of water molecules down a concentration gradient, through a semi-permeable membrane. **(1)**

3 The process is called osmosis **(1)**. More water molecules crossed the partially permeable **(1)** Visking tubing into the tubing than moved the other way **(1)**. This gave a net movement of water into the bag, so the level in the tube rose and the bag became fuller **(1)**.

4 (a) They are all methods of transport in cells **(1)**
   (b) Active transport requires energy from respiration **(1)** to move molecules against a concentration gradient **(1)**. The other two processes are passive and do not need energy from respiration to move substances down a concentration gradient. **(1)**

11. Osmosis in potatoes

1 (a) C Blot a piece of potato dry, measure and record its mass, then place it into one of the tubes, recording which tube **(1)**. Repeat for all tubes. **(1)**
       D After 20 minutes, remove the pieces of potato, blot them dry and remeasure the mass **(1)**. Record all the final masses, making sure you know exactly which piece of potato was in which tube. **(1)**
   (b) It removes surface water **(1)** and so helps to increase the accuracy and reliability of the results **(1)**

ANSWERS

2 (a)

Solute concentration (mol dm⁻³)	Initial mass (g)	Final mass (g)	Change in mass (g)	Percentage change in mass (%)
0.0	16.52	20.15	3.63	21.97
0.2	15.90	16.70	0.8	5.03
0.4	17.06	15.69	−1.37	−8.03
0.6	16.88	14.36	−2.52	−14.93
0.8	16.23	12.32	−3.91	−24.09

(2)

(b) (i) Look for clear labels and title, sensible scale, well drawn graph **(3)**

(ii) Approximately 0.28 mol dm⁻³ **(1)**

12. Extended response – Key concepts

Answers could include the following points **(6)**

• Collect five test tubes and fill with the different strength sugar solutions and one with water, using the same volume of liquid for each
• Label the tubes
• Cut five equal cylinders of sweet potato, dry and record the mass of each/cut cylinders into small sections/ measure the length and diameter of each/any other sensible suggestion and place one into each of the tubes
• Dry them to remove surface water and increase accuracy and reliability of results
• Make sure you record which cylinder went into which tube
• After 20–30 minutes remove the pieces of sweet potato, blot them dry and remeasure them
• Record all the final masses – making sure you know which cylinder was in which tube
• Plot the results on a graph – should show when the external solution is the same concentration as the cell contents and show that water moves by osmosis more when the concentration difference is greater

13. Mitosis

1 C **(1)**

2 (a) They have two sets of chromosomes **(1)**
(b) They get one set of chromosomes from the mother and one from the father **(1)**
(c) They are both identical to the parent cell **(1)**

3 (a) A prophase **(1)**   D telophase **(1)**
B metaphase **(1)**   E cytokinesis **(1)**
C anaphase **(1)**

(b) In stage A the nucleus starts to break down around the chromosome copies and spindle fibres appear **(1)**. In stage C the chromosome copies are separated and move to either end of the cell on the spindle fibres **(1)**. In stage E new nuclear membranes have formed around the chromosomes to make two new nuclei, and a cell surface membrane forms to separate the two cells **(1)** giving two genetically identical daughter cells. **(1)**

14. Cell growth and differentiation

1 D **(1)**

2 (a) zygote **(1)**
(b) Mitosis **(1)** – so all the cells of the new organism are genetically identical **(1)**
(c) The cells differentiate to form different types of specialised cells **(1)**. This is important because different types of cells are needed to do different jobs in the body. **(1)**

3 Cancer is the result of changes, in cells, which leads to uncontrolled cell division **(1)** and the formation of tumours **(1)**. If the noni fruit interferes with the stages of mitosis **(1)** it might be useful as a drug to stop uncontrolled mitosis (cell division) in cancer. **(1)**

4 (a) The region near the tip of a root or shoot where unspecialised cells are found and where cell division/mitosis takes place **(1)**
(b) Elongation **(1)** and differentiation **(1)**
(c) e.g. red blood cell has no nucleus to give more room for oxygen-carrying haemoglobin molecules **(1)**, and a large surface area for maximum diffusion of gases **(1)** e.g. xylem cell – loss of cell contents and end walls to make a hollow tube for water movement **(1)**, spiral lignin walls for strength and to withstand pressure. **(1)**

15. Growth and percentile charts

1 (a) A permanent increase in size **(1)**
(b) Increase in length/height **(1)**; increase in mass **(1)**

2 (a) (i) 1500 − 245 = 1 255 g (units must be given) **(1)**
(ii) 1950 − 250 = 1 700 g **(1)**
(b) (i) (1255/245) × 100 **(1)** = 512% **(1)**
(ii) (1700/250) × 100 **(1)** = 680% **(1)**
(c) 680 − 512 = 168% **(1)**
(d) The plants in set B are grown at 20 °C which is 10 degrees warmer than the other set. An increase in temperature means the reactions take place faster **(1)** and so the plants make more food and grow faster. **(1)**

3 (a) Growth **(1)**   (b) 75th percentile **(1)**
(c) That it is not growing properly – it is either too heavy or too light **(1)**

16. Stem cells

1 B **(1)**

2 (a) Unspecialised cells which divide to produce many different types of cell **(1)**
(b) Embryonic stem cells and meristem cells can both produce any type of cell needed in the organism **(1)** Embryonic stem cells are found in animals, meristem cells are found in plants **(1)**
(c) Embryonic stem cells and meristem cells can form any body cell **(1)**, but adult stem cells can only form a limited number of cell types. **(1)**

3 (a) Replacing or repairing damaged cells in the body, e.g. in the brain to treat Parkinson's, in the retina to reverse blindness **(1)** Growing new tissues in the lab to use for transplants or drugs testing **(1)**
(b) Stem cells are good at dividing. Sometimes they do not stop dividing and so may cause cancer in a patient instead of making them better. **(1)** An early human embryo is destroyed when the stem cells are removed. Some people think this is wrong and that the embryo has a right to life. **(1)**

4 The adult stem cells used in human medicine are usually extracted from the patient or from a willing donor, so no embryos are destroyed in the process **(1)**. This removes the ethical issue of using human embryos for some people **(1)**. Also, using adult stem cells extracted from the patient themselves removes any problems of tissue rejection **(1)**. In theory means it will be safer for the patient and avoids the need to take lifelong anti-rejection/immunosuppressant medication. **(1)**

17. Neurones

1 (a) A specialised cell that carries electrical impulses/ nervous impulses **(1)**
(b) Motor neurones carry impulses away from the central nervous system to effector organs **(1)** Sensory neurones carry impulses to the central nervous system **(1)** Relay neurones are found only in the central nervous system linking neurones in the CNS **(1)**

2 (a) A – Nerve ending, B – axon, C – myelin sheath, D – dendrite **(2)**

(b) (i) Part B carries the electrical impulse over long distances around the body **(1)**

(ii) Part C insulates the neurone **(1)**, making the impulse jump along the axon, speeding up transmission of the impulse. **(1)**

3

Motor neurone	Sensory neurone	Relay neurone
Impulse travels away from CNS	Impulse travels towards CNS	Impulse travels within CNS
Cell body at one end	Cell body between the axon and the dendron	Cell body central
Has sensory receptor at one end	Has nerve endings in an effector at one end	Links only to other neurones

(3)

4 (a) Electrical impulses from the receptor cells in the eye are transmitted through sensory neurones to the brain which processes the impulses and you see the fruit **(1)**. The brain sends impulses through the motor neurones to the muscles of the arm and hand **(1)**. When the effectors receive the impulses, they contract and you pick up the fruit. **(1)**

(b) The myelin sheaths protect the neurones **(1)** and they make the transmission of the electrical impulse faster **(1)**. As the myelin sheath is lost, the signals weaken and travel more slowly until eventually the signals do not reach the muscles, so they cannot contract. **(1)**

18. Responding to stimuli

1 (a) A gap between two neurones **(1)**

(b) A An electrical impulse travels along the neurone and reaches the end **(1)**, causing a chemical neurotransmitter to be released from vesicles in the neurone into the synapse (gap). **(1)**

B The neurotransmitter diffuses across the synapse/gap **(1)** and fits into the receptors on the membrane of the neurone on the other side. **(1)**

C A new electrical impulse starts up and travels along the second neurone. **(1)**

2 They allow new impulses to be generated in many neurones connected to the one initial neurone **(1)**, they make sure impulses only flow in one direction along a neurone **(1)**

3 (a) Automatic, very rapid response to a stimulus **(1)**

(b) Reflex arcs only involve three neurones **(1)**. If the impulses went to the conscious areas of the brain to be processed it would involve many more synapses which would slow the response down. **(1)**

(c) They protect the body from harmful stimuli **(1)** They allow basic functions of the body such as breathing to take place without conscious thought **(1)**

4 Stimulus (e.g. pinprick) → sensory receptor in skin → impulse in sensory neurone to synapse in spinal cord → synapse with relay neurone in spinal cord → impulse travels along relay neurone to synapse → synapse with motor neurone in spinal cord → impulse travels along motor neurone to effector (e.g. muscle in arm) → muscle contracts to move away from pinprick **(4)**

19. Extended response – Cells and control

Answers could include the following points **(6)**

• Motor neurones carry electrical impulses from the central nervous system to the muscles. The impulse causes a neurotransmitter to cross the synapse from the end of the axon of the motor nerve to the muscle cells.

• When these neurotransmitter chemicals reach the muscle cells they stimulate them to contract. Muscle contraction causes many different responses in the body – for example, they move the limbs so an animal can move around and move the ribs so an animal can breathe.

• Synapses are tiny gaps between two neurones or between a motor neurone and a muscle cell (effector). When an electrical impulse arrives at the end of the axon of the motor nerve, it causes a chemical transmitter to be released from vesicles in the neurone into the gap between the neurone and the muscle cell.

• The neurotransmitter diffuses across the gap and fits into receptors in the membrane of the muscle cell, and this stimulates it to contract.

• The poison curare binds to the receptors in the synapse between a motor neurone and a muscle cell.

• As a result, when an impulse travels down the motor nerve and causes the neurotransmitter to be released into the synapse, the neurotransmitter cannot bind to the receptors on the muscle cell. They are already taken up with curare. So, the nerves cannot stimulate the muscle cells, the muscle cells cannot contract and the animal is paralysed. Because the breathing muscles are also paralysed, the animal will die.

20. Meiosis

1 A and B **(1)**

2 (a) Diploid means a cell has two sets of chromosomes and haploid means a cell has one set of chromosomes **(1)**

(b) Because two gametes join together to form a new diploid cell **(1)**

(c) The original cell is diploid, but the daughter cells are haploid. **(1)**

3 Cell A is the cell which is going to divide to make the gametes. It is diploid – it has two sets of chromosomes **(1)**. The chromosomes replicate (make copies of themselves) and the copies stay stuck together (see Stage B) **(1)**. The cell divides in two, rather like mitosis, producing two cells with two sets of chromosomes (Stage C) **(1)**. Then these two cells immediately divide again. Each of the final four daughter cells is haploid/has only one set of chromosomes (Stage D). **(1)**

21. DNA

1 C **(1)**

2 A chromosome consists of a long molecule of DNA tightly coiled up and held together by proteins **(1)** A gene is a section of DNA which codes for a protein **(1)** DNA is the genetic material making up the chromosomes in the nuclei of cells **(1)**

3 (a) double helix **(1)**

(b) A phosphate groups **(1)**
B sugar **(1)**
C complementary base pairs **(1)**

(c) X is a hydrogen bond **(1)**. Hydrogen bonds are formed when the slightly negative charged part of one base is attracted to the slightly positive part of another base **(1)**. These weak forces of attraction hold the DNA molecule together. **(1)**

4 (a) It is made up of many monomers/small units joined together **(1)**

(b) The same bases always link together, e.g. A with T **(1)**

(c) Complementary base to adenine is thymine (T) **(1)** and to guanine is cytosine (C) **(1)**

(d) DNA makes up the chromosomes which are held inside the nucleus of the cell **(1)**. Both the nucleus and the cell are surrounded by membranes **(1)** so to extract the DNA from the nucleus you need to use detergent break open both the cell and nuclear membranes. **(1)**

22. Genetic terms

1 Base, allele, gene, chromosome, genome **(2)**

2 (a) A short piece of DNA on a chromosome which codes for a particular characteristic **(1)**

   (b) Alleles are different forms of the same gene **(1)**, which code for different variations of the same characteristic. **(1)**

3 (a)

	b	b
B	Bb	Bb
b	bb	bb

(1)

   (b) Genotype: the alleles present in an organism for a particular characteristic **(1)**

   (c) Bb **(1)**

   (d) (i) B **(1)**   (ii) b **(1)**

   (e) B **(1)**

   (f) (i) Phenotype: the characteristics of an individual as a result of its genotype, including its physical appearance **(1)**

      (ii) Recessive allele: the characteristic coded for only appears in the phenotype if two copies of the allele are present in the genotype **(1)**

4 (a) Homozygous, round **(1)**

   (b) Homozygous, wrinkled **(1)**

   (c) Heterozygous, round **(1)**

23. Monohybrid inheritance

1 (a) ½ of the kittens will have the genotype Tt and so their phenotype will be Manx/tailess. This is 2/4 × 100 = 50% **(3)**

	T	t
t	Tt	tt
t	Tt	tt

   (b) Manx cat genotype Tt

	T	t
T	TT	Tt
t	Tt	tt

(2)

   (c) The ratio of kittens with a dominant allele which gives the Manx form to kittens who inherit homozygous recessive alleles is 3:1 **(1)**

   (d) 2:1 **(1)**, because any kittens born with the homozygous TT will die before they are born **(1)**

2 Possibility 1: Purple flowers are homozygous dominant, RR, and white flowers are homozygous recessive, rr. **(1)** 100% of the offspring have the genotype Rr and the phenotype purple flowers **(1)**

	R	R
r	Rr	Rr
r	Rr	Rr

Possibility 2: Purple flowers are heterozygous, Rr, and white flowers are homozygous recessive, rr. **(1)** 50% of the offspring have the genotype Rr and the phenotype purple flowers;

	R	r
r	Rr	rr
r	Rr	rr

50% of the offspring have the genotype rr and the phenotype white flowers **(1)**

24. Family pedigrees

1 (a) C **(1)**

   (b) They both have the dominant phenotype so must have at least one dominant allele A **(1)**. They have an albino child so they must both have carried and passed on a recessive albino allele a **(1)**. So, they must both be heterozygotes (Aa). **(1)**

   (c) Individual 3 does not have albinism **(1)**. The allele for normal colouring A is dominant. So, the genotype of individual 3 could be AA or Aa. **(1)**

AA × aa
All the children are unaffected by albinism which is what we see **(1)**

	A	A
a	Aa	Aa
a	Aa	Aa

Aa × aa
There is a 1 in 4 chance that a child will have albinism **(1)** but in this case they all inherited a normal allele from their father and all are unaffected. **(1)**

	A	a
A	AA	Aa
a	Aa	aa

2 The combination of alleles from the mother and father that combine to form a zygote is always a matter of chance **(1)**. In both couples, one parent has a dominant Huntington's allele and the other does not, so the genetic cross is the same in both cases. **(1)** (Individuals 4 and 8 are not HH as their mother does not have Huntington's disease and so must be hh.)

	H	h
h	Hh	hh
h	Hh	hh

Hh × hh
Each time one of these couples conceives, there is a 50% chance their baby will be affected by Huntington's and a 50% chance it will be healthy **(1)**. Couple 3 and 4 were lucky both times they had a child, couple 8 and 9 were lucky twice but in one case the sperm which fertilised the egg was carrying the dominant allele for Huntington's and so the child was affected. **(1)**

25. Sex determination

1 D **(1)**

2 C **(1)**

3 (a)

	X	Y
X	XX	XY
X	XX	XY

(2)

   (b) Each baby gets one set of chromosomes from the mother and one from the father **(1)**. Each time a baby is conceived there is a 50% chance it will be a boy and 50% it will be a girl **(1)**. This genetic situation is not affected by the sex of any other children a couple may have so the new baby has a 50-50 chance of being a boy or a girl **(1)**. Both sets of friends are wrong. **(1)**

4 Gametes are produced by meiosis which gives haploid cells (with a single set of chromosomes). As the sex chromosomes in a woman's diploid body cell are both X, all the eggs she produces will contain one X chromosome so they can all form half of a female zygote **(1)**. The sex chromosomes in a man's diploid body cells are XY, so when they divide by meiosis to form the gametes 50% of his sperm will contain one X chromosome so they can form a female zygote **(1)** and the other 50% will contain one Y chromosome so they can form a male zygote. **(1)**

26. Variation and mutation

1 Genetic variation, e.g. eye colour, natural hair colour: environmental variation, e.g. scars, being able to drive **(1)**

2 B **(1)**

3 (a) A change in the sequence of bases in the DNA which forms a new allele **(1)**

   (b) Mistakes made when a cell divides **(1)**, radiation damage **(1)**

   (c) The sequence of bases in the DNA codes for the amino acids which are joined together in protein synthesis to make a protein **(1)**. If a mutation affects the base sequences so that different amino acids are joined in the protein chain **(1)**, this will affect the properties of the protein which in turn may affect the phenotype of the organism. **(1)**

4 (a) The number of times it appears in a population **(1)**

(b) That the characteristic measured shows continuous variation **(1)**

27. The Human Genome Project

1 (a) The human genome is all of the bases in all the DNA in a human cell **(1)**

(b) A collaboration between scientists set up to decode the human genome **(1)**

(c) It may enable them to look at how the genome of the person interacts with the medicine **(1)** as some alleles make people more or less affected by a particular drug **(1)**

2 (a) Advantage 1:
A person who is at risk from a genetic condition or has a genetic tendency towards a particular condition such as heart disease can make lifestyle changes to minimise their risks **(1)**
Advantage 2:
Doctors may be able to tailor treatments to an individual when their alleles mean they are particularly sensitive to or affected by a medicine/ can distinguish between different forms of a disease so the best medicine can be used. **(1)**

(b) If you know you have an increased risk of developing something like heart disease or breast cancer you may have to pay more for life insurance. **(1)**

3 If you know you have a number of alleles increasing your risk of developing heart disease you can try to protect yourself, e.g. lifestyle changes such as low-fat diet and plenty of exercise, regular check-ups, monitoring weight and blood pressure, etc. **(1)**. So a test could give you the power to reduce your risks as much as you can **(1)**. However, you would have the stress of knowing you had a higher risk which could increase the risk further **(1)**. Life insurance could be expensive **(1)**. Knowing you don't have the high risk alleles for heart disease could lead to you living a very unhealthy lifestyle and getting other problems, e.g. type 2 diabetes. **(1)**

28. Extended response – Genetics

Answers could include the following points **(6)**

• A mutation is a change in the arrangement of the bases in the DNA, which may or may not affect the phenotype. The mutated allele H is dominant, which means if you inherit the allele from just one parent you will develop the disease. In the case of Huntington's disease, it causes changes which usually appear in middle age and lead to serious illness and death.

• Key: h = normal; H = Huntington's disease

• OR: If one of your parents has the allele, you have a 50% chance of inheriting it/ If you have the allele, you have a 50% chance of passing it on to your children.

	H	h
h	Hh	hh
h	Hh	hh

• HGP enables us to identify the faulty allele that causes Huntington's disease and develop a test to show if someone has the allele. The main advantage of having the test for the Huntington's mutation is that you know what is coming. If you don't have the allele you can forget about it. If you do have the allele, although there is nothing you can do to stop the disease developing, you can plan your life, make choices about whether to have children or, if you do have children, choose

whether to use preimplantation diagnosis to be sure your children are not going to be affected. You can plan your finances, etc.

• The disadvantages of having the test include the fact that other members of your family, e.g. your parents, may not want to be tested but your result could tell them if they have the allele. Also, it is an incurable disease and the knowledge you are going to become ill could be difficult to deal with as there is nothing you can do to reduce the risk.

29. Evolution

1 Adult organisms usually produce more offspring than the environment can support. As a result, there is competition between the young to survive and reproduce themselves. **(1)**

↓

Some of the offspring inherit advantageous variations making them better adapted to survive in a particular environment. Others inherit variations which are less well suited to that particular environment. **(1)**

↓

Individuals with the advantageous variations are more likely to survive and reproduce, passing the advantageous variations on to their offspring. **(1)**

↓

The number of individuals with the advantageous variations in the population will increase. **(1)**

2 Evolution by natural selection states that the individuals which survive to reproduce will be the ones with the most advantageous variations for a particular environment **(1)**. Those advantageous characteristics will become more common. Eventually, if populations are separated, they will become separate species adapted for different environments **(1)**. Aloes and agaves both live in very similar desert environments. They both show characteristics which help them survive in a desert, such as fleshy leaves, ability to store water, spines to stop animals eating them **(1)**. As a result of natural selection, these characteristics will have survived and become more and more common in each generation, so the different species have ended up looking very similar even though they are in very different parts of the world **(1)**. They may have had a common ancestor but have evolved/changed due to the separation of land mass. **(1)**

30. Human evolution

1 (a) Fossils **(1)**

(b) The lack of fossils **(1)**

(c) The volume of the skull gives us a measure of the brain volume **(1)**, and the big increase in the size of the brain in relation to the size of the body was an important factor in human evolution. **(1)**

2 The layers of rock where stone tools were found have been dated. The earliest stone tools found [about 3.3 million years old] are relatively simple, because those human ancestors had relatively small brains **(1)**. More modern stone tools are more sophisticated – scientists think this reflects increasing brain volume – thought and coordination improved. **(1)**

3 Any four, e.g.
Species have got taller **(1)**
Skull volume and therefore brain volume has increased from $350\,cm^3$ to $1450\,cm^3$ **(1)**
The relative length of the arms has reduced **(1)**
The arrangement of the toes has changed from big toes sticking out for gripping in trees to modern toes aligned to the front **(1)**
Teeth have changed – got smaller and less specialised **(1)**

Dome of the skull has got bigger and rounder to accommodate the brain **(1)**
Brow ridge has reduced **(1)**

31. Classification

1 D **(1)**

2

Kingdom	Characteristics
Animals	1 multicellular 2 cells have nuclei 3 no cell walls
Plants	1 multicellular/cell have nuclei 2 chloroplasts for photosynthesis 3 cellulose cell walls
Fungi	1 multicellular (apart from yeasts)/cells have nuclei 2 all feed off dead matter or other living organisms/saprophytes or parasites 3 cell walls contain chitin but NOT cellulose
Protists	1 mostly unicellular 2 cells have nuclei 3 some cells have cell walls, but not made of chitin or cellulose
Prokaryotes	1 unicellular 2 cells do not have nuclei 3 cell walls are flexible, not made of chitin or cellulose

(5)

3 (a) A system of classifying all living organisms into one of three domains **(1)**

(b) Archea – cells with no nucleus, genes contain unused sections of DNA **(1)**
Bacteria – cells with no nucleus and no unused sections in the genes **(1)**
Eukaryota – cells with a nucleus and unused sections in the genes **(1)**

(c) The three domain classification system is based on differences in the way the DNA of the different organisms is organised and how it works **(1)**. It is also based on chemical differences in the ribosomes **(1)**. These differences could not be detected until the technology needed to read the DNA code and analyse cell organelles had been developed and this only happened from the 1970s onwards. **(1)**

32. Selective breeding

1 D **(1)**

2 (a) It is when plants or animals with desirable characteristics are chosen to breed together so the offspring produced inherit the favourable characteristics **(1)**

(b) Any three from: disease resistance **(1)** increased yield **(1)** faster growth **(1)** better flavour **(1)** ability to cope with difficult conditions **(1)**

3 First, the breeder would choose two cats – male and female – with very little hair **(1)**. Then, they would choose the kittens with the least hair and when they grew up, breed them with other cats with very little fur **(1)**. This would be repeated for many generations until a breed of cats with little or no hair is produced. **(1)**

4 (a) They remained stable and relatively low until after 1945–50 **(1)**. Then the yields increased steadily and significantly from just over 2 tonnes per hectare to over 8 tonnes per hectare until around 1980 **(1)**. Since then yields have stabilised and continued to increase, but very slowly. **(1)**

(b) Selective breeding – artificial selection of the wheat which gives the highest yield and breeding it for generations **(1)**; adding high quality fertilisers **(1)**

(c) If the wheat ears become too heavy, they break the stalk and then they can't be harvested or they stop growing **(1)**. So, have to find a balance between wheat which gives a big yield and wheat which doesn't get blown over if there is a storm **(1)**. Can selectively breed for shorter, stronger stems as well as high yield to get the maximum crop. **(1)**

33. Genetic engineering

1 (a) Genetic engineering is changing the DNA of an organism, often by inserting genes (sections of DNA) from another organism. **(1)**

(b) Genetically engineer crop plants such as rice to contain extra vitamins/any sensible suggestion **(1)**

2 (a) An organism which has had its DNA altered, often by having a gene from a different organism added **(1)**

(b) Advantage: they can be very useful to humans, e.g. make chemicals we need, resist pests and help us identify pollutants, etc. **(1)**
Disadvantage: some people feel it is wrong because it is not natural/if genetically modified organisms breed with wild organisms it could upset the balance of nature **(1)**

3 (a) No bacteria contain the human gene to make human insulin **(1)**. They only have bacterial genes. They had to genetically modify the bacteria to add the human gene they needed. **(1)**

(b) The gene for making insulin was identified and cut out of a human chromosome **(1)**. It was then inserted into the bacterial chromosome, so that the bacterium made insulin **(1)**. When the bacterium divides, it makes new copies of the human gene in its DNA so the offspring can also make human insulin. **(1)**

34. Extended response – Genetic modification

Answers could include the following points **(6)**

• Evolution is a process of natural selection which often takes place over long periods of time. The organisms with alleles which give them adaptations suited to their environment are most likely to survive and reproduce, passing on their alleles until a new species arises.

• Selective breeding is when the characteristics selected for are chosen by people, and only organisms with the desired characteristics are allowed to breed. It can take many years.

• In genetic engineering scientists choose specific alleles and insert them in organisms to give them desired characteristics. It can be very rapid.

• Selective breeding has produced many very useful organisms for people over time BUT the organisms can only interbreed with organisms of the same species so the changes that can be achieved are limited.

• Genetic engineering makes it possible to take genes from one type of organism and place them in an entirely different type of organism in a relatively fast process. This means we can make some extremely useful organisms but there are some ethical issues about moving genes between species, and so far, there are limits to what can be engineered.

35. Health and disease

1 (a) A disease which can be passed from one person to another **(1)**

(b) Pathogens **(1)**

(c) B **(1)**

2 (a) Being free from disease **(1)**

(b) Getting on well with other people/having a good social network supporting you **(1)**

(c) Feeling good about yourself **(1)**

3 (a) A microorganism which causes communicable disease **(1)**

(b)

Pathogen	How do they make you ill?
Bacteria	May release toxins in their host/ damage body cells
Viruses	Take over the DNA of a body cell, so the cell makes new viruses which damage the cell when they are released
Fungi	Eukaryotic organisms which dissolve and damage cells
Protists	Eukaryotic organisms which can live in the body and damage cells

(4)

4 Any two from:

If you have a disease which affects the immune system, you will be more likely to get other infectious diseases as your immune system will not be able to fight them. **(1)**

If you have a disease which stops one organ working properly you will be unwell and so more likely to get another infectious disease. **(1)**

If you have a disease due to poor nutrition your whole body will be affected and you may be more likely to get both communicable and non-communicable diseases. **(1)**

36. Common infections

1 C **(1)**
2 (a) 8000 **(1)**
   (b) (6000/8000) × 100 = 75% **(2)**
   (c) HIV is a viral infection which attacks the immune system **(1)**. When the immune system is not working properly people are much more likely to pick up another infection such as TB **(1)** because their immune system cannot fight the infection. **(1)**

3

Pathogen	Disease	Symptoms
Bacterium	Cholera/ tuberculosis/ stomach ulcers	Diarrhoea/lung damage/ damage to stomach lining
Virus	HIV/Ebola	Mild infections followed by damage to immune system and many other infections/ internal bleeding, fever, severe headaches, diarrhoea
Protist	Malaria	Fever, weakness, chills, sweating

(6)

37. How pathogens spread

1 D **(1)**
2 (a) Bacteria **(1)**
   (b) Large amounts of pale, watery diarrhoea **(1)**
   (c) The bacteria that cause cholera pass out of the body in diarrhoea **(1)**. If there is a good sewage system, they do not come into contact with other people so the disease does not spread **(1)**. After natural disasters sewage systems are often destroyed so diarrhoea gets into water used for drinking, washing, etc. and so it spreads rapidly from one person to another. **(1)**
3 A pathogen is a microorganism which causes an infectious disease. **(1)**
   A vector is a living organism (e.g. mosquito) which carries a pathogen from one host to another. **(1)**
4 (a) Pathogens pass out of the body in the faeces **(1)**. Washing your hands removes the pathogens so you cannot pass them on to someone else. **(1)**
   (b) Pathogens from bodily waste can find their way into the drinking water if there is poor sewage treatment **(1)**. Boiling water kills pathogens such as bacteria and protists and prevents the spread of disease. **(1)**
   (c) The pathogens causing the disease are trapped in the tissue and then thrown away, avoiding droplet

infection in the air **(1)**. Washing your hands then removes any pathogens which might be left so if you touch surfaces you don't pass the pathogens to other people who touch the surfaces and then put their fingers in their mouths. **(1)**

38. STIs

1 D [STIs are usually curable; HIV is the exception] **(1)**
2 (a) STIs are spread by contact with sexual fluids containing the pathogens **(1)**. If a man wears a condom, it prevents him coming into contact with the sexual fluids of his partner **(1)** and prevents his partner coming into contact with his semen which will contain pathogens if he is infected with an STI. **(1)**
   (b) A woman can have these STIs without knowing **(1)**. The pathogens can be passed from a mother to her unborn child and cause it damage **(1)**. If the infection is picked up by screening it can be treated which protects the baby, or the baby can be treated as soon as it is born. **(1)**
3 (a) Prevents sexual/bodily fluids from an infected person coming into contact with a healthy person and infecting them **(1)**
   (b) The pathogens causing STIs can be passed into a healthy person through an infected blood transfusion **(1)**. Screening blood for STIs before it is used prevents that happening. **(1)**
   (c) Many people do not understand much about STIs, e.g. that you can have an STI without knowing, or that they can be passed from mother to baby **(1)**. They also do not know how to treat or prevent STIs. Better education would mean people who are likely to have different sexual partners, would be better informed and better able to protect themselves from STIs and get appropriate treatment if they become infected. **(1)**
   (d) If someone infected with an STI uses a needle to inject drugs, and someone else who does not have an STI then uses the same needle, that person may become infected with the STI **(1)**. If drug users are all provided with sterile needles, they will not need to share needles and the spread of STIs will be reduced. **(1)**

39. Human defences

1 C **(1)**
2 (a) Unbroken skin forms a physical barrier between pathogens and the inside of the body **(1)** because it is too thick and tough for most pathogens to get through. **(1)**
   (b) The acid in the stomach acts as a chemical barrier to pathogens **(1)**; it destroys most of the pathogens you take into your body in food and drink/swallow in your mucus. **(1)**
   (c) Tears act as a chemical barrier to pathogens **(1)** as they contain the enzyme lysozyme which breaks down the cell walls of bacteria and destroys them. **(1)** (They also wash bacteria out of the eyes)
3 (a) A mucus **(1)**
       B cilia **(1)**
       C ciliated epithelial cell **(1)**
   (b) Mucus in the nose and tubes leading to the lungs traps pathogens such as bacteria **(1)**. Some of the cells lining the nose and the tubes in the breathing system have cilia. The cilia beat and move mucus away from the lungs to the throat where it is swallowed and the pathogens are destroyed by the stomach acid. **(1)**

(c) Chemicals in cigarette smoke paralyse/damage the cilia in the nose and trachea **(1)**. The paralysed/damaged cilia cannot move the mucus to the back of the throat to be swallowed **(1)**. The mucus travels down to the lungs, taking the pathogens with it. The pathogens can cause chest infections. **(1)**

40. The immune system

1 A **(1)**
2 (a) White blood cells called lymphocytes have antibodies on their surface **(1)**. The shape of each antibody matches the shape of the antigens on a specific pathogen **(1)**. If the pathogen is present, a lymphocyte with the right antibody will attach to it. **(1)**
   (b) A lymphocyte is activated when an antigen from a pathogen fits into the antibodies on the surface of the lymphocyte **(1)**. The lymphocyte then divides over and over again to produce clones of identical lymphocytes **(1)**. These cloned lymphocytes release large amounts of antibodies which bind to the antigens on the pathogens and destroy them. **(1)**
   (c) Some of the activated lymphocytes form memory cells **(1)**. When you meet the same pathogen again, they can make the right antibodies and destroy the pathogens before you develop symptoms of disease. **(1)**
3 (a) The person has a second infection with the same pathogen **(1)**
   (b) A is the primary response to the pathogen **(1)**, B is the secondary response to the same pathogen **(1)**
   (c) After the primary response, memory cells are formed which have the right antigens ready for that particular pathogen. They remain in your system **(1)**. If that pathogen enters your body for a second time, there is an immediate production of antibodies and an immediate rapid cloning of activated cells to make even more antibodies **(1)**. This is why the response is both faster and results in more antibodies being made. **(1)**

41. Immunisation

1 (a) Immunisation is when you give a person a vaccine to prevent them from becoming ill from a particular disease in the future. **(1)**
   (b) A vaccine is a medicine made of inactivated pathogens injected into the body of a person, or taken by mouth **(1)**, to produce immunity to the disease caused by that type of pathogen. **(1)**
2 Natural immunity results from your exposure to a live pathogen, when you get a disease **(1)**. In artificial immunity, inactivated pathogens are injected into the body, (or taken by mouth/nose) so you never get the disease **(1)**. In both natural and artificial immunity, the antigens on the pathogens/inactivated pathogens trigger an immune response and so the body builds up memory cells carrying the antibodies for the antigens on the pathogens/inactivated pathogens **(1)**. If you then meet the live pathogen, a normal secondary immune response takes place, with the rapid production of many antibodies which will destroy the pathogen before it can cause disease. **(1)**
3 (a) It contains the inactivated pathogens of five different diseases **(1)**
   (b) When a lymphocyte becomes activated, it produces many cloned lymphocytes making many antibodies **(1)**. These attach to the antigens on a particular

type of pathogen and destroy it **(1)**. The antigen-antibody reaction depends on the exact shape of the antigen and the antibody **(1)**. Antibodies produced against one pathogen would not fit onto the antigens on the surface of a different type of pathogen **(1)**, and so would not be able to destroy it and prevent disease. **(1)**

42. Treating infections

1 D **(1)**
2 (a) Because they affect bacterial cells but do not affect human cells **(1)**
   (b) They can kill bacteria or they can inhibit their cell processes **(1)** which stops them growing and reproducing **(1)**
   (c) Colds are caused by viruses **(1)**. Antibiotics do not have any effect on viruses so they would not help the child get better. **(1)**
3 (a) 875/100 000 live births **(2)**
   (b) The beginning of widespread use of antibiotics to treat infections in women after they gave birth **(1)**
   (c) The over-use of antibiotics has led to an increase in antibiotic resistance in pathogens **(1)**. This means they are no longer harmed by the antibiotics **(1)**. If the number of antibiotic-resistant bacteria keeps increasing, the time will come when antibiotics are no longer effective against them, and so people will once more die in large numbers from infectious diseases **(1)**.
   On the other hand, new medicines are being developed all the time and doctors and scientists are working to reduce the development of antibiotic resistance so this may never happen. **(1)**

43. New medicines

1 C **(1)**
2 (a) Because they don't know exactly which chemical is doing what **(1)**. There may be side effects **(1)**
   (b) (i) Testing new medicines in the laboratory **(1)** to check that the drugs are taken into the cells and seem to have the desired effect **(1)**
       (ii) Testing on cultures of cells **(1)**
           Testing on cultures of tissues **(1)**
           Testing on whole living animals **(1)**
   (c) It goes into clinical testing **(1)**. First it is tried on a small number of healthy people to make sure the drug is not toxic **(1)**, and then it is tried on a larger number of people with the disease the drug is intended to treat, to see if it has the desired effect. **(1)**
3 (a) In case they have unexpected side effects which may be harmful **(1)**
   (b) A measure of how well it works **(1)**
   (c) The best dose to give the patient – usually the lowest dose that treats the disease **(1)**
   (d) It means it is harmful to the patient **(1)**
   (e) Because there is always a limit to the number of people in clinical trials **(1)**. Once the medicine is being prescribed by doctors, thousands of people will be using the drug **(1)** and so there is more chance of picking up any adverse side effects. **(1)**

44. Non-communicable diseases

1 (a) They cannot be passed directly from one person to another **(1)**
   (b) Genes **(1)**, age **(1)**, lifestyle **(1)**, environment/sex **(1)**

2 (a) 51 − 2 = 49% **(1)**
  (b) 87% risk for breast cancer compared with 63% risk for ovarian cancer **(1)**
  (c) [For those with the BRCA gene] Age increases the risk **(1)** – from around 51% by the age of 50 to around 87% by the age of 70 **(1)**. Over those 20 years the gene stays the same but the risk increases. **(1)**
  (accept mark for description of data without the gene)

3 Age: the older you get, the more likely it is that cells will develop mutations leading to cancer / that you build up cholesterol which can cause heart disease / Females have more oestrogen until they are around 50 and this protects them against some non-communicable diseases such as heart disease. **(1)**
Lifestyle factors: the way we live can affect our risk of developing diseases, e.g. if we don't get enough to eat we may develop deficiency diseases such as lack of vitamin C (scurvy), lack of protein (kwashiorkor), lack of exercise (heart disease), smoking (lung/throat cancer) **(1)**
Environmental factors: Factors in the environment can cause non-communicable disease, e.g. air pollution / asbestos can cause lung disease / toxins in food or water can cause health problems / UV levels in sunlight affecting melanoma rates **(1)**
Sex: Sex is biological and it is the presence of XX or XY chromosomes that have an impact on non-communicable diseases, regardless of the gender an individual identifies with. Some non-communicable diseases are more common in one gender, e.g. breast cancer rates are 100 times higher in women than men, 10% more men than women suffer from high blood pressure and are therefore more at risk of strokes. **(1)**

45. Alcohol and smoking
1 (a) Brazil, USA, Australia, Russia/UK, UK/Russia **(1)**
  (b) Australia, USA, UK, Brazil, Russia **(1)**
  (c) A Russia is one of the countries which drinks the most alcohol per person per year, and also has the most deaths from liver disease, which is linked to drinking alcohol. **(1)**
    B The UK appears to drink a similar amount of alcohol to Russia but far fewer people die of liver diseases, Australia drinks a lot of alcohol but has the lowest number of deaths from liver disease **(1)**. Facts like these suggest that other factors are also important. **(1)**
  (d) If the actual amount of alcohol taken in above 12.5 dm³ per person per year was shown it might make the impact of drinking in Russia clearer / No indication of the type of alcohol drunk **(1)**
2 (a) A disease which is caused by particular aspects of the way we live such as diet, smoking, alcohol, etc. **(1)**
  (b) Carbon monoxide reduces the amount of oxygen which can be carried by the blood **(1)**
    Nicotine is an addictive drug **(1)**
    Tar contains chemicals which can cause cancers **(1)**
    Chemicals in the smoke can make the blood vessels narrow, which increases blood pressure and can lead to cardiovascular disease **(1)**

46. Malnutrition and obesity
1 (a) When someone eats too little or too much of a nutrient in their diet **(1)**
  (b) E.g. anaemia through lack of iron in the diet / rickets through lack of vitamin D or calcium in the diet **(1)**
2 (a) Body mass index **(1)**
  (b) BMI = $\frac{\text{weight (kg)}}{(\text{height (m)})^2}$ **(1)**

  (c) BMI = $70/1.6^2$ = 70/2.56 **(1)** = 27.34 **(1)**
    A BMI of over 30 is obese, so this man is not obese. **(1)**
3 (a) An alternative way to BMI of measuring obesity **(1)**, where the waist measurement is divided by the hip measurement **(1)**
  (b) They show that an increase in obesity appears to increase the risk of death from cardiovascular disease **(1)**, although a very low BMI also seems to be linked to a slight raise in the risk of death from cardiovascular disease. **(1)**
  (c) Waist: hip ratio gives reliable estimate of obesity levels regardless of the activity levels **(1)** and body makeup of an individual **(1)**. BMI can be an unreliable indicator of obesity in people who are very fit and muscular, when they may be heavy but as a result of muscles not fat. **(1)**

47. Cardiovascular disease
1 A Substances from tobacco smoke damage the artery lining **(1)**
  B Fat builds up on the artery wall at the site of the damage **(1)**, making the artery narrower **(1)**
  C A blood clot may block the artery where it is damaged **(1)**, or break off and block an artery in another part of the body **(1)**, causing a heart attack or stroke. **(1)**
2 (a) Lose weight **(1)**; give up smoking **(1)**; take more exercise **(1)**; eat a healthy diet (low fat, salt and sugar) **(1)**
  (b) Advantages (any two): no side effects **(1)**; cheap **(1)**; may help prevent other diseases **(1)**. Disadvantages (any one): may not work **(1)**; may be too late **(1)**
3 (a) The coronary arteries supply blood to the heart muscle **(1)**. If they become narrowed or blocked the heart muscle cannot get enough oxygen, the cells die **(1)** and the person has a heart attack. **(1)**
  (b) A wire frame inserted into an artery to hold it open **(1)**
  (c) A blood vessel taken from somewhere else in the body is inserted to bypass blocked coronary arteries **(1)**
  (d) Surgery carries a risk that the patient will die / may develop an infection after surgery **(1)**. It is more difficult and time consuming / more expensive than giving medication **(1)**. Lifestyle changes or medication are cheaper and less risky so they are usually tried first. **(1)**

48. Extended response – Health and disease
Answers could include the following points **(6)**
• The risk of any individual developing a non-communicable disease such as lung cancer and heart disease is the result of a number of different factors. These include age, sex, genetic inheritance, the environment you live in and the lifestyle you lead.
• Strong scientific evidence from many studies shows that smoking regularly increases the risk of developing a number of diseases such as lung cancer and heart disease. Based on statistics, most smokers live less long than most non-smokers.
• Similar evidence shows that drinking relatively large amounts of alcohol regularly over time increases the risk of a person developing liver or brain diseases.
• In an individual like the woman in the newspaper reports, she has lifestyle factors such as smoking and drinking which increase her risk of developing lung cancer, heart disease, liver disease, etc. She is also old, which increases her risk of developing many diseases including different types of cancers.

- However, she is a woman, which may have protected her against some diseases, e.g. heart disease for many years until she was over the menopause. Most importantly, she may have inherited alleles which mean she is very unlikely to develop certain cancers and heart disease, whatever her lifestyle or environment.

49. Photosynthesis

1 (a) C **(1)**
   (b) carbon dioxide + water **(1)** → glucose + oxygen **(1)**
   (c) Chloroplasts **(1)**
2 (a) The materials which make up an organism **(1)**
   (b) Plants and algae can make their own biomass by photosynthesis **(1)**. Almost all other life on Earth use this biomass as food **(1)**. So, plants and algae produce the biomass for all the food chains and this is why they are known as producers. **(1)**
3 (a) To make sure the plant had used up all of the starch stored in its leaves **(1)**, so any starch detected in the investigation is the result of new photosynthesis. **(1)**
   (b) A is blue-black all over, indicating the presence of starch because the leaf had been in the light and photosynthesising during the day **(1)**, so it has made glucose which has been converted to starch. **(1)**
   (c) B is orange (iodine colour) all over, because the black card stops light reaching the leaf **(1)** so it cannot photosynthesise and make starch. **(1)**
   (d) C is orange where the black card has covered the leaf and it couldn't photosynthesise **(1)**, with a blue-black circle where light reached the leaf and it could photosynthesise and produce starch. **(1)**
   (e) Test several of each type of leaf for starch. **(1)**

50. Limiting factors

1 Any three from: light intensity **(1)**, carbon dioxide concentration **(1)**, temperature **(1)**, water. **(1)**
2 (a) At point A, light intensity is limiting the rate of photosynthesis **(1)**. As the light intensity increases, the rate of photosynthesis also goes up. **(1)**
   (b) Light is no longer the limiting factor on the rate of photosynthesis **(1)**. However much the light intensity increases, the rate of photosynthesis will not change **(1)**. Another factor/temperature or carbon dioxide is limiting the rate of photosynthesis. **(1)**
3 (a) Because carbon dioxide is a reactant of photosynthesis **(1)** and so the more there is, the more photosynthesis can potentially take place **(1)**
   (b) Initially, as the temperature increases the kinetic energy of the molecules goes up, increasing the rate of the enzyme-controlled reactions so the rate of photosynthesis goes up **(1)**. Once the temperature goes above a certain level the enzymes controlling photosynthesis will start to be denatured, so photosynthesis will slow **(1)**. If the temperature gets too high the enzymes will be permanently denatured and the plant will no longer be able to photosynthesise. **(1)**

51. Light intensity

1 (a) The effect of light intensity on the rate of photosynthesis **(1)**
   (b) By counting the number bubbles/volume of oxygen produced **(1)** in a measured time interval **(1)**
   (c) Make sure that the temperature of the water stays the same / use a water bath to keep the temperature constant. **(1)**

2 (a)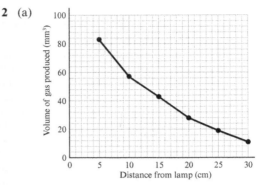
   (2)
   (b) 37 mm³ or 38 mm³ **(1)**
   (c) Plants need light to photosynthesise. When there is a lot of light the plants can photosynthesis fast and give off a lot of gas **(1)**. When the light is moved away, the light intensity falls, the plants cannot photosynthesise as much so the amount of gas produced falls. **(1)**

52. Specialised plant cells

1 (a) Xylem **(1)**   (b) Water **(1)**
   (c) Two features and explanations from: Dead cells **(1)** – more space for water containing minerals to move through. **(1)**
   Cell walls strengthened with lignin rings **(1)** – makes them strong and prevents collapsing. **(1)**
   No end walls **(1)** so they form continuous tubes for water transport. **(1)**
2 (a) The uptake of water and mineral ions from the soil **(1)**
   (b) The root hair has a big surface area **(1)** for absorbing water and mineral ions **(1)**. The root hair has a thin cell wall **(1)** to make it quicker for water and ions to move into the cell. **(1)**
   (c) Structure B is a mitochondrion. They provide the energy needed **(1)** for the root hair cell to move mineral ions into the cell against a concentration gradient. **(1)**
3 (a) Phloem **(1)**
   (b) Sieve tube elements which have very little cytoplasm so there is a lot of space to transport sucrose **(1)** Companion cells with lots of mitochondria to supply energy for the active transport of sucrose into and out of the phloem vessels **(1)**

53. Transpiration

1 D **(1)**
2 (a) The movement of water from the roots of a plant to the leaves and into the air **(1)**
   (b)   Water enters the roots by osmosis through the root hair cells

   ↓ **(1)**

   Water is drawn up the stem through the xylem from the roots

   ↓ **(1)**

   Water is drawn into the leaves and then evaporates from the leaf cells into the air spaces

   ↓ **(1)**

   Water diffuses out through the stomata down a concentration gradient

   (1)

3 (a) They allow carbon dioxide to diffuse into the leaf **(1)** and allow oxygen and water vapour to diffuse out of the leaf down concentration gradients. **(1)**

(b) A – guard cells   C – vacuole
B – stoma   D – chloroplast **(2)**

(c) In the light chloroplasts make sugar and water moves into the guard cells by osmosis, making them swell and become rigid **(1)**. The cell wall is thicker on one side of the cell than on the other, so when the cell swells, an opening appears between the two guard cells. This is the stoma **(1)**. At night, when there is no photosynthesis, water moves out of the guard cells by osmosis **(1)**. They lose their rigidity and the stoma closes. **(1)**

54. Translocation

1 B **(1)**

2 (a) Translocation is the movement of sucrose around a plant in the phloem. **(1)**

(b) Translocation of sucrose depends on sucrose being moved by active transport into and out of the phloem sieve tubes by the companion cells **(1)**. If the poison inhibits active transport, the companion cells will no longer be able to move sucrose into and out of the sieve tubes and translocation will stop. **(1)**

3

	Transpiration	Translocation
Tissue where it takes place	Xylem	Phloem
Substances transported	Water	Sucrose dissolved in water
Direction of transport	From the roots to the leaves	From the leaves, both up and down the plant

(3)

4 (a) Cellular respiration in growing regions, e.g. the bud **(1)**. Converted to starch and stored in leaves and storage organs for use when needed. **(1)**

(b) Scientists can show that radioactive water is found above the ring of dead tissues, showing that the movement of water up the plant in the xylem is not affected as the xylem cells are already dead **(1)**.
Radioactive sucrose is only found in areas below the ring of dead tissue, showing that the movement of sucrose is an active process which relies on living phloem cells **(1)**, and so it does not take place if the cells are killed. **(1)**

55. Water uptake in plants

1 (a) The uptake of water from a cut stem **(1)**

(b) (i) The air flow moves across the leaf increasing the concentration gradient between the inside and the outside of the leaf **(1)**. This increases the loss of water by evaporation and diffusion from the plant **(1)** and so the air bubble moves across the scale faster. **(1)**

(ii) Water vapour diffuses out of the leaf through the stomata **(1)**. Most of the stomata are on the underside of the leaf. If the underside of the leaf is covered in petroleum jelly, gases will not be able to leave the leaf **(1)** so the rate of water loss will slow down and the bubble will move very slowly or stop. **(1)**

2 (a)

Movement of air bubble in 5 minute interval (mm)	Plant A at 15 °C	Plant B at 25 °C	Plant C at 25 °C with a fan blowing at the leaves
Reading 1	50	80	105
Reading 2	45	84	106
Reading 3	55	91	104
Mean result	50	255/3 = 85	315/3 = 105
Mean rate of water uptake (mm/min)	50/5 = 10	85/5 = 17	105/5 = 21

(4)

(b) To make sure the experiment is repeatable and the data is as precise as possible **(1)**

(c) (i) Plant A is photosynthesising at 15 °C and the rate of uptake of water as measured by the distance moved by the air bubble is 10 mm/min **(1)**. Plant B was at 25 °C and the rate of uptake of water was 17 mm/min **(1)**. As the temperature increases, water molecules move around faster and so more water evaporates from the cells in the leaves **(1)** so more water was taken up by plant B in the transpiration stream. **(1)**

(ii) The rate of water uptake in plant B is 17 mm/min **(1)**. Plant C is also at 25 °C BUT it takes up 21 mm water/min **(1)**. The difference is that a fan is blowing on plant C. This blows away the water vapour from the surface of the leaf, increasing the concentration gradient between the inside and the outside of the leaf **(1)**. This increases the water lost from the leaf by evaporation and diffusion, so more water is pulled up into the shoot by the transpiration stream. **(1)**

56. Extended response – Plant structures and functions

Answers could include the following points **(6)**

- Plants need carbon dioxide, water, light and chlorophyll in their chloroplasts to make their own food through the process of photosynthesis. They take in carbon dioxide from the air by gas exchange through the stomata on the leaves. At the same time, water vapour is lost through transpiration.
- In the desert, there is very little water most of the time, so plants need to prevent water loss or they will die.
- Cactus: the stem has become a water store. It is also green (contains chloroplasts) so can carry out photosynthesis. Leaves have become hard spines so no stomata and no water loss, also protect plant from being eaten.
- Palo verde: sheds leaves so it does not lose water through transpiration from the stomata. Bark contains chloroplasts and is green for photosynthesis. In wet periods, tree grows leaves to maximise photosynthesis when water is available and transpiration losses do not matter.

57. Hormones

1 B **(1)**

2 A hormone is a chemical produced by an endocrine gland and released directly into the blood **(1)**. It travels around the body in the blood until it reaches its target organ or organs **(1)**. It causes a response in the target organ. **(1)**

3 (a) Pituitary **(1)**, produces TSH, ADH, FSH, LH **(1)**

(b) Thyroid gland **(1)**, produces thyroxine **(1)**

(c) Pancreas **(1)**, produces insulin **(1)**

4

Hormone	Produced in	Target organ/s and tissues
TSH	Pituitary gland	Thyroid gland
Insulin	Pancreas	Liver, muscles and fatty tissue
Adrenaline	Adrenal glands	Heart, liver, skin, other organs
Oestrogen	Ovaries	Ovaries, uterus, pituitary gland

(4)

58. The menstrual cycle

1 D **(1)**

2 (a) When the ovary releases an egg cell in the middle of the menstrual cycle **(1)**

(b) The event which marks the start of a new menstrual cycle, when the thickened part of the uterus lining and the unfertilised egg cell are lost during the monthly bleed or period **(1)**

(c) When a sperm meets and fuses with an egg cell in the oviduct **(1)**

3 (a) The thickened lining of the uterus and the unfertilised egg are lost through the vagina if pregnancy has not occurred (period). **(1)**

(b) An egg is released from the ovary/ovulation. **(1)**

(c) The lining of the uterus thickens ready to receive a fertilised egg. **(1)**

4 (a) A method used to try to prevent fertilisation/the joining of the egg and sperm. **(1)**

(b) Day 14–16 **(1)** when the egg is released. **(1)**

(c) Condoms **(1)** – Barrier methods put a physical barrier between the egg and the sperm to stop them meeting. **(1)**

(d) They release hormones which interfere with the menstrual cycle **(1)** and prevent ovulation **(1)**

(e) Barrier contraception is easily available and doesn't involve medical professionals **(1)** Used properly with spermicides it is very reliable BUT can go wrong, which increases the risk of pregnancy **(1)** Hormonal contraception requires prescribing by a medical professional **(1)** oral tablets have to be taken daily (or injections received regularly at the correct time in your cycle), it is 99.9% effective when taken properly BUT if tablets/injections are missed or if not all of the hormone is absorbed, e.g. from diahorea or vomiting, it can be ineffective. **(1)**

59. Blood glucose regulation

1 A **(1)**

2 (a) It is broken down in the cells during respiration **(1)**

(b) The pancreas **(1)**

(c) When carbohydrates are digested in the gut, glucose is released **(1)**. It passes from the gut into the blood so the blood glucose levels rise. **(1)**

(d) If the blood glucose levels/concentration are too low, the cells will not have enough glucose for respiration and the body will not function effectively and will eventually die **(1)**. If the blood glucose levels/concentration get too high it can damage organs and cause coma and death. **(1)**

3 (a) At point A the blood glucose concentration is increasing/rising. **(1)**
The person has just had a meal so they are digesting the carbohydrates from the food, breaking them down into sugars such as glucose **(1)**. The glucose is absorbed into the blood from the digestive system causing the blood glucose concentration to rise. **(1)**

(b) At point B the blood glucose concentration is decreasing/falling. **(1)**

The pancreas is releasing insulin in response to a rise in the blood glucose concentration after the meal **(1)**. Insulin makes cells in the liver and other organs convert glucose to glycogen as a store. As a result, the concentration of glucose in the blood falls. **(1)**

60. Diabetes

1 (a) The blood level would rise and continue to rise until it reached a plateau/levelled out. **(1)**

(b) The blood glucose concentration increases after a meal as normal but the pancreas does not release insulin **(1)**. As a result, the blood glucose is not converted into glycogen in the liver and muscles **(1)**. The glucose level continues to rise until all of the glucose from the meal has been absorbed into the blood **(1)**, and then it will stay the same as the glucose cannot get into the cells. **(1)**

(c) An insulin injection replaces the natural insulin **(1)** and allows the liver and muscle cells to store glycogen so the blood glucose levels fall. **(1)**

2

	Type 1 diabetes	Type 2 diabetes
Cause	Immune system damages insulin-producing pancreatic cells so they cannot produce insulin **(1)**	Person produces insulin but the liver and muscle cells have become resistant to it **(1)**
Control	Injecting the right amount of insulin at regular intervals to keep the blood glucose concentration within safe limits **(1)**	Most people can control type 2 diabetes by losing weight, eating low-carbohydrate foods and exercising more. There are medicines available if needed. **(1)**

3 (a) There appears to be a correlation between BMI category and type 2 diabetes in women **(1)**. In men, there is a higher percentage of normal BMI men than overweight men with type 2 diabetes **(1)**. Being obese appears to correlate closely with type 2 diabetes in both men and women. **(1)**

(b) The data covers all adults in the UK so should be reliable **(1)**. In each BMI category given, a higher percentage of men have type 2. So, the claim could seem reasonable. **(1)**
BUT – don't know what happens in other BMI categories **(1)**; don't know if there are any other factors involved, e.g. smoking, drinking, etc.
So, can't make that claim without qualifying it. **(1)**

61. Extended response – Control and coordination

Answers could include the following points **(6)**

• In fertilisation, a sperm penetrates an egg to form a new cell. Contraception aims to prevent the sperm and the egg fusing. Barrier methods put a layer between the sperm and the eggs (condoms are placed over the penis, diaphragms are placed across the cervix). Hormonal contraception uses female sex hormones or similar chemicals to interfere with the menstrual cycle so ovulation does not take place. They also affect the mucus around the cervix so it is harder for sperm to get to the egg.

• From the data given, hormone-based contraception appears several percentage points more effective than barrier contraception, with a mean effectiveness of over 99% compared with a mean effectiveness of 96% for barrier methods. The percentage effectiveness of a method of contraception is measured by the number of women who would get pregnant out of 100 women using the method of contraception correctly for a year – so 98% effective means two women out of the hundred using it correctly for a year would get pregnant.

- To use a contraceptive correctly, the instructions must be followed exactly every time, e.g. no pills forgotten, spermicide used with condoms, etc. In real life, many people do not use contraception correctly every time and so real life failure rates are probably higher than those shown in the data.
- Although hormone methods are more effective, barrier methods have several advantages – they do not require a visit to medical professionals, they have no associated health risks and they are available at any time. Both forms of contraception meet people's needs.

62. Exchanging materials

1 C **(1)**
2 (a) Smaller organism SA = $1 \times 1 = 1\,cm^2$
Volume = $1 \times 1 \times 1 = 1\,cm^3$
sa : vol = 1 : 1 or 1
Larger organism SA = $6 \times 6 = 36\,cm^2$
Volume = $6 \times 6 \times 6 = 216\,cm^3$
sa : vol = 1 : 6 or 0.17 **(2)**

(b) Substances are transported into and out of cells through the outer surface **(1)**. As an organism gets bigger, the surface area to volume ratio gets smaller and it would take too long for materials to diffuse in or out **(1)**. So large multicellular organisms need exchange surfaces with large surface areas to move substances in and out and transport systems to carry substances to and from where they are needed. **(1)**

3 (a) Any two from: lungs **(1)** small intestine **(1)** kidneys **(1)**
(b) The circulatory system **(1)**
(c) Large surface area **(1)**, thin/short distances to travel **(1)**

4

Substance	Site of exchange	Reason for exchange
Oxygen	Alveoli in lungs	Needed for respiration
Carbon dioxide	Alveoli in lungs	Waste product of respiration
Dissolved food molecules	Small intestine	Needed for respiration/ cell metabolism
Mineral ions	Small intestine	Needed for cells to function properly
Urea	Nephrons in kidney	Waste product of breakdown of amino acids/metabolism

(5)

63. Alveoli

1 (a) The movement of air in and out of the lungs **(1)**
(b) Oxygen diffuses from the air in the alveoli of the lungs into the blood **(1)**. Carbon dioxide diffuses from the blood into the air in the alveoli. **(1)**
(c) It removes air relatively high in carbon dioxide and replaces it with air relatively high in oxygen **(1)**. This maintains a steep concentration gradient between the air and the blood **(1)** so diffusion of gases in and out of the blood is as fast and efficient as possible. **(1)**

2 Large surface area – lots of area over which gas exchange can take place **(1)**
Good blood supply – constantly delivers carbon dioxide-rich blood to the alveoli and removes oxygen-rich blood **(1)**. This maintains steep concentration gradients for diffusion of gases. **(1)**

Thin walls – give short diffusion distances between the air and the blood, making diffusion more efficient. **(1)**

3 (a) The larger air sacs will have a smaller surface area : volume ratio **(1)**, so there will be less gas exchange and so less oxygen will get into the blood and less carbon dioxide will be removed, causing breathlessness. **(1)**
(b) The tumour takes up the space of the lung tissue made up of alveoli, greatly reducing the surfaces available for gas exchange by diffusion **(1)**. This makes the person breathless and lowers blood oxygen concentration. **(1)**
(c) The blood cannot get into the capillaries around the alveoli of the lungs, there is little or no gas exchange between the air in the lungs and the blood **(1)**. As a result, the person becomes breathless with low blood oxygen. **(1)**

64. Blood

1 D **(1)**
2 (a) A = plasma, B, C = white blood cells /platelets, D = red blood cells **(2)**
(b) Plasma: transport of dissolved substances /food/ carbon dioxide/mineral ions **(1)**
White blood cells: attack pathogens in the body **(1)**
Platelets: help in clotting the blood to prevent bleeding/protect damaged skin **(1)**
Red blood cells: carry oxygen around the body **(1)**

3 Red blood cells contain haemoglobin which binds with oxygen in the lungs and carries it around the body to the tissues **(1)**
Their biconcave shape gives a big surface area for gas exchange so oxygen can diffuse in and out easily **(1)**
They have no nucleus which makes more space for haemoglobin in the cell so more oxygen can be carried **(1)**

4 (a) Some white blood cells called phagocytes **(1)** surround foreign cells/pathogens and digest them **(1)**. White blood cells called lymphocytes **(1)** produce chemicals called antibodies that stick to foreign cells/pathogens and help to destroy them. **(1)**
(b) White blood cells protect us against infection by engulfing pathogens or producing antibodies **(1)**. Children with SCID don't produce healthy white blood cells **(1)** so any pathogens which enter their body can easily cause an infection as they are not attacked by the white blood cells of the immune system. **(1)**

65. Blood vessels

1 (a) A = vein
B = artery
C = capillaries **(2)**
(b) Blood pressure is highest in blood vessel B **(1)** because the heart squeezes blood into these vessels at high pressure with each heartbeat. **(1)**

2 (a) Walls thinner than arterial walls, **(1)** large space in the middle, valves **(1)**
(b) Thin walls as blood is not under high pressure **(1)**, wide lumen allows large volume of blood to flow **(1)**, valves prevent backflow of blood **(1)**

3 (a) Blood is squeezed into the arteries by the heart at high pressure **(1)**. The elastic walls of the arteries stretch so they are not damaged **(1)**. After they have been stretched, the muscles and elastic fibres contract, returning the artery to its original size and helping the blood to flow smoothly. **(1)**

ANSWERS

(b) As you move, your muscles squeeze the blood along the veins towards the heart **(1)**. The valves open to allow the blood to flow towards the heart but close to stop it flowing backwards. **(1)**

4 (a) Capillaries are very small blood vessels with walls which are only one cell thick. **(1)** (They are so narrow red blood cells move through them in single file.)

(b) Because capillaries transport food and oxygen to the cells and remove waste products **(1)**. They are the site of exchange between the blood and all the cells. **(1)**

(c) They have a very large surface area as they are so small and there are so many of them **(1)**. Their walls are only one cell thick so the diffusion distances for dissolved food, oxygen and waste products are very short, allowing for rapid, efficient exchange **(1)**. Blood flows through them continually from the arteries to the veins maintaining concentration gradients between the blood and the cells, so diffusion takes place as quickly and efficiently as possible. **(1)**

66. The heart

1 C **(1)**

2 (a) A = right and left atria **(1)**
B = right and left ventricles **(1)**

(b) Valves **(1)** – prevent the blood flowing backwards through the heart **(1)**

(c) Muscle wall of the left ventricle is thicker than the muscle wall of the right ventricle **(1)**. Left ventricle pushes blood all around the body whilst the right ventricle pushes it only to the lungs. **(1)**

3 Blood <u>returns to</u> the heart from <u>the organs</u> in <u>the veins</u> **(1)** → the <u>atria</u> contract forcing <u>blood into the ventricles</u> **(1)** → the <u>valves</u> close preventing <u>blood flowing the wrong way</u> through the heart **(1)** → the <u>ventricles</u> contract, forcing <u>blood out of the heart</u> into <u>the arteries</u> which carry it to the organs. **(1)**

67. Aerobic respiration

1 (a) It is a process that releases energy from glucose for use in cellular activities **(1)**, using oxygen. **(1)**

(b) Glucose + oxygen **(1)** → carbon dioxide + water **(1)**

(c) Mainly in the mitochondria **(1)**

(d) Glucose comes from digested food **(1)**, oxygen from the air in gas exchange in the lungs. **(1)**

2 (a) For metabolic processes/to build larger molecules from smaller ones for growth **(1)**
To enable muscle contraction **(1)**
In birds and mammals, to help maintain a steady body temperature **(1)**

(b) Building larger molecules from smaller ones **(1)**, e.g. using sugars and nitrates to build amino acids to make proteins **(1)**

3 (a) Enzymes are biological catalysts made of protein **(1)**. Protein is denatured if the temperature gets too high (above 40 °C) **(1)** or if the pH is not in the ideal range **(1)**. If the enzymes controlling cellular respiration are denatured, there will be no energy available for the cells so it is important to control the environment. **(1)**

(b) The poison affects the enzymes of the mitochondria and prevents aerobic respiration **(1)**, so energy is not released for cell metabolism **(1)**. Supplying useable energy provides the cells with what they need even though cellular respiration

is not taking place, so the normal reactions of metabolism can take place. **(1)**

68. Anaerobic respiration

1 B **(1)**

2 (a) Anaerobic respiration is the incomplete breakdown of glucose into lactic acid **(1)** when there is not enough oxygen for aerobic respiration to take place. **(1)**

(b)

Advantages of anaerobic respiration	Disadvantages of anaerobic respiration
1 Anaerobic respiration is useful to muscle cells because it can release energy to allow muscle cells to continue contracting even when the heart and lungs cannot deliver oxygen and glucose fast enough for aerobic respiration 2 Respiration can continue in organisms that have no, or a very limited supply of, oxygen	1 Anaerobic respiration releases much less energy from each molecule of glucose than aerobic respiration 2 Lactic acid is not removed from the body. It builds up in the muscles and blood, and must be broken down using oxygen after exercise

(4)

3 (a) Aerobic **(1)**

(b) The muscles respire anaerobically, so glucose is not completely broken down **(1)**. Lactic acid is formed **(1)** and much less energy is released for the cells to use. **(1)**

(c) The heart rate falls back to normal relatively quickly **(1)** but the breathing rate remains raised for some time. **(1)**

69. Rate of respiration

1 (a) Soda lime absorbs the carbon dioxide produced by the seeds during respiration so it doesn't affect the respirometer reading, which measures uptake of oxygen. **(1)**

(b) As the peas absorb oxygen from the air as they respire, the liquid moves along the scale **(1)**. If the distance the blob moves in given intervals of time is measured, the rate of respiration can be calculated indirectly by dividing the distance travelled by the time. **(1)**

(c) No movement of the liquid/no uptake of oxygen **(1)**. Boiling the peas kills them so they no longer respire. **(1)**

2 (a) Carbon dioxide **(1)**

(b) The mealworms must be handled very carefully to minimise any trauma or damage **(1)**, changes in conditions must be relatively small and never up to a level that would damage the animals. **(1)**

(c) Mealworms would respire at a faster rate than germinating peas. **(1)**

(d) Mealworms are animals so they move around which requires energy from respiration **(1)**. They are active and so respire relatively fast **(1)**. Germinating peas are actively growing but they do not move. Their energy needs are lower **(1)** and so respiration rate would be slower. **(1)**

70. Changes in heart rate

1 B **(1)**

2 (a) The volume of blood pushed out of the heart into the aorta with each heartbeat **(1)**, measured in litres **(1)**

(b) The number of times the heart beats in a minute **(1)**, measured in beats/minute **(1)**

(c) The volume of blood pushed into the aorta per minute **(1)**, measured in litres/minute **(1)**

(d) cardiac output = stroke volume × heart rate **(1)**

3 (a) Person C is the fittest **(1)** because they had the highest cardiac volume, fitter people have larger stroke volumes and pump more blood to the muscles during exercise. **(1)**

(b) Person A **(1)** – people who are unfit usually have small stroke volumes and their hearts beat very fast during exercise to try to get enough blood to the muscles to supply them with the food and oxygen they need. **(1)**

(c) B = 0.095 × 120 = 11.4 litres/min **(1)**
C = 0.15 × 100 = 15.0 litres/min **(1)**

(d) 3.6/11.4 × 100 **(1)** = 31.6% more blood per minute **(1)**

71. Extended response – Exchange
Answers could include the following points **(6)**
- The muscles need a good supply of glucose and oxygen to carry out aerobic respiration to release as much energy as possible for muscle contraction.
- If the muscles don't get enough oxygen, they will undergo anaerobic respiration when glucose is broken down without oxygen to form lactic acid, releasing very little energy. This also makes the muscles hurt because lactic acid builds up in the muscles.
- In the gas exchange system of the lungs, oxygen needed by the muscles moves from the air to the blood down a concentration gradient by diffusion, and waste carbon dioxide produced in aerobic respiration diffuses from the blood into the air in the alveoli of the lungs to be removed from the body.
- During exercise Tom will breathe faster and more deeply to supply more oxygen for aerobic respiration in the contracting muscles and to remove more carbon dioxide.
- As the race progresses, Tom's heart beats faster and the stroke volume of the heart at each beat increases, increasing the cardiac output.
- This increases the flow of blood to the muscles, carrying oxygen and food to the contracting cells and removing the waste carbon dioxide, carrying it to the lungs to be removed from the body.

72. Ecosystems and abiotic factors
1 D **(1)**
2 (a) A single, living individual **(1)**
(b) All of the organisms of the same species in an area **(1)**
(c) All of the different populations in an area **(1)**
(d) All the living organisms/communities in an area along with all the non-living components which affect them **(1)**
3 (a) Three from: light levels **(1)**, average temperature **(1)**, average rainfall **(1)**, oxygen levels in water **(1)**
(b) The soil of bogs is very poor with few mineral ions/low nitrate levels **(1)**. The sundew gets mineral ions/nitrates from the insects it digests **(1)**. Ordinary plants cannot do this so they can't survive. **(1)**
(c) Baby birds eat a lot of caterpillars **(1)**. If the weather is cold it will kill the caterpillars, so there are fewer available for the parents to find/heavy rain can wash small caterpillars and insects off leaves, again making them harder to find **(1)**. There is less food and some of the chicks starve to death. **(1)**

73. Biotic factors
1 C **(1)**
2 (a) Territory **(1)** and mates **(1)**
(b) Competition **(1)**
(c) Any species with explanation, e.g. rabbits and sheep **(1)** both eat grass and compete for it in fields **(1)**; beavers and elk **(1)** compete for trees in America **(1)**; puffin and haddock **(1)** both eat sand eels and compete for them **(1)**; any other sensible answer
3 In early spring, the trees have no leaves, so the light the ground plants need to grow reaches them and they grow fast and flower, avoiding competition with the trees **(1)**. As the leaves open on the trees, less light reaches the ground plants and they die back because there is not enough light for them to continue photosynthesising **(1)**. By summer the trees have many leaves and very little light reaches the ground beneath them so other plants cannot compete and grow. **(1)**
4 (a) An animal which hunts and eats other animals **(1)**
(b) An animal which is hunted and eaten by other animals **(1)**
(c) As snowshoe hare numbers fall, they are followed by a fall in the lynx numbers **(1)**. Then as snowshoe hare numbers rise, this is followed by a rise in lynx numbers. **(1)**
(d) The hare numbers fall because they are being eaten by the lynxes **(1)**. But once the number of hares gets too low, there isn't enough food for all the lynxes so the lynx numbers fall **(1)**. Once there are fewer predators, the hare numbers go up as they reproduce and fewer are eaten **(1)**. But when there is more prey, the lynx do better and so their numbers go up again. **(1)**

74. Parasitism and mutualism
1 D **(1)**
2 (a) An organism that benefits from feeding off a host organism **(1)** and causes harm to the host **(1)**
(b) Any three examples of parasitic feeding, e.g.

Parasite	How it feeds
Flea	Sucks blood after piercing skin with sharp mouthparts
Tapeworm	Lives in intestines, attaches to gut wall, absorbs digested nutrients through body
Mistletoe	Grows roots into host tree and absorbs water and nutrients

(3)
3 The hooks and suckers attach to the intestine wall of the host **(1)**. The thin flattened body gives a big surface area where food from the host can be absorbed **(1)**. Segments contain both male and female sex organs so fertilisation can take place inside the body of the host **(1)**.
4 (a) A relationship between two different types of organisms where both organisms benefit **(1)**
(b) The leguminous plant gets nitrogen compounds, which it needs to grow and make proteins, from the bacteria **(1)**; the nitrogen-fixing bacteria are protected from the environment and get food from the plant. **(1)**

75. Fieldwork techniques
1 (a) $\frac{10 + 2 + 15 + 9 + 3 + 22 + 14 + 12 + 20}{9} = \frac{107}{9}$ **(1)**
= 11.9 nests/100 m² **(2)**
(b) A good year compared to the previous years as there were more nests per 100 m² of beach **(1)**, 11.9/100 m² compared to 5.6/100 m² and 8.4/100 m² **(1)**
(c) Biotic factor: food supply/numbers of predators **(1)**
Abiotic factor: temperature/amount of heavy rain **(1)**

2 (a) A measure of how common something is in an area **(1)**

(b) Mean number of slugs in $1\,m^2 = \frac{10+6+5+9+2}{5} = \frac{32}{5} = 6.4$ slugs/m^2 **(2)**

Garden is $100\,m^2$ in area so approximate slug population in the garden is $6.4 \times 100 = 640$ slugs. **(1)**

3 (a) A non-living aspect of the ecosystem where an organism lives **(1)**

(b) The distribution of plants describes where they are found in an ecosystem **(1)**

(c) A quadrat is a square frame with a known area, used to indicate where to take samples of organisms in the field **(1)**

(d) Students are investigating the effect of abiotic factors on the distribution of plants in a park so a belt transect will give them the best results **(1)**. They need to sample organisms in relation to changes in abiotic factors which can be recorded and correlated with changes in plant numbers **(1)**. Random quadrats might all land in areas with similar abiotic factors **(1)** and so make it much more difficult to relate the abiotic factors of the environment to the distribution of plants. **(1)**

76. Organisms and their environment

1 (a) Transect A $= \frac{1+3+1+4}{8} = \frac{9}{8} = 1$ plant/$0.25\,m^2$ (to the nearest whole number) **(1)**

Transect B $= \frac{4+6+8+10+10+5+3}{8} = \frac{46}{8} = 5.75$ or 6 plants/$0.25\,m^2$ (to the nearest whole number) **(1)**

(b) Transect A has very few sundew plants so it is probably not through a bog **(1)**. However, there are a few sundews so it probably borders onto a bog **(1)**. Transect B has lots of sundew plants. Most are in the middle of the transect, so it probably goes across the middle of a bog, with the lowest numbers of sundews at the edges. **(1)**

(c) Carry out more transects/indicate where the transects are taken on a map/use larger quadrats for sampling/ do the samples closer together **(1)**, e.g. space quadrats every metre instead of every two metres. **(1)**

2 Need to be organised to start when tide is at its lowest **(1)**. Peg out a long tape measure from low tide to high tide mark up the beach **(1)**.
Decide on the intervals at which to place quadrats to count crabs, e.g. 1 m apart, and decide on the size of quadrat to use, e.g. $0.25\,m^2$, $1\,m^2$. **(1)**
Start at low tide and work up the tape counting the numbers of mussels on the rocks in each quadrat. Record numbers. **(1)**
Record any abiotic factors – most important is distance from low water. **(1)**

77. Human effects on ecosystems

1 B **(1)**

2 (a) Introduction of new non-indigenous species **(1)**

(b) A new species can out-compete indigenous species and take over an ecosystem very quickly, damaging the balance of the indigenous species **(1)**. New species can easily become pests. **(1)**

(c) New species may be introduced to control another species – indigenous or non-indigenous – which has got out of control **(1)**. They can be very effective as long as they only eat the pest species. **(1)**

3 (a) Fish farming involves growing fish in pens **(1)** where they can be fed and monitored as they grow. **(1)**

(b) Any three from: the fish grow faster because they have plenty of food **(1)**; fish are protected from

predators and disease **(1)**; fishermen don't have to risk their lives catching fish **(1)**; gives a reliable source of fish and more fish for people to eat **(1)**

(c) Uneaten food and faeces sink to the bottom of the sea/lake and change the environment **(1)**. Disease can spread from farmed fish to wild stock. **(1)**

78. Biodiversity

1 (a) The variety of species in an area **(1)**

(b) Any three from: to maintain the structure of ecosystems as organisms are interdependent/ to maintain the food chains in an ecosystem **(1)**; some species are useful to people; e.g. for potential medicines **(1)**; because morally people should respect other organisms **(1)**; people enjoy seeing a variety of different organisms in different habitats **(1)**

2 (a) Deforestation removes trees from an area **(1)**. This also removes the habitat of many different species and may remove the food source for some animals, so it reduces biodiversity in an area. **(1)**

(b) When an area where the trees have been removed in the process of deforestation is allowed to return to woodland/forest **(1)**. Can be by natural regrowth or replanting. **(1)**

(c) Rainforests contain about 500 species of tree per hectare and UK woodlands have around 12 species per hectare so rainforests have two orders of magnitude more types of tree than UK forests **(1)**. Trees in both places support huge numbers of other plants, fungi, bacteria and animals/organisms **(1)**. So, in terms of numbers of species lost, deforestation of a rainforest will lose more species than deforestation in the UK/the data doesn't compare the number of different species that live off the tree species in each location, so you cannot accurately support the statement. **(1)**

3 Any four from: Providing suitable habitat by planting conifer woodlands **(1)**. Connecting one conifer woodland with another by conifer corridors **(1)**. Feeding red squirrels to improve breeding success and killing grey squirrels in the feeding area **(1)**. Producing a vaccine against squirrelpox and giving it to red squirrels **(1)**. Keeping grey squirrels out of red squirrel strongholds. **(1)**

79. The carbon cycle

1 A **(1)**

2 (a) Decomposers respire using dead plant and animal material and animal waste products, releasing carbon dioxide into the air. **(1)**

(b) In combustion, the wood and other material reacts with oxygen, and carbon dioxide is produced and released into the air **(1)**. Trees take a lot of carbon dioxide from the air by photosynthesis **(1)**. If they are destroyed by burning, they can no longer remove carbon from the air **(1)** or act as carbon stores. **(1)**

3 (a) The carbon cycle is the movement of carbon through the biotic and abiotic components of the environment. **(1)**

(b) (i) Process A is respiration **(1)**. Respiration takes place in plants, animals and decomposers/all organisms **(1)**. It releases carbon back into the air as carbon dioxide, a waste product formed when glucose is broken down using oxygen to release energy. **(1)**

(ii) Process B is photosynthesis **(1)**. During photosynthesis, plants absorb carbon dioxide gas **(1)** and convert it to carbon compounds, e.g. glucose. **(1)**

    (iii) Process C is feeding **(1)**. Carbon compounds in plants are passed to animals when they eat plants, and from animal to animal along a food chain **(1)**. This provides the glucose for respiration. **(1)**

    (iv) Process D is combustion **(1)**. In combustion fossil fuels or plant material reacts with oxygen to burn **(1)**. Carbon dioxide is produced as a waste product and released into the air. **(1)**

80. The water cycle

1 (a) A model of how water moves through the abiotic (and some biotic) parts of an ecosystem **(1)**

  (b) Two from: water makes up a large percentage of the body mass of most organisms **(1)**; most of the reactions in cells take place in water **(1)**; we are constantly losing water to the environment and need to replace it. **(1)**

  (c) A = evaporation, B = transpiration, C = condensation/cloud formation, D = cooling/precipitation **(2)**

2 (a) Sea water contains lots of salt and this would upset the balance of our bodies. **(1)**

  (b) Desalination **(1)**

  (c) Seawater is heated until the water evaporates, forming steam. **(1)**
The steam is condensed in another container to give pure water. **(1)**
The salt and any other impurities are left behind in the very salty water remaining. **(1)**

3 Water evaporates from the surface of seas, rivers, lakes and the land. **(1)**
The water vapour condenses as it rises and forms clouds. **(1)**
The water continues to cool as it rises to form precipitation (rain or snow) that returns the water to the Earth. **(1)**
Some of the water evaporates again, but some runs off the land into the sea or enters rivers and flows back into the sea, and the process continues. **(1)**
Some of the water filters down to underground natural reservoirs. **(1)**

81. The nitrogen cycle

1 D **(1)**

2 (a) Plants need nitrates to make proteins and DNA so they can grow properly **(1)**. Growing crops every year can mean the nitrate levels in the soil get low **(1)**. Adding nitrate fertilisers means the growing crops have all the nitrates they need. **(1)**

  (b) Different types of plants take different combinations of minerals out of the soil **(1)** so by rotating the types of crops grown the farmer reduces the chances of a crop being low in the minerals it needs. **(1)**

  (c) Peas and clover have root nodules containing bacteria that can fix nitrogen from the air and convert it into nitrogen compounds in the soil **(1)**. They have a mutualistic relationship so the bacteria are protected in the plant roots **(1)** and the plants get nitrogen compounds directly from the bacteria **(1)**. If a farmer grows these crops and then digs the roots into the soil, the following year a different crop will benefit from the additional nitrogen compounds in the soil. **(1)**

3 (a) Bacteria **(1)**

  (b) A: Nitrogen fixation by bacteria in the root nodules of plants such as peas and clover **(1)**

B: Nitrogen fixation – nitrogen in the air being joined with other chemicals to form nitrogen-containing compounds by bacteria in the soil and by lightning **(1)**

C: Denitrification – breakdown of nitrogen-containing compounds to nitrogen by bacteria in the soil **(1)**

D: Breakdown of proteins and urea in animals and animal products by decomposers including soil bacteria **(1)**

E: Absorption of nitrates from the soil by plants **(1)**

82. Extended response – Ecosystems and material cycles

Answers could include the following points **(6)**

- Panda numbers fell as a result of hunting and loss of habitat. As the bamboo forests that were home to pandas were destroyed there would have been a general loss of biodiversity.

- The lowest recorded panda population was 1114 in the 1980s. Since then the populations have increased with a 16.8% increase in the last 10 years (1864 – 1596 = 268/1596 × 100). Numbers are still not up to the population in 1974–7 (2459).

- Ways of increasing panda numbers could include protecting the habitat by preventing the destruction of the bamboo forests, stopping the hunting and killing of pandas for their body parts by making it illegal, and perhaps captive breeding programmes to help increase the population to release in the wild.

- By conserving the bamboo forests for the pandas, the biodiversity of the whole area would be conserved and will possibly increase as all the plants and other animals which thrive in that habitat will be able to grow and reproduce successfully again.

Chemistry

83. Formulae

1 (a) K **(1)** (b) Cl **(1)** (c) Helium **(1)** (d) Sulfur **(1)**

2 Chlorine **(1)** element **(1)** molecules **(1)** atoms **(1)**

3 B **(1)** C **(1)**

4 Carbon **(1)** hydrogen **(1)** oxygen **(1)**

5 Sodium: 2 **(1)** carbon: 1 **(1)** oxygen: 3 **(1)**

84. Equations

1 Magnesium + copper chloride **(1)** → magnesium chloride + copper (the products can be either way round) **(1)**

2 Sodium + chlorine **(1)** → sodium chloride **(1)**

3 (s) **(1)** (s) **(1)** (g) **(1)**

4 A **(1)**

5 (a) There is one hydrogen and one chlorine on the left side of the equation **(1)** *but* there are two hydrogens and (two) chlorines on the right side of the equation. **(1)**

  (b) 2 **(1)**

6 C **(1)**

85. Hazards, risk and precautions

1 (a) Flammable **(1)**

  (b) The Bunsen burner will get hot, which can cause burns **(1)**
The magnesium will give out a bright light, which can damage the eyes **(1)**

  (c) Any **two** sensible precautions, for example, wear eye protection, do not touch the hot Bunsen burner, allow the Bunsen burner to cool down before touching it, do not look directly at the bright light, use tongs to hold the magnesium in the flame. **(2)**

2　(a) D **(1)**

　　(b) A risk is the chance that someone or something will be harmed **(1)** if exposed to hazard. **(1)**

　　(c) Any sensible precaution with reason, for example, wear eye protection **(1)** to protect the eyes because acid is corrosive and can damage them **(1)**

86. Atomic structure

1　Clockwise from top left: shell **(1)** proton **(1)** neutron **(1)** nucleus **(1)** electron **(1)**

2　(a) Proton **(1)** (b) Neutron **(1)** (c) Electron **(1)** (d) Electron **(1)** (e) Proton and neutron **(1)** (f) Proton and neutron **(1)**

3　Atoms have equal numbers of protons and electrons **(1)** so have the same amount of positive and negative charge. **(1)**

4　$2 \times 60\,000$ **(1)** $= 120\,000\,mm$ **(1)** $120\,000/1000 = 120\,m$ **(1)**

87. Isotopes

1　Mass number − The total number of neutrons and protons in an atom **(1)**
Atomic number − The number of protons (and electrons) in an atom **(1)**
Relative atomic mass − The average mass of atoms of an element, taking into account all its different isotopes and their abundances **(1)**

2　(a) 3 **(1)**　　　　　　(c) 4 **(1)**
　　(b) 7 **(1)**　　　　　　(d) 3 **(1)**

3　B **(1)**

4

Isotope	Number of protons	Number of neutrons	Number of electrons	
Sodium-23	*11*	*12*	*11*	**(1)**
Oxygen-16	8	8	8	**(1)**
Magnesium-26	12	14	12	**(1)**
Chlorine-37	17	20	17	**(1)**

88. Mendeleev's table

1　mass **(1)** group **(1)**

2　(a) 7 **(1)**

　　(b) They have similar properties/they react with water/oxygen in the same way **(1)**

　　(c) He left gaps for elements that he predicted had not yet been discovered **(1)**. He did not put titanium into group 3 because it did not share similar properties with the other elements in group 3. **(1)**

3　Any one from: they both use symbols to represent the elements/the elements are arranged in columns/the elements are arranged in rows/the elements are grouped into columns depending on their properties.

4　B **(1)** C **(1)**

89. The periodic table

1　Periods **(1)** number **(1)** properties **(1)** groups **(1)**

2　(a) Magnesium **(1)**
　　(b) Helium **(1)**
　　(c) Bromine **(1)**

3　(a) W **(1)** X **(1)**　　　(c) Z **(1)**
　　(b) Y **(1)** and Z **(1)**　　(d) W **(1)**

4　Any box in group 0 is shaded **(1)**

90. Electronic configurations

1　2,8,7 **(1)**

2　Two electrons drawn on the innermost shell **(1)**, six electrons drawn on the outer shell **(1)**

3　It has three occupied electron shells **(1)** so is in period 3 **(1)**
It has eight electrons in its outer shell **(1)** so is in group 0/8 **(1)**

4　(a) 2 **(1)**　　　　(b) 4 **(1)**　　　　(c) Carbon **(1)**

91. Ions

1　A **(1)** C **(1)**

2　(a) It loses an electron **(1)**
　　(b) +1 **(1)**
　　(c) The sodium atom has an equal number of positive protons and negative electrons **(1)** so has no overall charge **(1)**. When an ion is formed it loses one electron, so now has an overall charge of +1. **(1)**

3　(a) Mg^{2+} **(1)**　　　　(c) Al^{3+} **(1)**
　　(b) S^{2-} **(1)**　　　　(d) Br^{-} **(1)**

4

Ion	Number of protons	Number of electrons	
Li^{+}	3	2	**(1)**
Cl^{-}	17	18	**(1)**
Ca^{2+}	20	18	**(1)**
O^{2-}	8	10	**(1)**

92. Formulae of ionic compounds

1　(a) Lithium chloride **(1)**
　　(b) Lithium bromide **(1)**
　　(c) Magnesium oxide **(1)**
　　(d) Calcium carbonate **(1)**
　　(e) Sodium sulfate **(1)**
　　(f) Potassium hydroxide **(1)**
　　(g) Copper nitrate **(1)**

2　D **(1)**

3　(a) $NaCl$ **(1)**　　　　(c) MgO **(1)**
　　(b) Na_2O **(1)**　　　　(d) $MgCl_2$ **(1)**

93. Properties of ionic compounds

1　(a) cation **(1)**
　　(b) anion **(1)**
　　(c) anion **(1)**

2　B **(1)** C **(1)**

3　(a) Mg^{2+} **(1)** and O^{2-} **(1)**
　　(b) The ions have opposite charges **(1)** which attract **(1)**
　　(c)  **(1)**
　　(d) The bonds between the ions are very strong **(1)** so a lot of heat energy is required to break them. **(1)**

4　(a) No **(1)**, because the ions are held together by strong bonds so cannot move. **(1)**
　　(b) Yes **(1)**, because the bonds have been broken and the ions can move. **(1)**

94. Covalent bonds

1　Oxygen **(1)** carbon dioxide **(1)**

2　There is a single covalent bond between the atoms in hydrogen chloride. **(1)**
There are double covalent bonds between the atoms in carbon dioxide. **(1)**

3　A shared pair of electrons **(1)**

4　(a) Correct diagram, for example, one pair of dots and crosses in shared areas **(1)**; two pairs of dots/crosses on O only **(1)**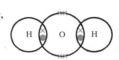

(b) Correct diagram, for example, one pair of dots and crosses in shared area **(1)**; three pairs of dots/crosses on each Cl **(1)**

5 $1 \times 10^{-9} \div 1 \times 10^{-10} = 10$ **(1)** one order of magnitude difference **(1)**

95. Simple molecular substances

1 B **(1)** C **(1)**
2 (a) Y: intermolecular force **(1)**
   (b) X **(1)** Y **(1)** Y **(1)** X **(1)**
3 They do not contain any charged particles **(1)**
4 The forces between the molecules are weak **(1)** so do not require a lot of heat energy to break them **(1)**

96. Giant molecular substances

1 A **(1)** C **(1)**
2 (a) It contains only carbon atoms/its atoms are all the same element **(1)**
   (b) Can conduct electricity – delocalised electrons between layers are able to move **(1)**
       Feels slippery (layers slide over each other) – weak intermolecular forces between layers **(1)**
       Solid at room temperature – strong covalent bonds between atoms **(1)**
3 Each atom is bonded to three others by strong covalent bonds **(1)**, so the atoms are held strongly together **(1)**, so diamond is harder than the materials it is cutting. **(1)**

97. Other large molecules

1 D **(1)**
2 (a) A **(1)** C **(1)**
   (b) 0.71×1000 **(1)** = 710 pm **(1)**
3 Similarity: They are both formed of interlocking hexagonal rings of carbon atoms **(1)**
   Difference: Graphite contains many layers, graphene only contains one **(1)**
4 Carbon nanotubes are very strong **(1)** because they contain strong covalent bonds between the carbon atoms **(1)** which means a lot of force is needed to break the structure they are reinforcing. **(1)**

98. Metals

1 (a) From the top: positive ions **(1)** delocalised electrons **(1)**
   (b) The (delocalised) electrons are free to move through the metal **(1)**
2 (a) Metal: W and Y **(1)**
       Non-metal: X and Z **(1)**
   (b) W **(1)** because it has a melting point lower than 20 °C **(1)** and can conduct electricity/is shiny **(1)**
   (c) Z **(1)** because it can conduct electricity **(1)** but it is dull at room temperature **(1)**

99. Limitations of models

1 A **(1)**
2 (a) Suitable diagram, for example:
       Single lines drawn between each C and H **(1)**
       Two lines drawn between the two Cs **(1)**
   (b) CH_2CH_2 **(1)**
   (c) CH_2 **(1)**
3 Advantage: Any one from: it shows the size of the atoms relative to their bonds/it shows the structure in 3D **(1)**
   Disadvantage: Any one from: it does not show how the electrons are shared/it does not show the symbols for the atoms **(1)**

100. Relative formula mass

1 $CH_4 = 16$ **(1)** $CO_2 = 44$ **(1)** $H_2O = 18$ **(1)** $NH_3 = 17$ **(1)**
2 (a) $63.5 + 16 = 79.5$ **(1)**
   (b) $12 + 16 = 28$ **(1)**
   (c) $14 + (16 \times 2) = 46$ **(1)**
3 (a) $24 + 12 + (16 \times 3) = 84$ **(1)**
   (b) $63.5 + ([16 + 1] \times 2) = 97.5$ **(1)**
   (c) $24 + ([14 + (16 \times 3)] \times 2) = 148$ **(1)**

101. Empirical formulae

1 (a) Magnesium + oxygen → magnesium oxide **(1)**
   (b) To allow the oxygen from the air to reach the magnesium **(1)** so the magnesium could fully react. **(1)**
2 (a) $23.98 - 23.82$ **(1)** = 0.16 g **(1)**
   (b) Mass of magnesium used = $23.82 - 23.58 = 0.24$ g **(1)**
       Mass of oxygen used = 0.16 g
       $\frac{0.24}{24} = 0.1$ $\frac{0.16}{16} = 0.1$ **(1)**
       $\frac{0.01}{0.01} = 1$ $\frac{0.01}{0.01} = 1$ **(1)**
       Empirical formula is MgO **(1)**
3 $12 + (3 \times 1) = 15$ **(1)**
   $30/15 = 2$ **(1)**
   Empirical formula is C_2H_6 **(1)**

102. Conservation of mass

1 (a) Copper + oxygen → copper oxide **(1)**
   (b) A **(1)**
2 (a) A change in colour shows a new substance has been made **(1)**
   (b) $2.2 + 1.6 = 3.8$ g **(1)**
3 (a) Use tongs/test tube holder/retort stand to hold the test tube **(1)** to avoid burns
   (b) $CuCO_3$ **(1)** → $CuO + CO_2$ **(1)**
   (c) $8.61 - 5.57 = 3.04$ g **(1)**

103. Concentration of solution

1 D **(1)**
2 (a) 1 dm³ **(1)**   (b) 0.1 dm³ **(1)**   (c) 0.35 dm³ **(1)**
3 (a) 2500 cm³ **(1)**   (b) 800 cm³ **(1)**
   (c) 50 cm³ **(1)**
4 (a) 0.04 g cm⁻³ **(1)**   (b) 40 g dm⁻³ **(1)**
5 $20 \times 2 = 40$ g **(1)**

104. Extended response – Types of substance

The answer may include some of the following points: **(6)**

Comparing melting and boiling points:
• Silicon dioxide has the highest melting and boiling point
• Oxygen has the lowest melting and boiling point
• Silicon dioxide is a solid (at room temperature)
• Bromine is a liquid (at room temperature)
• Oxygen is a gas (at room temperature)

Reason for oxygen's/bromine's melting and boiling points based on structure:
• Oxygen/bromine is made up of simple molecules
• The intermolecular forces between the molecules are weak
• Can be weakened with relatively little heat energy during melting
• Can be broken with relatively little heat energy during boiling

Comparison of oxygen and bromine:
• The intermolecular forces between the molecules in bromine are stronger than those between the molecules of oxygen
• More heat energy is required to melt/boil bromine compared with oxygen

Reason for silicon dioxide's melting and boiling point based on structure:
- Silicon dioxide has a giant covalent structure in a 3D structure
- Atoms are bonded by strong covalent bonds
- A relatively high amount of heat energy is needed to weaken/break all the bonds

105. States of matter
1 A (1)
2 (a) Melting (1)
  (b) Condensing/condensation (1)
  (c) Boiling/evaporating (1)
3 In a chemical change new substances are made, but in a physical change no new substances are made (1)
4 (a) Sublimation/subliming (1)
  (b) The particles move further apart so they are not touching (1), and move around randomly and fast (1)
5 (a) Gas (1)   (b) Liquid (1)   (c) Solid (1)

106. Pure substances and mixtures
1 Carbon – element (1); carbon dioxide – compound (1); air – mixture (1); helium – element (1)
2 It is a mixture/not a pure substance (1) so the boiling point will not be the same as pure water. (1)
3 (a) An element only contains one type of atom/atoms from only one element (1), but a compound contains two or more types of atoms (1) bonded together. (1)
  (b) Compound (1) mixture (1)
  (c) They are not bonded/joined together (1)
4 (a) C (1)   (b) 50 °C (1)
  (c) Pure (1) because it condenses/freezes at a certain temperature (not over a range) (1)

107. Distillation
1 (a) C (1)
  (b) Fractional (distillation) (1)
2 (a) It is where condensation takes place (1) and the steam condenses to form pure water. (1)
  (b) To make sure the water around the condenser stays cold enough (1) for condensation to take place (1)
  (c) It increases (1) because the volume of water decreases (1), but the mass of salt stays the same. (1)
  (d) Heat the water until it boils, measure the boiling point (1); it will boil at exactly 100 °C (1)
  Or, cool the water so it freezes, measure the freezing point; (1) it will freeze at exactly 0 °C (1)

108. Filtration and crystallisation
1 (a) Soluble (1); insoluble (1); solution (1)
  (b) From top to bottom: filter funnel (1) filter (1) beaker (or conical flask) (1)
  (c) They filter the mixture to remove the sand (1). It works because there are small holes in the filter paper that allow the salt solution to pass through (1), but the sand particles are too large so stay behind on the paper. (1)
  (d) 1. Heat the filtrate until it is saturated (1) 2. Leave the filtrate to cool (1) 3. Separate the crystals from the liquid by decanting/filtration (1)

109. Paper chromatography
1 (a) Water (1)   (b) Paper (1)   (c) Water (1)
  (d) To stop the solvent/water from evaporating (1)
2 To stop the solvent/water evaporating (1)
3 (a) There are three spots (1)
  (b) It contains three food colourings B, C (1) and an unknown (1)
  (c) 5.4 (1) / 10.2 (1) = 0.53 (1)

110. Investigating inks
1 D (1)
2 (a) The ink in the pen will dissolve in the solvent, pencil will not (1)
  (b) Waterproof pens are not soluble in water (1) so propanone is used because it will dissolve the ink (1) and act as a suitable mobile phase. (1)
  (c) Do not use the propanone near any naked flames (1)
  (d) To stop the fumes being inhaled because propanone vapour can cause dizziness (1)
  To protect the eyes because propanone irritates eyes (1)
3 (a) Each ink is attracted to both the mobile phase and stationary phase (1). The ink that travelled further is more attracted to the mobile phase than the other ink. (1)
  (b) Distance travelled by ink spot divided by distance travelled by the solvent (1)

111. Drinking water
1 (a) Water that is safe to drink (1)   (b) C (1)
2 (a) Chlorine is bubbled through the water (1)
  (b) To kill any microorganisms (1) that could cause disease (1)
3 (a) Aluminium hydroxide (1)
  (b) water (1) sulfuric acid (1)
4 Using distillation is a good idea because: it will provide clean drinking water/the country has plenty of coastline so a good supply of sea water/it will kill any microorganisms in the water/the Sun can be used to evaporate the water.
  Using distillation is not a good idea because: it can be expensive/it needs a lot of energy.
  Any four points from above but must include a disadvantage (4)

112. Extended response – Separating mixtures
The answer may include some of the following points: (6)

Separating the sand
- Use filtration to separate the sand from the mixture
- Sand is insoluble in water and ethanol
- Water and ethanol will go through the filter paper; sand will be left behind on the filter paper

Separating the ethanol
- Use fractional distillation to remove the ethanol from the water
- Ethanol and water are miscible liquids
- Heat the mixture to a temperature of 78 °C
- The ethanol will boil and turn into a gas
- The ethanol will cool in the condenser and turn into a liquid, which is collected
- The water will not boil and will stay in the flask as a liquid

113. Acids and alkalis
1 pH lower than 7 = acid (1) pH higher than 7 = alkali (1)
  (OH⁻) = alkali (1) (H⁺) = acid (1)
2 (a) H^+ (1)   (c) H^+ (1) NO_3^- (1)
  (b) NaOH (1)   (d) K^+ (1) OH^- (1)
3 (a) X (1) (b) Substance Z has a pH of 7 (1). The information shows this because it turns universal indicator green/litmus purple (1)
  (c) Blue (1)
4 Litmus will only show if the solution is acidic, alkaline or neutral (1). Universal indicator goes different colours according to the pH of the solution. (1)

114. Bases and alkalis

1 Salt **(1)** carbon dioxide **(1)** water **(1)**

2

Acid	Base		
	Sodium hydroxide	Potassium oxide	Copper carbonate
Hydrochloric acid	Sodium chloride	Potassium chloride	Copper chloride **(3)**
Sulfuric acid	Sodium sulfate	Potassium sulfate	Copper sulfate **(3)**
Nitric acid	Sodium nitrate	Potassium nitrate	Copper nitrate **(3)**

3 (a) It is not soluble in water **(1)**
 (b) Calcium chloride **(1)**
4 (a) Mg (s) + 2 **(1)** HCl (aq) → $MgCl_2$ (aq) + H_2 (g)
 (b) The magnesium is reacting to form the salt magnesium chloride. **(1)**
 (c) They would hear a pop noise **(1)** because the gas hydrogen was produced in the reaction. **(1)**

115. Neutralisation

1 (a) C **(1)** D **(1)**
 (b) A neutral solution is made **(1)**
2 (a) Calcium oxide is corrosive, whereas calcium hydroxide is an irritant **(1)** so there are fewer risks with using calcium hydroxide. **(1)**
 (b) 2 **(1)** 2 **(1)**
 (c) Universal indicator/pH probe **(1)**
 (d)

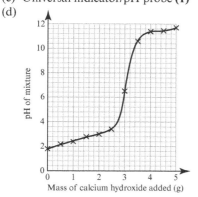

 (1)
 (e) 3 g **(1)**

116. Salts from insoluble bases

1 B **(1)** D **(1)**
2 (a) Copper oxide + sulfuric acid **(1)** → copper sulfate + water **(1)**
 (b) To increase the rate of reaction between the acid and the copper oxide **(1)**; to reduce the risk of burns/to stop acidic fumes being released **(1)**
 (c) There will be some copper oxide/a black powder left at the bottom of the beaker **(1)**
 (d) Use filtration **(1)** by pouring the mixture through filter paper in a funnel **(1)**, the liquid will go through the filter paper and can be collected **(1)**
 (e) Use a Bunsen burner to heat the mixture **(1)** until small crystals start to form **(1)** then leave the basin in a warm place to evaporate the rest of the water. **(1)**

117. Salts from soluble bases

1 Filter funnel **(1)** beaker **(1)** evaporating basin/dish **(1)**
2 (a) Burette **(1)** (b) Pipette **(1)**
3 (a) Indicator **(1)**   (b) Pink **(1)**
 (c) The solution will go colourless **(1)**
4 (a) 30.85 – 15.45 **(1)** = 15.40 (cm³) **(1)**
 (b) 15.45 + 15.40 + 15.40 = 46.25 **(1)**
   46.25/3 = 15.42 (cm³) **(1)**

118. Making insoluble salts

1 Soluble: sodium hydroxide **(1)** silver nitrate **(1)** potassium carbonate **(1)**
 Insoluble: lead sulfate **(1)**

2

Leave the salt to dry on the filter paper.	4
Pour distilled water through the filter paper.	3
Mix solutions of two substances that will form the insoluble salt.	1
Filter the mixture.	2

 (1)

3 (a) Copper hydroxide + sodium chloride **(1)** copper hydroxide is circled **(1)**
 (b) Potassium nitrate + lead sulfate **(1)** lead sulfate is circled **(1)**
 (c) Calcium carbonate + sodium nitrate **(1)** calcium carbonate is circled **(1)**
4 (a) Calcium nitrate **(1)** and sodium/potassium/ammonium carbonate **(1)**
 (b) Silver nitrate/sulfate **(1)**; any chloride (apart from silver and lead) **(1)**
 (c) Barium nitrate/chloride **(1)**; any sulfate (apart from lead, barium and calcium) **(1)**

119. Extended response – Making salts

The answer may include some of the following points: **(6)**

Making the solutions
• Add water to solid sodium sulfate and solid calcium chloride, and stir to create solutions

Carrying out the reaction
• Mix together the solutions
• Solid/a precipitate of calcium sulfate will be produced
• The reaction is sodium sulfate (aq) + calcium chloride (aq) → sodium chloride (aq) + calcium sulfate (s)

Purifying and drying the precipitate
• Filter the mixture
• The sodium chloride solution will pass through the filter paper
• The solid calcium sulfate will stay on the filter paper
• Pass distilled water through the filter paper to wash the calcium sulfate/remove any sodium chloride contaminating the calcium sulfate
• Leave the calcium sulfate to dry on the filter paper

120. Electrolysis

1 Electrolysis – a process where electricity is used to break down an ionic compound **(1)**
 Electrolyte – an ionic compound in the molten state or dissolved in water **(1)**
 Cation – positively charged ion **(1)**
 Anion – negatively charged ion **(1)**
2 Labels clockwise from top: d.c. supply **(1)** anode **(1)** electrolyte **(1)** cathode **(1)**.
3 (a) Melted/in the liquid state **(1)**
 (b)

Electrolyte	Product formed at the cathode	Product formed at the anode	
Copper chloride	Copper	Chlorine	**(1)**
Aluminium bromide	Aluminium	Bromine	**(1)**
Sodium oxide	Sodium	Oxygen	**(1)**

121. Electrolysing solutions

1 B **(1)** D **(1)**
2 (a) Cations: Na^+ **(1)** H^+ **(1)**
   Anions: Cl^- **(1)** OH^- **(1)**

(b) Negatively, cathode, gain **(1)** negatively, anode, lose **(1)**

(c) Negative: hydrogen **(1)** positive: chlorine **(1)**

3 (a) Negative: silver **(1)** positive: chlorine **(1)**

(b) Negative: hydrogen **(1)** positive: oxygen **(1)**

122. Investigating electrolysis

1 (a) Cathode: (+)0.15 **(1)** anode –0.18 **(1)**

(b) To remove liquid on the electrodes **(1)**, so the mass is accurate/to remove errors in the mass **(1)**

(c) The mass of the anode decreased **(1)** because copper atoms in the anode changed into copper ions, which went into the solution. **(1)**
The mass of the cathode increased **(1)** because copper ions in the solution changed into copper atoms, which were deposited on the cathode. **(1)**

(d) Any one from: some of the copper ions formed from copper atoms in the anode will still be in solution/will not have deposited on the cathode. Some of the copper deposited on the cathode may have fallen off when the cathode was moved. **(1)**

2 (a) The changes in mass to both electrodes will be higher **(1)**

(b) Any one from: current/voltage/concentration of copper sulfate solution/surface area of electrodes/ temperature of copper sulfate solution **(1)**

123. Extended response – Electrolysis

The answer may include some of the following points: **(6)**

Observation 1

• Hydrogen gas is being formed at the anode

• Hydrogen collects in test tube A

• Oxygen gas is being formed at the cathode

• Oxygen collects in test tube B

Observation 2

• Twice as much hydrogen as oxygen formed

• This is because the formula of water is H_2O

• There are twice as many hydrogen atoms in a molecule of water as oxygen atoms

Observation 3

• The test for hydrogen involves adding a lighted splint

• A 'pop' noise is a positive result

124. The reactivity series

1 Potassium hydroxide **(1)** Hydrogen **(1)**
K **(1)** H_2 **(1)**

2 (a) It is very reactive **(1)** so it is not safe to add it to acid **(1)** because the reaction would be very vigorous/it might cause an explosion **(1)**

(b) B, A, D, C **(1)**

(c) C **(1)** because it did not react with either water or acid **(1)**. Copper is an unreactive metal. **(1)**

3 (a) Hydrogen is produced. **(1)**

(b) Magnesium is not a very reactive metal. **(1)**

(c) Any two from: increase the concentration of the acid, increase the temperature of the acid, increase the surface area of the magnesium/use smaller pieces of magnesium **(2)**

125. Metal displacement reactions

1 (a) C **(1)** (b) B **(1)**

2 (a) Magnesium chloride **(1)** iron **(1)**

(b) Silver nitrate **(1)**

3 (a) Any one from: a colour change/an increase in temperature. **(1)**

(b) Y, X, Z **(1)**

Y can displace both X and Z from their salt solutions, so Y must be more reactive than both X and Z. **(1)**
X can displace Z, but not Y so it is more reactive than Z, but less reactive than Y. **(1)**
Z can displace neither and so must be the least reactive. **(1)**

126. Explaining metal reactivity

1 (these are the words that remain) More **(1)** loses **(1)** positive **(1)**

2 Sodium, aluminium, iron, gold **(1)**

3 (a) It is more reactive than hydrogen **(1)**

(b) A **(1)** D **(1)**

(c) Cations **(1)**

(d) −2 **(1)**

127. Metal ores

1 (a) Platinum **(1)**   (c) Iron ore **(1)**

(b) Zinc oxide **(1)**   (d) Sodium **(1)**

2 (a) The loss of oxygen from a substance **(1)**

(b) Reduced – zinc oxide **(1)**; oxidised – carbon **(1)**

3 (a) It costs more to extract the ore than the metal can be sold for. **(1)**

(b) $(0.4/56) \times 100$ **(1)** $= 0.71$ **(1)**

(c) In the future we may start to run out of copper **(1)** so it will be worth more money. **(1)**

128. Iron and aluminium

1

Extracted by electrolysis	Extracted by reduction	Does not need to be extracted – found pure
Aluminium	Iron	Gold
Potassium	Zinc	Silver

(1)

2 (a) Electrolysis is very expensive to carry out **(1)** because it uses a lot of electricity. **(1)**

(b) Iron **(1)** carbon monoxide **(1)**

(c) (i) 2 **(1)**   (ii) g **(1)** l **(1)**

3 (a) When aluminium is melted its ions are free to move **(1)** to the electrodes. **(1)**

(b) Anode: oxygen **(1)**; cathode: aluminium **(1)**

(c) The oxygen reacts with the carbon anode to produce carbon dioxide. **(1)**

129. Recycling metals

1 (a) It will be melted **(1)** and cooled to form new objects **(1)**

(b) B **(1)** C **(1)**

2 Aluminium **(1)**
If you recycle a metal it means that less of it has to be extracted from its ores.
Extracting the metal aluminium from its ores requires a lot of energy **(1)** because a lot of electricity is needed for electrolysis. **(1)**

3 Advantage: Any one from: less dust/noise, limited resources are not used up, environment not damaged **(1)**
Disadvantage: Any one from: fewer jobs for people, less money for company/country **(1)**

130. Life-cycle assessments

1 (a) Clockwise from top: obtaining raw materials, manufacturing the product, using the product, disposing of the product **(1)**

(b) An arrow linking the final box to the first **(1)**

2 (a) Plastic **(1)**

(b) They take up more space **(1)** so more vehicles are needed to transport them. **(1)**

(c) Any two from: they are made from a resource that can be replaced, less energy is used in manufacture, they are easily recycled **(2)**

131. The Haber process
1 (a) The reaction is reversible **(1)**
  (b) C **(1)** D **(1)**
2 B **(1)** D **(1)**
3 (a) Hydrogen **(1)** and nitrogen **(1)**
  (b) Ammonia **(1)**
  (c) Catalyst: iron **(1)**; Temperature: 450 °C **(1)**; Pressure: 200 atmospheres **(1)**
  (d) To increase the rate of reaction **(1)** so the ammonia is made in a shorter time **(1)**
  (e) To stop it breaking back down **(1)** into the reactants **(1)**

132. Extended response – Reactivity of metals
The answer may include some of the following points: **(6)**

Identification of metal X
• Metal X could be aluminium or zinc

Evidence from test 1
• Metal X does not react with water so it cannot be a reactive metal
• It cannot be potassium, sodium or calcium

Evidence from test 2
• Metal X does react with dilute acid so it must be above hydrogen in the reactivity series
• It could be magnesium, aluminium, zinc or iron

Evidence from test 3
• Metal X displaces iron from its salt
• Metal X must be more reactive than iron

Evidence from test 4
• Metal X does not displace aluminium from its salt
• Metal X must be aluminium or less reactive than aluminium

133. The alkali metals
1 First column on left (group 1) shaded **(1)**
2 B **(1)** C **(1)**
3 (a) It is very reactive **(1)**. The oil stops it reacting with water/air. **(1)**
  (b) To remove the oil **(1)** so the potassium would react with the water **(1)**
  (c) (i) The reaction gives out heat **(1)**, which ignites the hydrogen formed in the reaction. **(1)**
     (ii) The pH turned from neutral to alkaline **(1)** because potassium hydroxide is formed in the reaction. **(1)**
  (d) The lithium would not burst into flames **(1)** because lithium is less reactive than potassium. **(1)**
4 (a) They get bigger. **(1)**
  (b) As you go down the group the outer electron gets further from the nucleus **(1)** so it is more easily lost during a reaction. **(1)**

134. The halogens
1 7 **(1)**
2

Name	Formula	State at room temperature	Colour	
Fluorine	F_2	Gas	Pale yellow	**(1)**
Chlorine	Cl_2	Gas	Yellow-green	**(1)**
Bromine	Br_2	Liquid	Red-brown	**(1)**
Iodine	I_2	Solid	Grey	**(1)**

3 (a) x-axis labelled as 'halogen' **(1)**; y-axis labelled as 'boiling point (°C)' **(1)**; bar drawn correctly for bromine (59 °C) **(1)**
  (b) As you go down the group the boiling point increases **(1)**. This is because the intermolecular forces between the molecules get stronger **(1)** so more heat energy is needed to overcome them. **(1)**
  (c) Answer around 300 °C **(1)**

135. Reactions of halogens
1 (a) A **(1)**
2 (a) Sodium + chlorine **(1)** → sodium chloride **(1)**
  (b) Sodium fluoride **(1)**
  (c) Fluorine is more reactive than chlorine **(1)** so the reaction is too violent/might explode **(1)** and so is not safe/is a hazard **(1)**
3 (a) –1 **(1)**
  (b) Halogen atoms have seven electrons in their outer shell **(1)**. When they react with metals they gain one electron to complete the shell. **(1)**
4 A fluorine atom is smaller than a chlorine atom **(1)**, so its outer shell is closer to the nucleus **(1)**. The force of attraction between the outer shell and the nucleus is stronger **(1)** so fluorine gains an electron more easily. **(1)**

136. Halogen displacement reactions
1 More **(1)** less **(1)**
2 (a) Potassium chloride + bromine **(1)**
  (b) No reaction **(1)**
  (c) Sodium bromide + iodine **(1)**
  (d) No reaction **(1)**
3 (a) They are less hazardous **(1)**
  (b) $Cl_2(aq) + 2NaBr(aq) → 2NaCl(aq) + Br_2(aq)$
     1 mark for balancing, 1 mark for state symbols
  (c) The mixture would get darker **(1)** because bromine is made. **(1)**
4 (a) C **(1)** No halogens could displace it because chlorine is more reactive than iodine and bromine **(1)**
  (b) A **(1)** Chlorine could displace it but not iodine **(1)**

137. The noble gases
1 (a) 0/8 **(1)**
  (b) Atoms **(1)** 8 **(1)**
2 Helium – to fill airships – density lower than air **(1)**
  Argon – to fill filament lamps – unreactive **(1)**
  Krypton – shield gas in welding – denser than air **(1)**
3 (a) As you go down the group the density increases **(1)**
  (b) 5 × 1.78 **(1)** = 8.9 g **(1)**
  (c) Answer between 3 and 4 $g\,dm^{-3}$ **(1)**
4 2 electrons in the innermost shell **(1)** 8 electrons in the outer shell **(1)**

138. Extended response – Groups
The answer may include some of the following points: **(6)**

Identifying the halogens
• X is bromine
• Y is chlorine
• Z is iodine

Explanation for identification
• Y will displace both bromine and iodine from their compounds. Therefore, Y must be more reactive than bromine and iodine, and so must be chlorine.
• X will displace iodine, but will not displace chlorine. Therefore, X must be more reactive than iodine, but less reactive than chlorine, and so must be bromine.

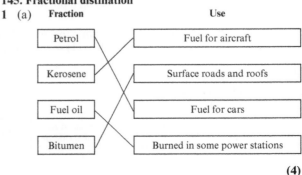

- Z will not displace either chlorine or bromine. Therefore, Z must be less reactive than chlorine and bromine, and so is iodine.

Explaining the pattern
- Reactivity decreases as you go down the group.
- This is because the atoms get bigger as you go down the group, and the outer electron shell is further from the nucleus, so the attractive force of the nucleus on the outer shell electron is lower.
- This means that an electron is gained less easily.

139. Rates of reaction
1 Reactant (1) energy (1) activation (1)
2 Iron rusting – 1 (1), lithium reacting with water – 2 (1), explosion between hydrogen and oxygen – 3 (1)
3 Any three from: increase the concentration of acid; increase the temperature of the acid; increase the surface area of the zinc; use a catalyst (3)
4 Steeper line than the small chips line (1); line flattens at 1.40 g (1)
5 (a) Increasing the pressure will increase the rate of the reaction. (1)
   (b) Increasing the pressure will push the particles of reactant together (1) so they are more likely to collide and react. (1)

140. Investigating rates
1 (a) To stop the acid spraying out (1), but to allow the gas/carbon dioxide to escape (1)
   (b) Independent variable: size of marble chip/surface area of marble chip (1)
      Dependent variable: change in mass (1)
   (c) Any two from: temperature of acid, volume of acid, mass of marble chips, concentration of acid (2)
   (d) Mass at start – mass at end (1)
   (e) 3.4/5 (1) = 0.68 g/min (1)
   (f) The smaller the marble chip the faster the rate of reaction (1). This is because there are more particles of the reactant available (1) so the frequency of successful collisions increases. (1)

141. Exam skills – Rates of reaction
1 (a) C (1)
   (b) 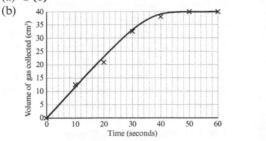 (3)
   (c) The reaction finished after 46 seconds (accept 44–47) (1). The graph shows this because the line flattens (1) as no more gas was produced. (1)
   (d)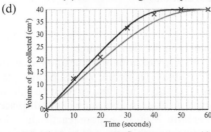
      Line is less steep (1) flattens out at 40 cm³ (1)

142. Heat energy changes
1 A (1) C (1)
2 (a) Polystyrene is an insulator of heat (1). It is used because it reduces energy transfer from the reaction mixture. (1)
   (b) 12.9 − 21.2 (1) = −8.3 °C (1)
   (c) Is an endothermic reaction: B and C (1)
      Is an exothermic reaction: A (1)
      Could be a neutralisation reaction: A (1)
3 (a) Exothermic (1)
   (b) The energy needed to break the bonds in methane and oxygen is less than the energy released when bonds are formed in carbon dioxide and water. (2)

143. Reaction profiles
1 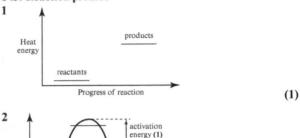 (1)

2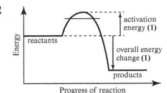

3 (a) The reaction is exothermic (1). The diagram shows this because the energy level of the reactants is higher than the energy level of the products. (1)
   (b) 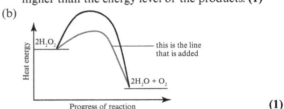 (1)

144. Crude oil
1 D (1)
2 New crude oil takes millions of years to form. (1)
3 A (1) D (1)
4 C_5H_{10} (1)
5 (a) Hydrogen (1) because it is a hydrocarbon/only contains carbon and hydrogen atoms (1)
6 As a starting material for industrial chemical processes (1), as a fuel (1) or any other correct use, for example, bitumen used for road building

145. Fractional distillation
1 (a)

Fraction	Use
Petrol	Fuel for aircraft
Kerosene	Surface roads and roofs
Fuel oil	Fuel for cars
Bitumen	Burned in some power stations

(4)
   (b) X (1)
   (c) Gases (1) bitumen (1) petrol (1)

2 The longer the molecule, the higher the boiling point **(1)** because the strength of the intermolecular forces between the molecules increases **(1)** so more energy must be transferred to overcome them. **(1)**

146. Alkanes
1 B **(1)** C **(1)**
2 A **(1)** D **(1)**
3

Name	Formula	Structure
Methane **(1)**	CH_4	H | H—C—H | H
Ethane	C_2H_6	H H | | H—C—C—H | | H H **(1)**
Propane	C_3H_8 **(1)**	H H H | | | H—C—C—C—H | | | H H H **(1)**

4 $C_{20}H_{42}$ **(1)**

147. Incomplete combustion
1 C **(1)**
2

Product	Complete combustion	Incomplete combustion	
Carbon		✓	**(1)**
Carbon monoxide		✓	**(1)**
Carbon dioxide	✓	✓	**(1)**
Water	✓		**(1)**

3 (a) Incomplete combustion is taking place **(1)** because the supply of oxygen is limited. **(1)**
   (b) Carbon monoxide attaches to the haemoglobin in red blood cells **(1)**, reducing the amount of oxygen being carried around the body. **(1)**
4 (a) Complete **(1)**
   (b) The safety flame is produced by incomplete combustion **(1)**. Complete combustion gives out more energy than incomplete combustion. **(1)**

148. Acid rain
1 Clockwise from bottom left: power station **(1)**; acidic gases **(1)**; rain cloud **(1)**; acid rain **(1)**; distant city **(1)**
2 A **(1)** C **(1)**
3 Any two from: damages trees, makes lakes more acidic, kills organisms in lakes, damages carbonate-containing rocks **(2)**
4 Oxygen **(1)** S **(1)** SO_2 **(1)**
5 Sulfur dioxide is produced, which dissolves in rainwater **(1)**
6 (a) 2 **(1)**
   (b) Vehicle engines **(1)** or any other correct answer, for example, lightning strikes

149. Choosing fuels
1 (a) Petrol **(1)** diesel **(1)** fuel oil **(1)**
   (b) Crude oil **(1)**
   (c) They are being used much faster than they are being produced **(1)**
2 B **(1)** C **(1)**
3 (a) 2 **(1)** 2 **(1)**
   (b) Advantage: burning hydrogen produces only water **(1)**, burning petrol produces ash/smoke/carbon dioxide/polluting gases **(1)**

4 Electrolysis uses electricity **(1)**, which may be produced by burning fossil fuels. **(1)**

150. Cracking
1 Alkanes/saturated hydrocarbons **(1)** shorter **(1)** alkenes/unsaturated hydrocarbons **(1)**
2 (a) B **(1)** C **(1)**
   (b) It produces shorter alkanes that are more useful as fuels **(1)** and alkenes, which can be used to make plastics. **(1)**
3 (a) Paraffin **(1)** ethene **(1)**
   (b) A catalyst/to increase the rate of reaction **(1)**

151. Extended response – Fuels
The answer may include some of the following points: **(6)**

Advantages of using hydrogen
- It has more energy per kilogram than petrol
- It produces only water, which is not a pollutant, but burning petrol produces polluting gases/carbon dioxide/ash/smoke
- It is very flammable/burns easily
- It can be produced from water, a renewable resource

Disadvantages of using hydrogen
- It has less energy per litre than petrol
- It is more difficult to store and transport than petrol/it has to be stored at high pressure
- It is dangerous/explosive
- Filling stations would need to be adapted in order to use hydrogen as a fuel
- It may be made from methane, which is a non-renewable resource
- Making it using electrolysis requires electricity, which may be generated by burning fossil fuels

152. The early atmosphere
1 D **(1)**
2 B **(1)** C **(1)**
3 (a)

Event	Order
Plant life evolves in the oceans	2
Oxygen builds up in the atmosphere	4
The Earth cools and oceans form	1
Oxygen builds up in the oceans	3

(1)

   (b) Photosynthesis **(1)**
   (c) The water vapour in the atmosphere **(1)** cooled and condensed. **(1)**
4 From top to bottom: oxygen, 21% **(1)** other gases, 1% **(1)** nitrogen, 78% **(1)**

153. Greenhouse effect
1 A **(1)** B **(1)**
2

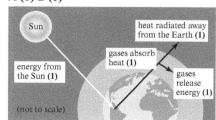

3 (a) Carbon dioxide is produced when fossil fuels burn **(1)**. More fossil fuels are being burned as the number of vehicles and power stations increases. **(1)**
   (b) Carbon dioxide is a greenhouse gas so more heat is absorbed **(1)** and released into the atmosphere. **(1)**
   (c) Any two from: change in weather patterns/climate change, melting ice/poles, rising sea levels **(2)**

154. Extended response – Atmospheric science

The answer may include some of the following points: **(6)**

Description of graph

- Temperature change has increased steadily since 1950
- The temperature change now is 0.8 °C higher than the mean temperature between 1850 and 1900
- The concentration of carbon dioxide has increased since 1850
- From around 280 parts per million to 380 parts per million

Conclusion

- A rise in carbon dioxide is linked to human activity
- This is because it is released when fossil fuels are burned
- Human population has risen/there are more vehicles on the roads/more fossil fuel-burning power stations
- There is a correlation between the rise in temperature and the rise in carbon dioxide concentration
- The rise in carbon dioxide could lead to a rise in temperature because carbon dioxide is a greenhouse gas

Validity of conclusion

- The measurements may have been taken from one place on Earth; the same pattern might not be seen in all places
- Some of the data was taken over a hundred years ago; it might not be accurate
- Just because there is a correlation, it does not mean that a rise in carbon dioxide has caused a rise in temperatures; there may be another explanation

Physics

Answers provided in workbook are not repeated here.

155. Key concepts

1 (a) mass = force/acceleration **(1)**
   (b) acceleration = force/mass **(1)**
2 Length – m, Mass – kg, Weight – N, Temperature – K **(1)**
3 (a) 50 kHz **(1)**
   (b) 4 m **(1)**
4 5 significant figures **(1)**
5 (b) 3.56 **(1)**
6 (b) 1.0300×10^4 **(1)**
   (d) 3.5×10^{-2} **(1)**
   (e) 4.29×10^5 **(1)**

156. Scalars and vectors

1 (a) Scalar quantity: magnitude only **(1)**; vector: magnitude and direction **(1)**
   (b) Any scalar quantity, e.g. temperature, mass, energy **(1)**. Any vector quantity, e.g. force, displacement, acceleration **(1)**
2 Acceleration is a vector quantity **(1)** because it has magnitude and direction **(1)**. Calculated from change in velocity divided by time/velocity is a vector. **(1)**
3 Speed: scalar as it only has magnitude **(1)**. Velocity: vector as it has magnitude and direction. **(1)**
4 (a) At constant velocity the resultant force is zero (i.e. the magnitude of the forwards and backwards forces are equal). **(1)** So the magnitude of the backwards force is 500 N. **(1)**
   (b) 0 N **(1)**
5 (a) 3 mph to the north is a vector quantity because there is a magnitude and a direction. **(1)**
   (b) 3 mph to the south **(1)**
6 Mass: scalar **(1)**; related to the number of particles / in kg **(1)**. Weight: vector (has size and direction) **(1)** is the gravitational force on a mass / in N **(1)**

157. Speed, distance and time

1 $v = \frac{x}{t}$ **(1)**
2 (b) Between 120–140 s **(1)** because slope is steepest **(1)**
   (c) 240 / 140 **(1)** = 1.7 m/s **(1)**
   (d) 0 m **(1)**
3 $v - u = at$ =, $v - 0 = 5 \times 10$ **(1)** so $v = 50$ m/s **(1)**
4 Distance = 100 000 m, time = 2×3600 s = 7200 s **(1)**; 100 000/7200 = 14 m/s to two significant figures **(1)**

158. Equations of motion

1 (a) C **(1)** (the equation is $a = \frac{v - u}{t}$ where v is final velocity and u is initial velocity)
2 $a = \frac{8 - 2}{1}$ **(1)** = 6 m/s² **(1)**
3 Driving force increases **(1)**, mainly air resistance/drag/friction plus smaller component from friction from tyres/other mechanical components/engine/other example increases **(1)**. Driving force is bigger than frictional force/wtte. **(1)**
4 $a = \frac{5^2 - 0^2}{2 \times 100}$ **(1)** = 0.13 m/s² **(1)**
5 $v = \sqrt{2 \times 1.5 \times 500 + 1^2}$ **(2)** = 39 m/s **(1)**
6 $x = \frac{13^2 - 2^2}{2 \times 2}$ **(2)** = 41.25 m **(1)**

159. Velocity/time graphs

1 (a) Acceleration **(1)** (b) The area under the graph **(1)**
   (c) Constant velocity **(1)**
2 (b) In the second section (70–80 s) the line is steeper / slope is greater / size of gradient is greater. **(1)** Therefore the acceleration will be higher. **(1)**
   (c) $a = \frac{20 - 10}{70 - 50}$ **(1)** = 0.5 m/s² **(1)**
   (d) 70 to 80 s: 150 m **(1)**; 80 to 90 s: 400 m **(1)**; total distance: 550 m **(1)**

160. Determining speed

1 Set up a ramp and measure the distance the car will be going **(1)**. One person lets the car roll down the slope, while a second student starts a timer and then stops the timer when the car goes past the finishing line. **(1)** Repeat three times. **(1)**
2 A typical speed for walking is 1.5 m/s (accept values between 1 and 2 m/s) **(1)**, whereas a typical running speed is 3 m/s (accept values between 2.5 and 4 m/s) **(1)**
3 $x = 11 \times 2 \times 60 = 1320$ m **(1)** = 1.3 km to two significant figures **(1)**
4 (a) 8 min = 8×60 s = 480 s **(1)** $v = \frac{x}{t}$ **(1)** = $\frac{5}{480}$ m/s = 0.01 m/s **(1)**
   (b) The equation for speed is $v = \frac{x}{t}$ **(1)**. If you divide the same distance by a bigger number, the result will be smaller. **(1)**
5 1333.3 s **(1)** = 22 min **(1)**

161. Newton's first law

1 Newton's first law states that if the forces on an object are balanced **(1)**, the object will either stay at rest **(1)** or it will continue to move at constant velocity. **(1)**
2 (a) Diagram showing a box with one arrow pointing one way labelled 'friction' and 10 N **(1)** and one arrow pointing in the opposite direction labelled 'pushing force' and 30 N **(1)**
   (b) The forces are not balanced **(1)**
   (c) 20 N **(1)**
3 Newton's first law states that the resultant force on an object must be zero for an object to be at rest **(1)**.

Therefore, if two forces are acting on an object, they must cancel out **(1)**. Two forces of the same magnitude could be acting on the object in opposite directions. **(1)**

4 Newton's first law states that an object at constant speed or at rest experiences a resultant force that is zero **(1)**. If there is a force acting on an object in constant motion, it will change velocity **(1)**. Because velocity is a vector, it has direction and magnitude. So the rocket might speed up or slow down and/or change direction. **(1)**

162. Newton's second law

1 C **(1)**

3 $F = 4 \times (5 - 0)$ **(2)** $= 20\,N$ **(1)**

4 A strong headwind will cause a lot of air resistance **(1)**, opposing the thrust force of the engine **(1)**. The resultant force in the forward direction is reduced. **(1)**

5 (a) $m = \frac{F}{a}$ **(1)** $= \frac{3750}{15}$ **(1)** $= 250\,kg$ **(1)**

   (b) $t = \frac{10}{15}$ **(2)** $= 0.67\,s$ **(1)**

163. Weight and mass

1 Vector, has magnitude, measured in N **(1)**

2 (b) 65×26 **(1)** $= 1690\,N$ **(1)**

   (c) $g = W/m = 725/65$ **(1)** $= 11.2\,N/kg$ **(1)**

3 (a) Independent: mass of objects **(1)**; dependent: weight of objects **(1)**

   (b) Straight line **(1)** through the origin **(1)**

4 (a) $g = \frac{198000}{55000}$ **(1)** $= 3.6\,N/kg$ **(1)**

5 Smallest on Earth **(1)** because smallest value for g **(1)**. Highest on a neutron star **(1)** because highest value for g. **(1)**

164. Force and acceleration

1 $F = ma = 5 \times 0.450$ **(1)** $= 2.25\,N$ **(1)**

2 $m = \frac{400}{0.4}$ **(1)** $= 1000\,kg$ **(1)**

3 $F = 400\,000\,N$ **(1)**, $F = ma$ **(1)** $a = F/m = 400\,000/2000 = 200\,m/s^2$ **(1)**

4 (a) $W = 70 \times 10$ **(1)** $= 700\,N$ **(1)**

   (b) $W = mg$: weight is dependent on the mass and the gravitational field strength **(1)**. The skydiver's mass and the gravitational field strength do not change during her fall. **(1)**

   (c) Initially downwards force /weight larger **(1)** than air resistance because effect of air resistance depends on speed and the vertical speed is small **(1)**. As the skydiver speeds up, air resistance goes up **(1)** until finally she will reach terminal velocity **(1)** where all forces are balanced. **(1)**

165. Newton's third law

1 For every action force there is an equal and opposite reaction force / If object X exerts a force on object Y, then object Y exerts a force on object X with the same magnitude, opposite direction and of the same type. **(1)**

2 20 N **(1)** upwards **(1)**

3 Any example that makes sense, e.g. a book staying on the table and not falling towards the centre of the Earth, since the force on the book from the Earth and the force on the book from the table cancel out **(1)**

4 Any two from: squirrel pushing on the ground ↔ ground pushing on squirrel **(1)**; nut pushing on paw ↔ paw pushing on nut **(1)**; wind or air movement pushing on squirrel ↔ squirrel pushing back with equal and opposite force **(1)**

5 Newton's third law states that for every action force there is an equal and opposite reaction force **(1)**. Without action-reaction forces, we wouldn't be able to move/

stand/stop/other suitable example. **(1)** Walking/standing/sitting: person pushing against the floor/chair/etc. ↔ floor/chair/etc. pushes back with equal force / friction when walking/running/stopping/etc. ↔ person pushing against friction / any suitable example **(1)**.

166. Human reaction time

2 Being tired, age, distractions, caffeine and alcohol ticked **(1)**

3 Person 1 holds a metre ruler, person 2 puts their index finger and thumb around the ruler at 0 cm leaving a gap **(1)**. Person 1 lets go of the ruler **(1)**. Person 2 grips the ruler as soon as they can, read off distance from 0 cm **(1)**. Repeat at least three times and calculate mean **(1)**. Calculate reaction time / $t = \sqrt{\frac{2x}{g}}$ (where t is reaction time, x is distance, and g gravitational field strength). **(1)**

4 $x = 10 \times 0.25$ **(1)** $= 2.5\,m$ **(1)**

5 (a) 0.27 m **(1)**

   (b) substitute x $(= 0.27\,m)$ and g into equation **(1)**, $t = 0.23\,s$ **(1)**

   (c) Typical reaction time 0.2–0.25 s **(1)**. Ruby's result is within this range / allow ecf. **(1)**

167. Stopping distance

2 Thinking distance: tiredness, alcohol and drugs, distraction **(1)**
   Braking distance: amount of friction between the tyres and the road, conditions of the brakes, mass of the car **(1)**

3 The slower car will have a shorter stopping distance **(1)** because both the thinking and braking distance are shorter **(1)** / reverse argument

4 Thinking distance = 3 m **(1)**. Stopping distance = 3 m + 14 m = 17 m **(1)**. The driver can stop before reaching the fox. **(1)**

5 Thinking distance not affected **(1)**. Braking distance increases **(1)** because less friction between the tyres and the road surface. **(1)**

168. Extended response – Motion and forces

Answer could include the following points **(6)**:

Definitions
- Vectors have direction and magnitude
- Whereas scalars have magnitude only

Examples
Any 2 examples of a vector and scalar, e.g.
- Mass/weight
- Velocity/speed
- Distance/displacement

Descriptions
Any 2 descriptions of a vector and scalar, e.g.
- Velocity has a certain direction such as north or south
- Speed only has magnitude
- Weight has direction towards the Earth's centre
- Mass only has magnitude
- Distance refers to how much ground has been covered by an object / only has magnitude
- Displacement has magnitude and direction

169. Energy stores and transfers

1 Any two from: chemical **(1)** kinetic **(1)** gravitational potential **(1)** elastic **(1)** thermal **(1)** magnetic **(1)** electrostatic **(1)** nuclear **(1)**

3 Any example relating to one of the four ways of energy transfers, e.g. electrical to light and heat (light bulb), chemical to electrical (battery), chemical to kinetic and sound and heat (motor) **(2)**

ANSWERS

4 (a) Battery (chemical store) **(1)** $\longrightarrow$

lamp **(1)** $\xrightarrow{\text{transferred as light}}$ environment **(1)**

$\xrightarrow[\text{energy (1)}]{\text{transferred as thermal}}$ environment

(b) Law of conservation of energy: total energy is conserved **(1)**. In the torch: total energy is conserved: chemical energy from battery is converted to light energy and thermal energy. **(1)**

5 fuel (chemical store) $\xrightarrow{\text{Mechanically (1)}}$ wheels (kinetic energy) **(1)**

motor (kinetic store) **(1)** $\xrightarrow[\text{(sound waves) (1)}]{\text{Thermally (1) + by radiation}}$ environment (heat store)

170. Efficient heat transfer

1 Thermal insulation can be put in to avoid heat loss by conduction from a house **(1)**. Any two methods of insulation, e.g. double glazing, cavity wall insulation, loft insulation, carpets, draught excluders, curtains **(2)**

2 House on the right **(1)** because it has no additional insulation and no double glazing **(1)**, so there will be faster thermal / heat transfer to the outside (which will mean having the heating on longer to compensate) **(1)**

3 (a) Diagram should show an arrow representing the energy input (600; suitable width of arrow) **(1)**, useful energy out horizontally (175; suitable width) **(1)**, the waste energies (270 for walls and windows with suitable width) **(1)**, 30 for ventilation with suitable width **(1)**, 125 for roof and floor with suitable width, i.e. 1 cm width for 100 kWh **(1)**.

(b) Efficiency = $\frac{175}{600} \times 100$ **(1)** = 29.2% **(1)**

171. Energy resources

1 Any three from: solar **(1)** wind **(1)** tidal **(1)** biofuels **(1)** hydroelectric **(1)**

2 Non-renewable energy resources will eventually run out **(1)** because the rate of use is higher than the rate of resources being replaced **(1)**

3 (b) Wind turbines need wind to generate electricity **(1)**. They need to be in places with lots of wind to work well **(1)**, so flat plains or out at sea is ideal as these are windy places. **(1)**

4 (a) Two from: provide large amount of energy **(1)** run most of the time (except for when maintenance is carried out) **(1)** no CO_2 emissions **(1)** copes well with changes in demand **(1)**

(b) Two from: nuclear waste has to be disposed of **(1)** nuclear waste remains radioactive for many thousands of years **(1)** potential of radioactive material escaping into the environment, e.g. when there is an accident **(1)** large amounts of CO_2 and toxic chemicals produced during the production of the fuel rods **(1)**

(c) Accept either yes or no; look for argument using points from (a) or (b) **(1)**. Student also needs to say that their chosen reason(s) are more important than any points from the other side of the argument **(1)** and why (environmental / health / financial / electricity demand / reliability) **(1)**

5 Fossil fuels readily available **(1)** compact form of energy / arguments such as solar panel would take up a lot of space on the car / cars are set up for fossil fuels and changing this would cost lots of money **(1)**

172. Patterns of energy use

1 Any two from: increase in world population **(1)** development of technology that uses power **(1)** power stations require energy to make electricity **(1)**

2 Two statements with explanation from: non-renewable so will run out **(1)** releases CO_2 which is a greenhouse gas **(1)** releases SO_2 causes pollution / acid rain **(1)** releases soot which leads to health problems **(1)** coal has to be mined which takes up land / destroys habitats **(1)**

3 (a) Most efficient: hydroturbine **(1)**; least efficient: nuclear power **(1)**

(b) Three from: mix of energy resources to meet demand all the time **(1)** some resources may only be available some of the time (e.g. solar or wind), but may be more environmentally friendly (2 marks for this statement) **(1)** some resources may be more expensive than others **(1)** impact on the environment: CO_2, habitats / size of land required, other toxic emissions or waste that is difficult to manage **(1)** preference of people in a certain area **(1)** investment by companies, e.g. companies advertising 'green energy' **(1)**

4 Student gives three reasons supporting the argument, or one reason against and two reasons supporting the argument: renewable energy resource **(1)** clean **(1)** cost-competitive **(1)** contributes to development of remote communities **(1)** use of lake that forms behind dam for recreation (boating, swimming, etc.) **(1)** environmental damage **(1)** high upfront cost **(1)** may lead to droughts **(1)** risk of flooding lower regions **(1)** CO_2 and methane emission **(1)** flooding of region behind dam may displace people or agriculture **(1)**

5 Any four from: world population has been growing over the past 100 (–200) years **(1)**. Energy consumption has increased similarly over the same time period **(1)**. More energy might be required in future to sustain a larger population using more energy / less energy might be required because of improved technologies **(2)**. Switch to more renewable energy resources **(1)**. More efficient production of energy **(1)** increases are different across nations (i.e. developing world has more rapidly changing energy demands as economies stabilise and grow) **(1)**

173. Potential and kinetic energy

1 C **(1)**

2 (a) GPE = $1 \times 2 \times 10$ **(1)** = 20 J **(1)**
(b) GPE = $2 \times 1 \times 10$ **(1)** = 20 J **(1)**

3 KE = $\frac{1}{2} \times 60 \times 33^2$ **(1)** = 32 670 J = 32.67 kJ **(1)**

4 (a) GPE = $4 \times 90 \times 10$ **(1)** = 3600 J/3.6 kJ **(1)**

(b) KE = GPE = 3600 J **(1)**; $v = \sqrt{\frac{2 \times 3600}{4}}$ **(1)** = 42 m/s **(1)**

174. Extended response – Conservation of energy

Answer could include the following points **(6)**:
Description of process:
- Water stored in tank has gravitational potential energy
- Water falls converting energy / turning turbine
- Electricity generated is used to generate heat in the heating element of the kettle
- Conduction

Energy conversions:
- Gravitational potential (water) → kinetic / sound / heat (turbine) (mechanical)
- Kinetic (turbine) → kinetic / sound / heat (generator) (mechanical)
- Kinetic (generator) → electrical
- Electrical → heat / sound (heating element / kettle)
- Heat (heating element / kettle) → heat (water)

Energy losses:
- Wasted energy conversions, e.g. sound energy, heat in generator / turbine
- Heat loss to environment from heating element

175. Waves

1 Transfers energy / information **(1)**, does not transfer matter **(1)**

2 Amplitude and wavelength correctly labelled **(2)**

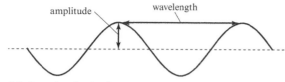

3 (a) Longitudinal: vibrations parallel to direction in which the wave is travelling **(1)**; transverse: vibrations of particles perpendicular / at right angles to the direction in which the wave is travelling **(1)**

(b) One from: both transfer energy / information, have amplitude / frequency / wavelength **(1)**

4 (a) 6.1 cm / answer read off 0 to intercept with x-axis (6.1 – 6.15) **(2)**

(b) Read off the height of a peak = 1 cm **(2)**

5 Longitudinal – sound: vibrations parallel to direction in which the wave is travelling **(1)** sound requires particles to travel/ cannot travel in vacuum **(1)**; Transverse – light: vibrations perpendicular / at 90° / at right angles to the direction in which the wave is travelling **(1)** light does not need particles / can travel through vacuum **(1)**

176. Wave equations

1 A **(1)**

2 $v = f\lambda = 600\,000 \times 500$ **(1)** $= 300\,000\,000$ m/s **(1)**

3 $\lambda = \frac{3 \times 10^8}{5 \times 10^{14}}$ **(1)** $= 6 \times 10^{-7}$ m **(1)**

4 $t = d/v = \frac{500}{50}$ **(1)** $= 10$ s **(1)**

5 (a) $v = f\lambda = 3300 \times 0.1$ **(1)** $= 330$ m/s **(1)**

(b) $t = d/v = \frac{500}{330}$ **(1)** $= 1.51$ s **(1)** (allow $\frac{500}{\text{their (a)}}$)

6 wavelength = 0.4 m, speed = 2 km/h $= \frac{2000\,\text{m}}{3600\,\text{s}} = 0.56$ m/s (convert the units correctly = 1 mark)

frequency $= \frac{\text{speed}}{\text{wavelength}}$ **(1)** $= \frac{0.56}{0.4} = 1.4$ Hz **(1)**

177. Measuring wave velocity

1 You could stand at a measured distance from a wall **(1)**. You would then make a loud noise **(1)**. Using stop watch measure the time it takes to hear the echo **(1)**. Use $v = \frac{d}{t}$ to work out speed / repeat / take average of repeats **(1)**

2 (a) Check the result is reliable / calculate the mean / identify any outliers **(1)**

(b) 2.15 s **(1)**   (c) 1.81 s **(1)**

(d) $v = \frac{d}{t} = \frac{2 \times 300}{1.81}$ **(1)** $= 330$ m/s **(1)**

(e) $\lambda = \frac{v}{f} = \frac{330}{500}$ **(1)** $= 0.66$ m **(1)**

3 $\lambda = \frac{v}{f} = \frac{0.02}{5}$ **(1)** 4×10^{-3} m **(1)** (plus 1 mark for converting units, 1 mark for converting to standard notation)

4 frequency = 50 000 Hz, wavelength = 1.25 m **(1)**
$v = f\lambda = 50\,000 \times 1.25$ **(1)** $= 62\,500$ m/s **(1)**
This wave is not an electromagnetic wave, as the velocity is not 300 000 000 m/s **(1)**

178. Waves and boundaries

1 Refraction is the change in direction of a wave when it enters a different medium. **(1)**

2 Drawing should show the refracted ray in the glass block being bent towards the normal **(1)**, and away from the normal when it exits the glass block **(1)** (the emergent should be parallel to the incident ray)

3 (a) Sound is a longitudinal wave **(1)** where particles vibrate back and forth / creating areas of compression and rarefaction **(1)**. Idea that something needs to be there to be compressed **(1)**

(b) Air molecules have less kinetic energy at cold temperatures **(1)**, so move more slowly and collide less **(1)**, so sound travels more slowly **(1)**

4 Light ray changes speed **(1)** as it enters a denser material **(1)**

5 No change in direction **(1)**

6 Refraction as light enters water **(1)** change in speed and direction of the light waves **(1)**, making the pencil appear kinked **(1)** (Image is formed by light reflecting off the pencil, being bent on the way **out** of the water and your eyes picking the rays up)

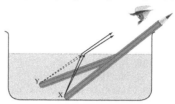

179. Waves in fluids

1 A, B, C **(1)**

2 Set up the ripple tank and produce waves **(1)**. Count the number of waves that pass a point per second. **(1)** Idea that this should be done for a period of time, e.g. one minute **(1)** to get more accurate value **(1)**

3 150/60 = 2.5 Hz **(2)**

4 Set up a ripple tank **(1)**. Use a stroboscope to 'freeze' the waves **(1)**. Use a ruler to measure the wavelength. **(1)**

5 (a) mean wavelength = (1.0 + 1.2 + 1.1 + 1.1) / 4 = 1.1 cm = 0.011 m. **(1)** To calculate mean frequency: convert 30 s to 1 min by multiplying the value by 2; add the frequencies together and divide the sum by 4 to get the mean, then multiply by 60 to convert from minutes to seconds;
mean frequency = 5.25 × 60 = 315 Hz. **(1)**

(b) speed = 0.011 m × 315 Hz = 3.465 m/s (accept calculations involving other units, e.g. 346.5 cm/s)

6 $v = f\lambda$ **(1)**. If frequency decreases, wavelength must increase for speed to remain the same **(1)**

180. Extended response – Waves

Answer could include the following points **(6)**:

• Set up the two microphones facing each other in a line at a set distance / 1 m apart / any other sensible value / use ruler / tape measure to measure distance.

• Connect them to the timer

• Make a sound using the two bricks right behind microphone 1

• Microphone 1 picks up the sound and activates timer

• Sound then picked up by microphone 2, which stops the timer

• Calculate speed of sound using $v = \frac{d}{t}$

• Repeat / calculate average

• Compare to literature value

181. Electromagnetic spectrum

1 Transverse wave; accept light wave **(1)**

2 Radiowaves, microwaves, infrared, visible, ultraviolet, X-rays, gamma rays **(1)**

3 Speed = wavelength × frequency **(1)**. As the frequency of an electromagnetic wave increases, the wavelength decreases **(1)**, so the speed is the same for all electromagnetic waves / speed of light / 3 × 10⁸ m/s **(1)**

4 Transverse waves **(1)**, transfer energy not matter **(1)**, vibrations are at right angles to the direction the wave is travelling **(1)**

5 $\lambda = \frac{v}{f} = \frac{3 \times 10^8}{300 \times 10^9}$ **(1)** $= 0.001$ m = 1 mm **(1)**

6 Wavelength of 4.3×10^{14} Hz has frequency of 700 nm / 0.0000007 m / 7×10^{-7} m: $\frac{3 \times 10^8}{4.3 \times 10^{14}}$ **(2)**

wavelength of 7.7×10^{14} Hz has frequency of 390 nm / 0.00000039 m / 3.9×10^{-7} m: $\frac{3 \times 10^8}{7.7 \times 10^{14}}$ **(2)**

182. Investigating refraction

1 The speed changes. If the light ray is incident at an angle, then the ray also changes direction. **(1)**
2 As ray enters glass block: bends towards the normal **(1)**. As ray exits glass block: bends away from the normal. **(1)**
3 Draw two normals (one at entry surface and one at exit surface) **(1)**, then measure angle between the normal and the ray in four places (incident and refracted at both surfaces). **(1)**
4 When the angle of incidence is 0° / the incident ray enters at 90° to the glass surface **(1)**
5 Any five from: Materials: glass block, pencil, sheet of paper, ruler, protractor, light source **(1)**. Draw the outline of the glass block on the sheet of paper and remove glass block **(1)**. Draw the normal on the surfaces using a protractor **(1)** and shine a light through the block entering the block where you have drawn the normal **(1)**. Mark path of light with crosses and draw line showing path of light through the block using the ruler **(1)**. Measure the angles using protractor. **(1)**
6 The eye **(1)**, light is refracted (by lens / cornea) to help focus it (on the retina) / so we can see **(1)**

183. Dangers and uses

1 Visible light
2 Cause mutations of the DNA **(1)** which can cause skin cancer / cause eye conditions **(1)**
3 (a) Cooking / heat up water **(1)**, communication **(1)**
(b) $\lambda = \frac{v}{f} = \frac{3 \times 10^8}{5 \times 10^8}$ **(1)** = 0.6 m **(1)**
4 Two uses and dangers
Uses: cooking / grills / toasters, thermal imaging, short-range communication / laptops / remote controls, optical fibres, security systems / burglar alarms / motion detectors
Dangers: can cause burns
5 Cause mutations of DNA **(1)**. This causes cancer **(1)**. It can also make cancer cells die **(1)** so it helps to treat certain cancers. **(1)**

184. Changes and radiation

1 Radiation is absorbed or emitted when electrons jump between energy levels **(1)**
2 Electrons, protons, neutrons **(3)**
3 Nucleus in centre containing protons **(1)** and neutrons **(1)** Electrons on energy shells surrounding the nucleus **(1)**
4 Certain / defined amount of energy required for electron to jump to a higher energy level **(1)**
5 Emitted from the nucleus of unstable atoms **(1)**
6 Both emit energy / radiation **(1)** Nuclear: gamma rays emitted / high energy radiation **(1)**. Electrons: lots of different wavelengths possible **(1)**
7 (a) Gamma rays are emitted from certain unstable nuclei **(1)** when the energy changes occur within the nucleus **(1)**. High-energy radiation produces mutations in cells **(1)** and kills cells. **(1)**
(b) Gamma radiation can kill cells / cause mutations **(1)**, can cause cancer / kill healthy cells / side effects during cancer treatment **(1)**

185. Extended response – Light and the electromagnetic spectrum

Answer could include the following points **(6)**:
- Waves listed from low to high frequency / energy: radiowaves, microwaves, IR, visible, UV, X-rays, gamma
- High frequency / small wavelength corresponds to high energy
- Examples of uses for each group given

At least one use and one danger for one group, and the rest of the marks allocated for the other groups (again minimum one use or one danger).

Dangers:
- X-rays / gamma rays: mutations to DNA / kills cells / causes cancer
- UV: sunburn / skin cancer / damages eyes
- IR: causes skin burns
- Microwaves: heating water inside cells can damage or kill them

Uses:
- Gamma: sterilise food / medical equipment / detection of cancer in scanners / treatment of cancer
- X-rays: e.g. medical use to look inside bodies / airport security scanners
- UV: detect security marks from special pens with fluorescent lamps / detection of forged banknotes / disinfect water
- Visible: eyes and vision / illumination / photography
- IR: cooking / thermal images / short-range communication / remote controls / information sent via optical fibres / burglar alarms
- Microwaves: mobile phones / satellite transmissions / cooking
- Radio waves: broadcasting radio and TV / communication with ships, planes, satellites

186. Structure of the atom

1 Neutrons, protons, electrons **(3)**
2 Nucleus containing neutrons **(1)** and protons **(1)** at centre **(1)**, electrons in energy shells around the nucleus **(1)**
3 Atom: 10^{-10} m, nucleus 10^{-14} m / 10^{-15} m **(1)**; atom is $10\,000/10^4$ or $100\,000/10^5$ times bigger than the nucleus **(1)**
4 Protons are positive **(1)**, electrons are negative **(1)**, number of electrons = number of protons **(1)**
5 (a)

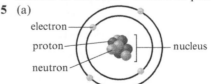

(4)

(b) Mass concentrated in nucleus **(1)** because protons and neutrons are the heaviest particles and electrons are very light **(1)**
(c) All atoms contain protons, neutrons and electrons **(1)**. Different elements have different numbers of protons. **(1)**

187. Atoms and isotopes

1 Same number of protons **(1)**, but different numbers of neutrons **(1)**
2 $^{35}_{17}\text{Cl}$ **(1)** and $^{37}_{17}\text{Cl}$ **(1)**
3 B and C **(1)** same number of protons **(1)**, but different number of neutrons **(1)**

4

	Number of protons	Number of neutrons	Number of electrons	
$^{7}_{3}\text{Li}$	3	4	3	(1)
$^{32}_{16}\text{S}$	16	16	16	(1)
$^{40}_{20}\text{Ca}^{2+}$	20	20	18	(1)
$^{19}_{9}\text{F}^{-}$	9	10	10	(1)
$^{200}_{80}\text{Hg}$	80	120	80	(1)

5 Drawing and labelled: in the nucleus 11 protons (1), 12 neutrons (1). Electrons: 11 electrons (1), 2 on inner shell and 8 on 2nd shell and 1 on outer shell (1)

188. Atoms, electrons and ions

1 An atom that has gained or lost electron(s) (so that it is charged) (1)
2 Electrons jump from lower to higher energy level (1) provided the amount of energy absorbed is exactly the required amount (i.e. the difference between energy levels) (1)
3 Bombarding atoms with alpha or beta particles / absorbing a certain amount of energy / chemically when forming bonds (1)
4 (a) Zero (1)
  (b) +1 / + / 1+ (1)
  (c) Protons = 19, neutrons = 39 – 19 = 20 (1) number of protons = number of electrons for a neutral atom (1) therefore 19 electrons (1)
5 Ions are charged species (1) so positive ions would be attracted to negative electrode (1), negative ions would be attracted to positive electrode. (1)
6 Protons and neutrons in nucleus (1), protons positively charged (1), neutrons neutral (1). Electrons in shells around the nucleus (1) and negatively charged (1)

189. Ionising radiation

1 Ionising radiation (1) consisting of 2 neutrons and 2 protons / He nucleus / helium nucleus (1)
2 Geiger counter (1), put a sheet of paper between source and Geiger counter / test at distance of more than 5 cm (1), if there is no radioactivity detected, it is an alpha source (1)
3 Opposite charge / β⁺-particles positive and β⁻-particles negative (1), deflected in opposite direction by magnetic field (1)
4 Stopped only by thick lead or concrete (1), so interacts weakly with matter / goes straight through materials (1)

5

Type of radiation	Relative Mass	Charge	Penetrating power	
Alpha	4	+2	Very low	(1)
Beta⁺	1/1840	+1	Low	(1)
Beta⁻	1/1840	−1	Low	(1)
Gamma	0	0	High	(1)
Neutron	1	0	High	(1)

6 Neutron radiation: (very) high penetrating power (1), travel through buildings / materials / long distances (1). Alpha particles: very low penetrating power (1), only travel through 5 cm of air / stopped by thin sheet of paper (1)

190. Background radiation

1 Low-level naturally occurring radiation we're exposed to all the time (1)
2 Radon gas (1) ground (rocks) and buildings (1)

3 Uranium in some rocks (1) decays to radon (1)
4 Any three from: nuclear power stations, nuclear weapons, hospitals, food and drink (3)
5 Radon gas emitted from rocks / gets into houses (1). Breathed in / inside a person's body (1) will interact with tissue / named organs / cause mutations (1) because it has very high ionising power (1)
6 Background radiation made up of (at least three of these) radon gas, ground and buildings, medical, nuclear power, cosmic rays, food and drink (1). Idea that some of these will vary depending on where you live, e.g. radon gas depends on type of rock where you live or how close you live to a nuclear power station (1)
7 Any sensible method, e.g. sealing cracks in the foundations, ventilation, building house on slabs of concrete, raised floor with cavity vented to outside, etc. (2) *Answer needs to include a description of the method and how this will reduce radon gas exposure.*

191. Measuring radioactivity

1 Geiger-Müller tube / photographic film (1)
2 Number of alpha, beta particles or gamma rays detected by a GM tube per specified time (1)
3 Dosimeter shows exposure to radiation (1). Work to keep workers safe / alert them of (high) exposure (1) Workers in nuclear power station at higher risk of exposure / possible leak / accident (1)
4 Control window records all radiation / accept background radiation (1), test windows containing aluminium / plastic / lead to block beta / gamma / neutron radiation (1), so when exposed to radiation the test windows would darken differently / would not darken compared to the control depending on material / would respond to radiation (1)
5 Radiation in tube ionises gas (1), allows current to flow as short pulse (1); tube connected to counter (1) to make a click / sound when radiation is detected (1)
6 GM tube / photographic film (1). Measure background radiation over several minutes and find average (1), measure count rate from rock (1) subtract background count rate from count rate from rock (1)

192. Models of the atom

1 Uniform positive mass / 'pudding' (1), (negative) electrons embedded / like currants in the dough (1)
2 (Observation →) ask a scientific question → hypothesis → experiment → conclusion → check against previous models / knowledge → new model (2)
3 There is a central positive nucleus (1), with electrons orbiting the nucleus (1)
4 In both models there is a central positive nucleus (1). In Rutherford's model, the electrons form a cloud around the nucleus (1). In the Bohr model, electrons are on (defined) energy levels (1) and can only move between levels (if they gain or lose energy) (1)
5 More (experimental) data has become available (1) which doesn't fit with earlier observations / conclusions / experiments (1), so new model is proposed (1)
6 Plum pudding model: positive 'mass' with electrons embedded (1); using the plum pudding model, most radiation expected to be deflected slightly. (1)

193. Beta decay

1 β⁺ positron (1) β⁻ electron (1)
2 Unstable neutron (1) to proton (1) and electron (1) or equation showing this
3 Carbon dating / PET scans / medical tracers / measuring thickness of materials (1)

4 $^{228}_{88}Ra \rightarrow \, ^{228}_{89}Ac$ **(1)** + β⁻ **(1)**

5 $^{10}_{6}C \rightarrow \, ^{10}_{5}B$ **(1)** + β⁺ **(1)**

6 Beta source emitting beta radiation **(1)** and detector opposite on the other side of the material picking up the amount of radiation passing through the material **(1)**. Detector connected to a device to control pressure of the rollers on one side **(1)**. The thicker the material, the more radiation is absorbed / the less radiation reaches the detector **(1)**. Detector sends signals to the equipment that adjusts the thickness of the material **(1)**.

7 β⁺ **(1)** $^{0}_{+1}$ β **(1)**

8 β⁻: negatively charged **(1)** electron **(1)** emitted from the nucleus **(1)**. Electrons in atoms found on shells around the nucleus **(1)**.

β⁺: positively charged **(1)** positron **(1)**

194. Radioactive decay

1

Radiation	Effect on the mass of the nucleus	Effect on the number of protons in the nucleus	
α	−4	−2	**(1)**
β⁺	0	−1	**(1)**
β⁻	0	+1	**(1)**
Gamma	0	0	**(1)**
Neutron	−1	0	**(1)**

(numbers and changes can be expressed in numbers or words)

2 (a) neutron **(1)** → proton **(1)** + electron **(1)**

(b) $^{73}_{30}Zn \rightarrow \, ^{73}_{31}Ga$ **(1)** + $^{0}_{-1}$β **(1)**

3 (a) nuclear charge decreases **(1)** by 2 **(1)**

(b) $^{226}_{88}Ra \rightarrow \, ^{222}_{86}Rn$ **(1)** + $^{4}_{2}α$ **(1)**

4 Gamma rays emitted when changes in the nucleus happen **(1)**. No change in mass **(1)** or proton number / nuclear charge **(1)**

5 (a) $^{125}_{53}I \rightarrow \, ^{125}_{53}I + γ$ **(1)**

(b) $^{90}_{38}Sr \rightarrow \, ^{90}_{39}Y + \, ^{0}_{-1}β$ **(1)**

(c) $^{238}_{92}U \rightarrow \, ^{234}_{90}Th + \, ^{4}_{2}α$ **(1)**

6 (b) $^{214}_{83}Bi$ **(1)** $\rightarrow \, ^{214}_{84}Po + \, ^{0}_{-1}β$ **(1)**

195. Half-life

1 Average time for half of the radioactive nuclei in a sample to have decayed / the average time for the (radio)activity of a sample to halve **(1)**

2 Random process **(1)**, which means chance event which nucleus will decay next **(1)**

3 After 10 days 2500 Bq, after 20 days 1250 Bq, after 30 days **(1)** = 625 Bq **(1)**

4 Accept values around 11–13 min **(1)**. Markings on graph to show how student worked this out, e.g. line across from half of original number/activity to curve, then down to time axis **(1)**

5 ½ × ½ × ½ = ⅛ **(2)**

6 Radioactive decay random process **(1)**. Half-life = time it takes for half of the nuclei to decay **(1)**. It will take many half-lives for activity of the waste to be reduced to a safe level. **(1)**

196. Dangers of radiation

1 Radiation burns / cancer / mutations / kills cells **(1)** because it produces **reactive** ions / remove electrons from atoms in the tissue **(1)**

2 Two from: limit time of exposure, wear protective clothing (or put other material between the source and the person), being at a distance from the radioactive material / using tongs / going out of the room **(2)**

3 Ionising radiation can form ions **(1)**. Non-ionising cannot / does not have enough energy to form ions **(1)**

4 (a) X-rays can be reduced / stopped by lead **(1)** wearing lead apron will reduce the amount of X-rays patient is exposed to **(1)**

(b) Go out of the room / go behind lead shield / accept wear lead apron **(1)**

5 (a) Benefits need to outweigh risk **(1)**, cancer treatment / detecting cancer / used in imaging techniques **(1)**

(b) Exposure monitored using film badges **(1)**. Two from: staff would use equipment like tongs / keep a distance from the radioactive materials / wear protective materials / lead apron / go out the room / reduce their exposure time **(2)**

197. Contamination and irradiation

1 B **(1)**

2 Irradiation = something is in contact with ionising radiation **(1)** sterilising herbs / sterilising medical equipment / any sensible example **(1)**

3 Irradiation = exposure to ionising radiation **(1)**, contamination = exposure to or moving of radioactive material / radioactive material on someone's skin / in their body **(1)**

4 External contamination: radioactive material on the outside of someone's body / hair / skin / clothing **(1)**; internal contamination: radioactive material inside someone's body / lungs / tissue / organs **(1)**, breathing in radon gas / any sensible example **(1)**

5 Irradiation **(1)**, just exposure to the radiation / not the source of radiation **(1)**

6 Food / drink can contain radioactive material **(1)**. When consumed it gets into the body **(1)**

7 Alpha particles **(1)** act over small distance / easily stopped / have low penetrating power so must be absorbed by the tissue and so interact strongly with the tissue inside the body **(1)** are highly ionising **(1)**

198. Extended response – Radioactivity

Answer could include the following points **(6)**:
- Exposure to iodine-131 highest during the first few weeks after the accident
- Because short half-life most of it will have decayed by 2017
- Exposure to caesium-137 will still be high
- Because first half-life not past / 30 years not past
- Contamination with the isotopes could lead to mutations and cancer
- Cancer of the thyroid for contamination with iodine-131
- Cancer of soft tissue for contamination with caesium-137

199. Work, energy and power

1 A **(1)**

2 Distance = 0.10 m, so WD = 50 × 0.10 **(1)** = 5 Nm = 5 J **(1)**

3 E = 1500 × 120 **(1)** = 180 000 J = 180 kJ **(1)**

4 Energy = 2000 × 60 = 120 000 J **(1)** force = $\frac{120000}{0.5}$ **(1)** = 240 000 N **(1)**

5 P = 14 400 000/(2 × 60 × 60) **(1)** = 2000 W / 2 kW **(1)**

6 Force required to lift 125 kg is 1250 N **(1)**. GPE per second = 5000 J **(1)**. Power = 1 s × 5000 J = 5000 W/5 kW **(1)**

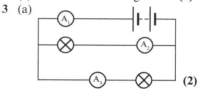

7 Energy = power × time = 60 000 × 7200 = 432 000 000 J **(2)**. Amount of fuel = $\frac{\text{Calculated energy}}{\text{Energy in 1l of fuel}}$ = $\frac{432\,000\,000}{36\,000\,000}$ = 12 litres **(2)**

200. Extended response – Energy and forces
Answer could include the following points **(6)**:
- Company needs to make the boat energy-independent from the grid / because boat may be cruising sometimes
- Boat needs heating / stove / oil heater / gas heater / water heater
- Insulation needed as boat hull made from steel / good conductor
- Insulation of the sides and ceiling, insulation of the floor / named examples of insulation such as polystyrene, rockwool, sprayfoam, small windows
- To reduce conduction through steel hull
- Double glazing / curtains
- To reduce heat loss via conduction / convection
- Close up vents (might want to mention carbon monoxide poisoning risk from stoves)
- To reduce draught
- Carpets
- To reduce heat loss via conduction

201. Interacting forces
2 Contact: thrust / normal force / friction / air resistance / any contact force **(1)**; non-contact: magnetism / gravity / electrostatic **(1)**

3 Force between masses **(1)**, no contact required / works over a distance / e.g. Sun and Earth or other valid example **(1)**

4 Magnetism is a non-contact force **(1)** magnets will repel or attract **(1)**, so there is a pair of forces either pulling magnets together or pushing them apart **(1)**; this could be shown as a diagram

5 Drawing showing: arrow pointing down labelled weight and same length arrow pointing up labelled normal force **(1)**, arrow pointing in direction of motion labelled pushing force and same length arrow in opposite direction labelled friction / air resistance **(1)**

6 Normal contact force from desk **(1)** which is upwards **(1)**. Weight force from Earth **(1)** which is downwards **(1)**. Normal contact force is same magnitude as weight force

7 Weight downwards with equal, but opposite, normal force **(1)**, friction / air resistance and pushing force acting in opposite directions **(1)** with pushing force exceeding / bigger than friction / air resistance **(1)**

202. Circuit symbols
1

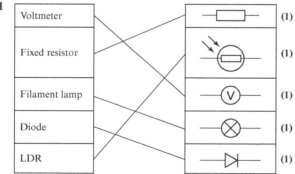

Voltmeter	▭	**(1)**
Fixed resistor	(LDR symbol)	**(1)**
Filament lamp	Ⓥ	**(1)**
Diode	⊗	**(1)**
LDR	▷	**(1)**

2 In parallel with a component **(1)** as it measures the potential difference across the component **(1)**

3 Correct circuit symbols (1 mark each). Fixed resistor: fixed resistance to the flow of current / resistance cannot be changed **(1)**. Variable resistor: resistance can be varied / changed **(1)**

4 Light-dependent resistor **(1)**, resistance decreases as the light intensity increases **(1)**. Any sensible uses, e.g. street light / light meter / weather station **(1)**

5 Electrical energy → kinetic energy **(1)** + sound / heat **(1)**

203. Series and parallel circuits
1 Series circuit: all components are in a loop **(1)**; parallel circuit: components in separate branches **(1)**

2 (a) Correct drawing (as shown) **(1)** Ammeter readings / current is the same everywhere in the circuit **(1)**
  (b) Voltmeter in parallel across each light bulb **(1)**
  (c) 1.5 V across each light bulb **(1)**

3 (a)

(circuit diagram with ammeters A_1, A_2, A_3 and light bulbs) **(2)**

  (b) 6 V across each light bulb **(1)**
  (c) 1.5 A in each branch **(1)**

204. Current and charge
2 D **(1)**

3 $I = \frac{Q}{t} = \frac{60}{60}$ **(1)** = 1 A **(1)**

4 Time = energy/power = 120 000/2000 = 60 s **(1)** Current = charge/time = 600/60 **(1)** = 10 A **(1)**

5 $t = \frac{Q}{I} = \frac{100}{15}$ **(1)** = 6.7 s **(1)**

6 Conventional current: from positive to negative terminal **(1)**, electrons: from negative to positive terminal **(1)**

7 Power = $\frac{\text{energy}}{\text{time}}$ **(1)**. While the LED is on, same amount of energy is required per each time unit / energy is proportional to time **(1)** so power remains constant **(1)**

205. Energy and charge
1 B **(1)**

2 Measure potential difference **(1)** and current **(1)**. Use $Q = It$ first **(1)** then $E = QV$ **(1)** [or use $E = VIt$ **(2)**]

3 $E = QV = 9 \times 500$ **(1)** = 4500 J **(1)**

4 $E = QV$, so $V = \frac{E}{Q} = \frac{460000}{2000}$ **(1)** = 230 V **(1)**

5 (a) Use $E = Pt$; Energy = 2000 × 120 **(1)** = 240 000 J **(1)**
  (b) Rearrange $E = QV$; Charge = $\frac{240000}{230}$ **(1)** = 1043 C **(1)**
  (c) Rearrange $Q = It$; Current = $\frac{1043}{120}$ **(1)** = 8.7 A **(1)**

206. Ohm's law
1 The magnitude of current flowing through a component is directly proportional to the potential difference across the component **(1)** at constant temperature **(1)**

2 $R = \frac{V}{I} = \frac{3}{6}$ **(1)** = 0.5 Ω **(1)**

3 Connect an ammeter in series to the component **(1)**, connect a voltmeter in parallel (accept circuit diagram with an ammeter in series and a voltmeter in parallel to the component) **(1)** and then calculate $R = V/I$ **(1)**

4 B **(1)** because the current flowing through the component is lower than the current in A for the same potential difference **(1)**

5 (a) $R = \frac{V}{I} = \frac{1.5}{4}$ **(1)** = 0.375 Ω **(1)**
  (b) (i) Potential difference = 1.5 + 3 **(1)** = 4.5 V **(1)**
     (ii) Resistance = 4.5/4 **(1)** = 1.125 Ω ($\frac{accept\ their\ b}{4}$) **(1)**

207. Resistors
1 Resistance in series circuits add up **(1)**

2 (a) $R = \frac{V}{I} = \frac{4.5}{0.5}$ **(1)** = 9 Ω **(1)**
  (b) $I = \frac{V}{R} = \frac{4.5}{25}$ **(1)** = 0.18 A **(1)**

(c) Total current = 0.5 + 0.18 = 0.68 A **(1)**
(accept 0.5 + error carried from (b))

3 (a) (i) current = 10 − 6 = 4 A **(1)**
  (ii) resistance = *V/I* = 12/4 = 3 Ω **(1)**
 (b) Total resistance = *V/I* = 12/6 **(1)** = 2 Ω **(1)**,
   resistance of K = 2 − 0.5 **(1)** = 1.5 Ω **(1)**

208. I–V graphs

1 Ohmic resistor / suitable example such as fixed resistor **(1)**

2
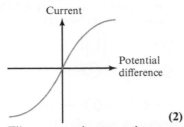

(2)

Filament gets hotter as the current increases **(1)**, leading to increased resistance **(1)**

3 (a) Any suitable example, e.g. fixed resistor **(1)**
 (b) Suitable example from (a) connected in series with ammeter **(1)** and variable resistor **(1)**, and in parallel with a voltmeter **(1)**. Collect several values of *I* and *V* **(1)** by setting variable resistor to different settings **(1)**
 (c) $R = \frac{V}{I} = \frac{10}{20}$ **(1)** = 0.5 Ω **(1)** (*read off any pair of values from the graph*)

4 In one direction very high resistance **(1)** so no current flows / line horizontal on zero / along p.d. axis **(1)**. In the other direction (from a certain threshold value) current (starts to) flow **(1)** and resistance doesn't change / behaves like fixed resistor / ohmic resistor **(1)**

209. Electrical circuits

1 The bulb/lamp gets hot **(1)**
2 Accurate = close to true value **(1)**, reliable = not much spread / values all close to one another **(1)**
3 Ohmic resistor: straight line through the origin **(1)**, resistance doesn't change / remains the same **(1)**; non-ohmic resistor: different shapes, e.g. a curve / description of an example **(1)**, resistance changes with voltage **(1)**
4 Potential difference = 3 V everywhere / across both light bulbs **(1)**, current in each branch will be half the total current **(1)**
5 Connect the light bulbs and an ammeter in series **(1)**, connect voltmeters in parallel / across each bulb **(1)**. Use *V* = *IR* to calculate the resistance of each light bulb **(1)**. Add both resistances together to get total resistance **(1)**.

210. The LDR and the thermistor

1 The higher the light intensity, the lower the resistance **(1)** at decreasing rate / non-linear **(1)**
2 Thermistor **(1)**
3 Electrical energy to heat energy **(1)**, so decreases the current in a circuit / lower current for higher resistance at same p.d. **(1)**
4 (a) Thermistor **(1)**

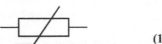

(1)

 (b) Resistance decreases with increasing temperature **(1)**, so if there is a fire a current would be able to flow and set off the alarm **(1)**

(c)
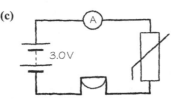

5 Resistance decreases with increasing light intensity **(1)**. This would be connected in a way that turns the street light on when it's dark / off when it's light **(1)**

211. Current heating effect

2 Useful: any use, e.g. fuse, electric heater, kettle **(1)**, not useful: any example, e.g. light bulb, computer **(1)**
3 Given off / dissipated to the environment as well as warming up the component **(1)**
4 Electrons flowing through wire collide with metal ions (accept atoms) **(1)**. This causes kinetic energy of electrons **(1)** to be converted to thermal energy **(1)**. The higher the current, the higher the heating effect. **(1)**
5 Fuse cuts the circuit if current gets too high **(1)**. Too much current means higher heating effect **(1)** which will break the fuse wire. **(1)**
6 Kettle transfers heat/thermal energy to water **(1)**. Current flowing through heating wire inside kettle heats up the wire by heating effect **(1)**. Electrons flowing through wire collide with metal ions (accept atoms) **(1)** and convert kinetic energy to thermal energy. **(1)**
7 Heating effect = heat produced because of current flowing through a wire **(1)**. Could damage circuits in / components in / computer **(1)**. Could use a fan / ventilation to reduce heat. **(1)**

212. Energy and power

1 Rate of electrical energy transferred into other forms **(1)**
2 Power = *VI* = 230 × 10 = 2300 W **(1)** energy = *Pt* = 2300 × 50 **(1)** = 115 000 J **(1)** (can also use *E* = *IVt* directly)
3 Power = *IV* **(1)** = 60 (accept 60.3) **(1)** W **(1)**
4 (a) *E* = *Pt*, so Power = $\frac{E}{t} = \frac{288420}{120}$ **(1)** = 2400 W **(1)**
 (b) *P* = *I²R*, so Resistance = $\frac{P}{I^2} = \frac{2400}{10.45^2}$ **(1)** = 22 Ω **(1)** (this can also be calculated using *V* = *IR*)
5 D (current flowing is 8.7 A) **(1)**

213. a.c. and d.c. circuits

1 Flat line above zero line **(1)**
2 d.c.: direction of current doesn't change **(1)** a.c.: direction of the current frequently/repeatedly/continually reverses or changes **(1)**
3 Any sensible examples, e.g. d.c.: torch, portable radio; e.g. a.c.: kettle, hairdryer **(4)**
4 Power = energy / time **(1)**, so 1700 J transferred per second **(1)**
5 Flow of electrons through an electric circuit **(1)**, supplied by (the potential difference of) the battery **(1)** **or** current is a rate **(1)** of flow of charge **(1)**

6
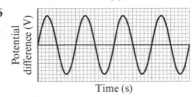

(1)

7 (a) *P* = *VI* = 19.5 × 2.31 **(1)** = 45 W **(1)**
 (b) *E* = *Pt* = 45 × 600 **(1)** = 27 000 J **(1)** (accept error carried from 7(a) × 10 × 60)

214. Mains electricity and the plug

1 Live: brown **(1)**, neutral: blue **(1)**, earth: green **and** yellow **(1)**

2 Fuse breaks circuit **(1)** by having the wire inside the capsule melt **(1)** if the current goes above the rating on the fuse **(1)**. This protects the device and cables supplying the device from overheating **(1)** or protects the user if the current has surged because the metal case has become live. **(1)**

3 Earth wire not part of circuit / safety feature / will only carry current if there is a fault **(1)**, live 230 V with respect to earth and neutral **(1)**, neutral 0 V **(1)**

4 Protects circuit / protects consumer / similar to fuse **(1)**, easy to reset / doesn't need to be replaced every time **(1)**

5 Safety feature **(1)** to prevent electrocution **(1)**, earth wire connected to the metal outer casing **(1)** provides a low resistance path for the electrons to flow down in the event of the casing becoming live **(1)**

6 (a) Any loose wire might come into contact with the metal casing **(1)** and give anyone touching it an electric shock **(1)**

(b) Live wire can't touch the outer casing **(1)**, so no chance of electric shock (even if wires inside become loose) **(1)** Plastic is an insulator so no current can flow through it **(1)**

215. Extended response – Electricity and circuits

Answer could include the following points **(6)**:

- Electricity made in power station, converted to high voltage
- Using step-up transformer
- Which has more turns on the secondary coil than primary coil
- Then transported at high voltage through cables **to reduce energy loss**
- **Via the current heating effect**
- As high voltage means low current
- From V = IR
- Then voltage reduced to 230 V
- Using step-down transformer
- Which has fewer turns on the secondary coil than on the primary coil.

216. Magnets and magnetic fields

1 D **(1)**

2

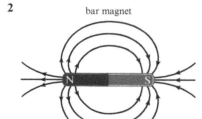

bar magnet

Shows field lines correctly, no overlapping field lines **(1)** with each field line with an arrow from N to S pole **(1)**

3 Stroke the nail with one pole of the bar magnet **(1)** in one direction only many times **(1)**

4 Permanent magnet: repulsion if like poles face each other **(1)** or attraction if unlike poles face each other **(1)**; unmagnetised iron: attraction **(1)**

5 (a) Can be used to trace the shape and direction of magnetic field lines **(1)**

(b) Contains tiny bar magnet **(1)** which aligns with Earth's magnetic field **(1)** and points north **(1)**

6 Put bar magnet on a piece of paper **(1)**, put plotting compass by one pole and draw a dot where the needle

is pointing **(1)**. Move compass so that the other end of the needle is by the dot and draw new dot **(1)**. Continue to map around the magnet. **(1)**

217. Current and magnetism

1 The larger the size of the current, the stronger the magnetic field **(1)**; the larger the distance from the wire, the smaller the magnetic field **(1)**

2 Series of concentric circles with an increased distance between each field line to show weaker field strength with distance from the wire **(1)**

3 (Fleming's) right-hand rule **(1)**, point thumb of right hand in direction of **conventional** current **(1)**, direction that your fingers curl is the direction of the magnetic field **(1)**

4 Directly proportional **(1)**, so as current decreases, magnetic field strength decreases **(1)**

5 Strong **and** uniform inside **(1)**, weaker outside **(1)** as field lines cancel **(1)**

6 (a) As one variable increases, the other decreases at the same rate **(1)**

(b) Increasing distance = weaker magnetic field **(1)**, decreasing distance = stronger magnetic field **(1)**

7 Materials: iron nail, copper wire, battery / power source **(1)**. Wrap the wire around the nail **(1)** and connect to the battery. **(1)**

218. Extended response – Magnetism and the motor effect

Answer could include the following points **(6)**:

For each of the three types, 1 mark for description of each material which needs to be linked to an example. 1 mark for link to property:

Permanent magnet:
- Magnetic all the time
- (North and south) poles
- Attract opposite poles
- Repel like poles
- Made of magnetic material
- E.g. door magnets, magnetic screwdriver, any sensible example
- Link to properties, e.g. since the magnetic screwdriver is always magnetic, it will attract screws to help guide them / so they aren't lost

Temporary magnet:
- Magnetic for a short period of time
- (North and south) poles
- Attract opposite poles
- Repel like poles
- E.g. MRI magnets / scrap yards / any sensible example
- Link to properties, e.g. since the magnet on a crane on a scrapyard can be turned on and off, cars / magnetic objects can be picked up and moved to different area

Unmagnetised magnetic material:
- Only attracted to other magnets
- Does not repel magnets
- Made of magnetic material
- E.g. sorting rubbish in a recycling plant / separating mixtures / other sensible example
- Link to properties, e.g. magnetic materials are attracted to a magnet and can be separated from a mixture

219. Transformers

1 Electromagnetic induction **(1)**

2 Two coils around iron core **(1)**. Primary coil has fewer turns than secondary coil **(1)**; primary coil connected to an a.c. power supply **(1)**; no electrical connection between the coils **(1)**

3 Produces higher voltage **(1)** which means low current **(1)**

4 $I_s = (V_p \times I_p)/V_s = (230 \times 1)/19 = 12$ (allow 12.1) A **(1)**; step-down transformer **(1)**

5 Transported through national grid at very high potential difference **(1)**, needs to be converted / reduced to 230 V for use at home **(1)**

6 $I_s = \frac{575 \times 2}{230}$ **(1)** = 5 A **(1)**

220. Extended response – Electromagnetic induction
Answer could include the following points **(6)**:
At least one point from each section is required:
Structure/function of dynamo
- Dynamo generates electricity / direct current
- Voltage produced when a magnet moves in a coil of wire
- Dynamo has a wheel which touches the tyre, wheel turns as bicycle moves
- Makes magnet inside turn / wheel turns magnet inside a coil
- Generates electricity / induces potential difference

Comparison with a.c. generator
- In a.c. generator, a coil rotates inside magnet / a.c. current produced

Disadvantage
- The faster the bike moves the higher the induced potential differences and hence the brighter the lights / when bike stops no electricity produced / lights are off/ cyclist can't be seen

Advantage
- Don't need to carry a battery / no battery to go flat
- Electricity generated as the cyclist moves / only takes a little bit more effort / is free

221. Changes of state
1 Gas **(1)**
2 Fixed positions **(1)** ordered lattice / arrangement **(1)**, vibrate in fixed positions **(1)**
3 Particles not in fixed positions / can slide past each other **(1)**. Any two from: liquids flow / take up the shape of the bottom of their container **(1)**, can be compressed (but not visibly/not to same extent as gases) **(1)**, usually less dense than solids / usually denser than gases **(1)**
4 Melting **(1)** heating required **(1)** to give particles more potential energy **(1)**
5 Substance gets colder / transfers energy to environment **(1)**, particles come closer together / move around less **(1)**
6 Gas **(1)**, particles moving randomly / fast / lots of potential energy **(1)**, not touching **(1)**
7 More potential energy in a liquid **(1)** so they can move past each other **(1)** whereas arranged in fixed lattice / arrangement in solid **(1)**

222. Density
1 Amount of matter / mass in a certain volume / density = mass/volume **(1)**
2 Density = mass/volume **(1)** = 98/70000 = 0.0014 **(1)** g/cm³ **(1)**
3 Mass = density × volume = 7.87 × 6.35 **(1)** = 50 g (accept 49.97) g **(1)**
4 (a) Liquid expands when heated / it evaporates / boils **(1)** so the volume of a gas is bigger than that of the liquid **(1)**. Dividing the same mass by a larger volume gives a smaller density for the gas. **(1)**
   (b) Solid normally denser than liquid **(1)** because the liquid has a larger volume than the solid of the same mass **(1)** so the density of liquid should be less **(1)**
5 Volume = mass/density = $\frac{20}{0.8}$ **(1)** = 25 cm³ **(1)**

223. Investigating density
1 Volume = 1432.4375 cm³ **(1)** density = $\frac{2800}{1432}$ **(1)** = 1.95 g/cm³ (accept 2 g/cm³) **(1)**
2 (a) Use a balance / scales / specified type of balance **(1)**
   (b) Either: measuring cylinder filled to known volume / enough water to cover stone **(1)**, read off the new volume **(1)**, take the difference **(1)**; or fill Eureka can to the spout with water **(1)**, measure volume of water that is displaced **(1)** into a measuring cylinder **(1)**
   (c) Density = mass/volume = 50/19 = 2.63 g/cm³ **(2)**, quartz **(1)**
3 Measuring cylinder **(1)**, read off bottom of the meniscus **(1)**
4 Mass = (2 × 3 × 4) × 3 **(1)** = 72 g **(1)**

224. Energy and changes of state
1 Thermal energy required to raise the temperature of 1 kg by 1 °C **(1)**
2 Latent heat of fusion: energy to turn 1 kg of solid to liquid / liquid to solid / to melt / freeze **(1)**; latent heat of vaporisation: energy to turn 1 kg of gas to liquid / liquid to gas / to condense / boil **(1)**
3 Energy = 2 × 4200 × (95 − 25) **(1)** = 588 000 J **(1)**
4 Specific latent heat relates to changes of state **(1)** where temperature remains constant / doesn't change **(1)**
5 Mass = Q/L = $\frac{16700}{334000}$ **(1)** = 0.5 kg = 50 g **(1)**, so 50 cm³ **(1)**
6 $\Delta\theta = \frac{32000}{10 \times 128}$ **(1)** = 25 °C **(1)**, $T - 25 = \Delta\theta$, so new temperature $T = 50$ °C **(1)**

225. Thermal properties of water
1 (a) Reduces heat loss to environment / dissipation **(1)** so more accurate value for specific heat capacity **(1)**
   (b) Read off the thermometer scale at eye level **(1)**, parallax error **(1)**

2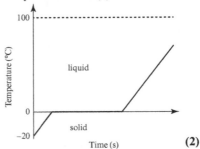
(1 mark for correct shape, 1 for labelling y-axis temperature and x-axis time)
3 Changes state / melts / boils / do not accept 'evaporates' **(1)**, interactions / bonds between particles loosen / break **(1)**
4 $c = \frac{460.5}{0.05 \times 20}$ **(1)** = 460.5 J/kg °C **(1)**
5 Correct conversions, i.e. 500 g = 0.5 kg and 10 min = 600 s **(1)** $c = \frac{230 \times 0.76 \times 600}{0.5 \times 50}$ **(1)** = 4200 J/kg °C **(1)**

226. Pressure and temperature
1 Particles moving randomly **(1)** and colliding with / hitting the inside of the balloon **(1)**
2 (a) As temperature rises, gas pressure increases **(1)** provided the volume stays constant **(1)**
   (b) Increasing temperature = particles move faster / more kinetic energy **(1)** so particles collide more frequently and harder with walls of balloon **(1)**, so pressure is higher **(1)**
3 −273 °C / 0 K **(1)**, vibration of particles zero **(1)**
4 (a) 288 K **(1)**   (c) 177 °C **(1)**
   (b) 373 K **(1)**   (d) 0 °C **(1)**
5 Smaller space **(1)** so more frequent collisions of the particles with the walls of the container **(1)**, so increased pressure **(1)**
6 Correct equation **(1)**, workings **(1)**, 5 Pa **(1)**

227. Extended response – Particle model
Answer could include the following points **(6)**:
- Put an electric heater in an insulated beaker, attach a power source and connect a voltmeter and an ammeter
- Add a known amount of water and a thermometer
- Measure the temperature before starting to heat the water
- Start the time when you start to heat and leave it for 10 min (600 s) / use stopwatch
- Measure the temperature again
- Calculate the temperature difference
- Measure the potential difference and the current
- Energy = current × voltage × time
- Convert volume of water to mass
- Calculate the specific heat capacity using $E = m \times c \times \theta$
- Repeat/take average

228. Elastic and inelastic distortion
2 Pulling it stretches it / makes it longer **(1)**, then letting go returns it to its original length **(1)**. If you stretch it too much it snaps / breaks / is inelastically distorted **(1)**
3 Inelastic distortion **(1)**
4 When object is distorted past the elastic limit **(1)** so won't return to its original shape **(1)**
5 Directly proportional **(1)**
6 Two arrows in opposite direction pushing object inwards. **(2)**
7 Any relevant examples, e.g. elastic distortion: elastic band / rubber / spring **(1)** returns to original shape when deforming forces removed **(1)**; e.g. inelastic distortion: brick / rocks / elastic material past the elastic limit **(1)** do not return to original shape when deforming forces removed **(1)**
8 Any two sensible examples plus explanation **(2)**, e.g. seat belt: designed to stretch a bit; air bags: provide barrier between head and dashboard; plastics such as foam: elastic deformation **(1)** to absorb energy during a collision / to convert kinetic energy into heat by bending materials / accept explanation linking to momentum (increases time taken for body's momentum to reach zero / reduces force) **(1)**; collapsible steering column to avoid drivers being impaled **(1)**; rigid passenger cell to protect passengers from being crushed **(1)**; bumper: small elastic deformation for small bumps / large collision inelastic deformation to absorb energy and avoid bouncing **(1)**

229. Springs
1 B **(1)**
2 $F = 0.05 \times 25$ **(1)** $= 1.25\,\text{N}$ **(1)**
3 Cannot calculate the extension **(1)** because spring has gone past the elastic limit **(1)** and is permanently / inelastically distorted **(1)**
4
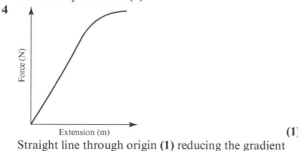
(1)
Straight line through origin **(1)** reducing the gradient past elastic limit **(1)**

5 The energy stored in the spring is the area under graph **(1)**, but this only applies up to the elastic limit **(1)**
6 $E = \frac{1}{2} \times 0.5 \times 0.3^2$ **(1)** $= 0.0225\,\text{J}$ **(1)**

230. Forces and springs
1 Spring could snap / ping off the clamp **(1)**. Wear eye protection / goggles **(1)**
2 Weight is a force and mass describes how much matter there is / weight in N/newton and mass in kg **(1)**
3 (a)

Length of spring (mm)	Extension of spring (mm)	Mass (g)	Weight (N)	
50	0	0	0	
60	10	100	1	**(1)**
70	20	200	2	**(2)**
80	30	300	3	**(2)**

   (b) No **(1)**, extension is directly proportional to weight **(1)**
4 $e = \sqrt{\frac{2 \times 5}{5}}$ **(1)** $= 1.41\,\text{m}$ **(1)**
5 $E = 0.5\,\text{J}$, $e = 5\,\text{cm} = 0.05\,\text{m}$ $k = \frac{2 \times E}{e^2}$ **(1)** $= 400\,\text{N/m}$ **(1)**

231. Extended response – Forces and matter
Answer could include the following points **(6)**:
Answer must include at least one point from each section:

Spring
- Spring inside newton meter has a certain stiffness
- Which will affect the force that it can take / by how much it can extend

Extension
- Attaching a mass / pulling on the spring extends the spring
- By a known amount

Force
- $F = ke$
- So if k is known
- Extension can be converted to force

Elastic limit
- Only works up to a certain force because once force extends the spring past the elastic limit
- It is inelastic
- And won't return to the original shape / length.

The Periodic Table of the Elements

1	2												3	4	5	6	7	0
																		4 **He** helium 2
7 **Li** lithium 3	9 **Be** beryllium 4												11 **B** boron 5	12 **C** carbon 6	14 **N** nitrogen 7	16 **O** oxygen 8	19 **F** fluorine 9	20 **Ne** neon 10
23 **Na** sodium 11	24 **Mg** magnesium 12												27 **Al** aluminium 13	28 **Si** silicon 14	31 **P** phosphorus 15	32 **S** sulfur 16	35.5 **Cl** chlorine 17	40 **Ar** argon 18
39 **K** potassium 19	40 **Ca** calcium 20	45 **Sc** scandium 21	48 **Ti** titanium 22	51 **V** vanadium 23	52 **Cr** chromium 24	55 **Mn** manganese 25	56 **Fe** iron 26	59 **Co** cobalt 27	59 **Ni** nickel 28	63.5 **Cu** copper 29	65 **Zn** zinc 30		70 **Ga** gallium 31	73 **Ge** germanium 32	75 **As** arsenic 33	79 **Se** selenium 34	80 **Br** bromine 35	84 **Kr** krypton 36
85 **Rb** rubidium 37	88 **Sr** strontium 38	89 **Y** yttrium 39	91 **Zr** zirconium 40	93 **Nb** niobium 41	96 **Mo** molybdenum 42	[98] **Tc** techuetium 43	101 **Ru** ruthenium 44	103 **Rh** rhodium 45	106 **Pd** palladium 46	108 **Ag** silver 47	112 **Cd** cadmium 48		115 **In** indium 49	119 **Sn** tin 50	122 **Sb** antimony 51	128 **Te** tellurium 52	127 **I** iodine 53	131 **Xe** xenon 54
133 **Cs** caesium 55	137 **Ba** barium 56	139 **La*** lanthanum 57	178 **Hf** hafnium 72	181 **Ta** tantalum 73	184 **W** tungsten 74	186 **Re** rhenium 75	190 **Os** osmium 76	192 **Ir** iridium 77	195 **Pt** platinum 78	197 **Au** gold 79	201 **Hg** mercury 80		204 **Tl** thallium 81	207 **Pb** lead 82	209 **Bi** bismuth 83	[209] **Po** polonium 84	[210] **At** astatine 85	[222] **Rn** radon 86
[223] **Fr** francium 87	[226] **Ra** radium 88	[227] **Ac*** actinium 89	[261] **Rf** rutherfordium 104	[262] **Db** dubnium 105	[266] **Sg** seaborgium 106	[264] **Bh** bohrium 107	[277] **Hs** hassium 108	[268] **Mt** meitnerium 109	[271] **Ds** darmstadtium 110	[272] **Rg** roentgenium 111								

Key

relative atomic mass
atomic symbol
name
atomic (proton) number

Example:

1
H
hydrogen
1

Elements with atomic numbers 112–116 have been reported but not fully authenticated

*The lanthanoids (atomic numbers 58–71) and the actinoids (atomic numbers 90–103) have been omitted.

Physics Equations List

(final velocity)^2 − (initial velocity)^2 = 2 × acceleration × distance

$v^2 - u^2 = 2 \times a \times x$

energy transferred = current × potential difference × time

$E = I \times V \times t$

change in thermal energy = mass × specific heat capacity × change in temperature

$\Delta Q = m \times c \times \Delta\theta$

thermal energy for a change of state = mass × specific latent heat

$Q = m \times L$

energy transferred in stretching = 0.5 × spring constant × (extension)^2

$E = \frac{1}{2} \times k \times x^2$

Notes

Notes

Notes